# THE BEAT OF
# THE PENDULUM

Also by Catherine Chidgey

*In a Fishbone Church*
*Golden Deeds*
*The Transformation*
*The Wish Child*

# THE BEAT OF
# THE PENDULUM

[ A FOUND NOVEL ]

## CATHERINE CHIDGEY

Published in 2018
by Lightning Books Ltd
Imprint of EyeStorm Media
312 Uxbridge Road
Rickmansworth
Hertfordshire
WD3 8YL

www.lightning-books.com

First published in 2017 by Victoria University Press (New Zealand)

ISBN: 9781785630903

Cover design by Ifan Bates

British Library Cataloguing in Publication Data
A catalogue record for this book is available from the British Library.

Printed by CPI Group (UK) Ltd, Croydon CR0 4YY

In theory one knows that the earth is turning, but in reality one does not perceive it; the ground on which one walks seems not to move, and one exists undisturbed. So it is with Time in one's life. And to make its flight perceptible, novelists are obliged, by wildly accelerating the beat of the pendulum, to transport the reader in a couple of minutes over ten, twenty, or thirty years.

—Marcel Proust, *In Search of Lost Time*

I confess I do not believe in time. I like to fold my magic carpet, after use, in such a way as to superimpose one part of the pattern upon another. Let visitors trip.

—Vladimir Nabokov, *Speak, Memory*

*for Alan*

# [ JANUARY ]

## 1

I think your door is open.

People sometimes hear something but they don't hear it correctly. How's wee darling? Did she see the New Year in?

No no no, gentle gentle gentle with the pearls.

Is he playing hard to get? You won't catch him. He's stupid but he's not that stupid. Shall we put you in the chair?

She looks at everything. I don't know how she looks so long without blinking.

She'll knock that off there. That's not going to stay there. Try the other hand.

Some babies at that age really can't eat. They can still just only have bottles. You're a show-off aren't you? Yes, you're a big show-off. She's keeping her eye on you, isn't she? That shortbread was lovely. Did you make it? Oh. Well it just tasted like homemade. When you can buy things as nice as that—I presume you bought it—it's hardly worth turning your oven on, is it?

So were there lots of admirers talking about the baby paraded at lunch the other day?

Oh yes—how old is she, what's her name? Yes, they thought she was beautiful. They all like to see something like that, because you know . . .

That was a nice guy at your table, with Gwen. He said she's got more hair than he does.

Yes he's lovely. He's got an artificial leg. He had his leg removed about three years ago. He's good fun. Gwen's quite a quiet lady. Les and I have lots of jokes and she joins in, you know. I have a feeling she didn't have a happy marriage. She's never quite said, but I think he went to the pub and football and left her alone quite a lot. We have a good table, Les and Gwen and me. There used to be another guy there, but I don't know whether he's died or gone upstairs or what's happened to him but he's not there, and nobody seems to know. And we've now got a lady there who doesn't even get a joke.

She hasn't done anything interesting for the last thirty-six hours or so.

Nana's having a cup of tea. Stop laughing at Nana and eat your carrot. Tea's so different just made in a cup, compared to sixty cups in a teapot.

Where's my laptop? I'll show you some photos Helen posted.

What's she standing on?

It's Charlie's hoverboard.

In the news, a lot of them have been spontaneously combusting. They just burst into flames.

Why?

Because there's videos of them all over the internet. Because of the batteries or something. And there's videos of people veering out of control and then coming off horrendously. They're back early from their holiday over there. The neighbours. They were meant to be away for four days and they've been away for two. Perhaps they'll do the lawns. Careful . . . careful . . . gentle! Gentle! Take control of that hand, because it'll get onto your hair or your pearls and the pearls will be all over the floor in seconds.

Do you want Nana's pearls? You can't have them yet. No. You're supposed to sit down. Bend your knees. Bend your knees and sit down. You're supposed to be just sitting down quietly. You don't like me holding on to you, do you? Do you want to go on the floor? Do you want to go on the floor? I'm trying to think how old that is.

That? I thought it was your father's.

Yes it was. And he came out from Ireland. It would be in the 1890s, before the turn of the century. I think about '98. Of course Dad had no idea when he came out.

Well he didn't know how old he was.

You can't imagine somebody hardly going to school, can you.

Why do you have to go off getting into trouble? Always getting into trouble.

Have you got a problem? Daddy's got a problem more like.

Rebel with a cause. Her toenails need doing too, Catherine.

They're so tiny at that age, the toenails, aren't they. I don't really want to see her with only four toes. I used to hate cutting your nails.

No need to look worried. Trust me, I'm a professional.

What's Mummy doing?

2

You can't just call a child Bill when it's not short for anything. You think they understand things. I'm not a positive person, but I'm a logical person. I've got my head round having an only. You don't want to look like a copy.

It sounds like a lot of hard work, changing my name. It's not that I'm anti-marriage, it's just that after fifteen years, if we could fill in some forms online . . .

Is that even a real name?

No, it's a butterfly name.

It feels like being difficult for the sake of it. They spend a life correcting everyone. When our babies are not the norm anyway—sperm donor babies, surro babies—you don't want to give them something else.

I'm the only one eating.

She was telling us about the farewell afternoon tea they threw for her and she gave her speech and she said you all think I work night shift, but it's because I don't like any of you. She said they all laughed.

I put an order in for the dimples. It was like a train you could never get off.

I think we were just at the wrong end of the bell curve.

I'm actually worn out. I just need to get on with my life.

There's nothing wrong with only children. He's fine. He's a good boy. It's all how you make the world around them. I get annoyed when people post that they're struggling to have a second one, and they post my child cries every day and asks for a sibling every day. I'm thinking, that's you putting that into their head.

Some of the things that children cry about that they want but don't get—I want a bike, I want a brother or sister.

I don't have it in me any more.

They had a UN-level conversation with a three-year-old about it, and it's because they live out in the country and the three-year-old's a bit bored some days. She's three. She doesn't understand what a sibling is anyway.

Harry's the best sharer I've ever come across. He'd give you his last lolly. He went to his dad's on Christmas night and he didn't really want to go. They had the girlfriend's nieces and nephews over and they were allowed free rein of the house, which includes his bedroom. If kids come to our place, they're not allowed free rein of the bedrooms. He says all of his stuff gets touched. You should be able to have a bedroom at your dad's.

My brother used to do it, looking for money, because it's what he's like.

Look at the deaths we've had. Look how many we've had in the last couple of years.

But wait, there's more! You'll also get the pressure oven recipe book. This is a present from my kitchen to yours. Shh, shh, shhhhh. Say daddy and I'll let you go. You can be sure that you will have results you never dreamt of. I was ecstatic. I almost fainted.

Give me the child.

It cooks before your eyes. I think I stood two feet taller.

You could just change the name—the Hermann Göring pressure oven.

You're being recorded.

I really didn't want to cook any more; I kind of lost that desire. It has totally sparked a new creativity in me. And my husband hasn't been this happy in a long time, because he's like part of you has come back. We can't get enough of this meatloaf.

Trips to restaurants and carry-out can cost the average Australian family hundreds every month. But wait, there's more! You'll also get the pressure oven recipe book. This is a present from my kitchen to yours.

Hold everything.

He's asleep with his eyes open.

You don't have to save cooking a fourteen-pound turkey for only the holidays.

You're quite a strange person, aren't you. Do you like the taste of the stars?

Flavour free with a great taste.

If you need to return it you only have sixty days from their ship date. The customer service rep was rude and unprofessional and laughed at me when I asked for a refund. She said, 'You are two days past your sixty days, do you have any other questions. No? Goodbye.'

4

REDUCE SPEED. When I say left, I mean right. REDUCE SPEED NOW. If you can see this, I've lost the boat!

Look at the light out there. I'm tired of suppressing myself to get along with white people.

You're a carrion bird of conversation. You pick out the bits of meat.

What a horrible mother.

What's coming to New Zealand? Family Feud. Tonight the beauties get lost in translation, and the geeks attempt to become perfect partners. We are so close to the grand finale, I can almost taste it. When James said that this challenge was on linguistics, all I could think about was pasta.

There's blood in my eggs.

I've been told that I could talk underwater with a mouthful of marbles. If I could speak any language in the world, I would love to be able to speak Mexican. Because I love Mexican food.

Do you know what that means? Blood in the eggs?

Like in folklore?

No, I just mean . . .

Why is there blood in the eggs.

Why is there blood in the eggs.

Wow, the Republicans really don't understand how they created Donald Trump. And it's too hard to pick out because it's right in the yolk.

There's probably a reason for that.

Dylan is a good teacher. I think he gets really frustrated because he feels like he's always talking to a brick wall. I am a pretty brick wall. My English is terrible. Sometimes I feel like people smile and nod at me when I'm speaking the same language as them. Shakespeare also speaks English, and he writes books. Who comes up with this stuff? I should write a book; it'd be more logical than anything Shakespeare wrote.

I'm feeling pretty masculine right now. It's the manliest I've ever felt. Eat, eat, eat. Be a man. A real man focuses. Are you a man, Oliver? The hotdogs weren't great, they tasted a bit like sadness.

Going into the challenge, I'm feeling more masculine than ever. I think my best physical feature would be the shade of blue my eyes are. Sometimes when I'm looking in the mirror even I get lost in them.

I guess I'll go to bed and read about Nazis.

That very night in Max's room a forest grew.

5

I'm worried that if I put her to sleep she won't wake up again. Eye bags just disparaged in sixty seconds.

This screen here is to arrive the patient. Now her clock is ticking away. This man is having a heart attack. A heart attack is not always as dramatic as you think. Will you be killed by your sofa? Do you have childcare on your mind? We asked people to show us what a heart attack looks like.

Have you ever had your neck clicked? Do you hate it or do you not mind it? Because this just is not moving. And short of getting out a mallet, I think the step before that is we might try a wee bit of a click. Now obviously there's an inherent danger, which is pulling your head off. We do try and avoid that. Take a deep breath. Cutting is huge at the moment. They say it's proof you're alive. I listen to the most horrendous talk from teenage girls—and boys. What they think they should look like is a hundred times worse than we had it. Today the deal is that you're really nice to yourself. Something to get your shoulders away from your ears.

Is that private? And you know about the convenience fee? More people pass away at the beginning of the year, having got through Christmas.

You've got to be careful, and then you've just got to let it go.

It could have been fatal. With anything kids do, they're always at a crossroads—it's going to be fatal or it's going to be nothing. And if you always treat it as fatal, you're going to be dead before she's five. Our house used to finish here, so in that wall was a great big window. And I was on the phone one day and I heard Hannah talking away to herself and then getting very quiet and then starting to go oooh-hooo-hooo, and I thought, that's sounding like she's scared, but she doesn't know whether she should be or not. I turned round and she was at the open window, hanging on to the frame, ready to fall out onto the concrete path. But by the time you've traumatised yourself over that—she's gone down the stairs. They're just an accident on two legs, they're just waiting to happen. If she doesn't bang her head she won't know the consequences. That girl we met yesterday looked like you could snap her in half. She's become so strong, it's like wrestling a grown-up.

I always said I was going to be a better parent than this. Go in the Jolly Jumper for a while. I'm off to have a drink. They can do their counselling when they're thirty.

Even though we're not believers, we ended up going to mass anyway. We've been to that particular service for a few years—it's the one at the Catholic cathedral, it's where the families go. It's the children's mass. And we've always been there without having a family. And so this year: I don't care, we're going, and we're taking the baby, and shoving it in all their faces.

Eventually it gets like that. You do what makes them happy, which feels like you're ignoring them, and leaving them. We'd go out and visit Mum, and she was more comfortable just being left alone in a room by herself.

Be prepared, because you can guarantee it'll be when the wind's coming this way that they'll light it. It won't be when the wind's going to their house. I've been working on my tapping because I was sabotaging myself.

The thing is, now it's Christmas tree dumping season. They're not the best for pregnant cows. It causes abortion. You've got this neighbour trained, haven't you? I wonder if the skin needs to come off?

I worry about her eyes drying out. She doesn't blink.

We'll go to Cathedral Cove. I love swimming there. That's where you can either do that really hellish walk, or you take the water taxi.

I don't know which we'll do, with her.

We'll take the water taxi. Took him half an hour to get Alice across the road and he's thinking: hellish walk, we could do that.

But then you're out on the water, and if the boat capsizes or sinks or something . . .

John's nickname when we were farming was Think of the Worst First John. That's what the workers called him.

I was a health and safety dream come true. Don't wear your woolly scarf next to the tractor hydraulics.

You have all these little knots from all your accidents and operations. Margherita, remember your mother? She had that broken rib. Hugged her too tight. Imagine a swan lying on the ground with its neck hanging out.

6

Did you get one of these little booklets? It's got some ideas for menus with iron. Clever girl. You're very clever. And making sounds? Knows her name?

She knows no.

Good girl. Can I just pop around and give you a snack chart? And PlunketLine's always there.

He's not wearing a mask. That's not Steve cleaning the spouting, is it?

I think it's the wife . . . what's her name? I think it's her brother.

He doesn't look Indian.

Yes he does.

Does he?

Look, lesbians on the cover. Because they're known for having malnourished children.

They look like sisters.

They do. Are they the Ulmer twins?

No, no, the rowing sisters.

Yes, the Ulmer twins. Because they advertise beef and lamb.

Oh is that what it is.

Yes. Not lesbians, then. Oh the Evers-Swindells.

Yes. They're the rowing twins.

Is your baby getting enough iron?

It's all meat, meat, meat, meat.

Maybe she can have fish. It mentions fish at the start.

Well it's a good way to get mercury.

When we were rowing, we needed iron-rich beef and lamb to ensure we performed at our best. Now we're helping Tom and Lucy do the same. Their favourite is beef mince and kumara: Tom needs it puréed and Lucy loves it mashed!

God, she was wearing very pungent perfume. I don't know. I just smile and nod.

This is put out by the Beef and Lamb Board.

I don't know what to do, I really don't. I feel like we should already have made the decision.

Let's put you in your chair. Shall we put you in your chair?

Man finds revenge dildo in his shopping basket after leaving a bad review on Amazon. Look.

Plunket's such a whore, with the Beef and Lamb and the Wattie's.

Oh dear, the place has gone mad here. You knew about my Christmas decorations . . . ? She's since taken my rubbish bins. I've got them back again, but I think she's gone a bit weird. She's holding my fingers. I can see your little teeth.

You're going to stand up, are you?

Can you see how that goes together, Alan? Are you going to help Daddy? Are you going to help Daddy?

No, ist kaputt. We'll have to get you a new one.

Could you do that?

Don't they supply them here?

We'll talk to Denise.

Nana's going to shut the door. Yes I am. Boo. Boo. Boo. I can't do it any more. No.

She was quite grizzly this morning, I'm surprised she's being so docile.

No, you're beautiful, I don't believe Daddy. No, you weren't grizzly, were you.

Hello! We got terribly lost, and then I lost Barbara. Oh poor Alice, all this noise. And then we thought—the bank, somebody'll know there, but no, I can't help you he said. And then I found a nice lady who had a map on her phone. We should have gone round that roundabout.

I think Hamilton is a silly city.

Well it's all different. Totally different.

How are you, old thing? Behaving yourself?

No.

Good.

Actually I can never find anything to be naughty about, living in here.

You've got a nice little room.

No, it's lovely, I'm very happy here.

And is she a good little girl?

As if our family would be naughty.

She's not telling any tales. Goodness, I'd almost forgotten how to hold a small spud. Oh dear—no tears. No tears, no tears, there's Dad. I've lost my touch. They've got a lovely feel about them. Their skin's beautiful. We're saying how lovely you are. No no no. No tears. And I hope she hung her stocking up?

She did. She got a cage for Christmas. Nana gave her a cage, didn't she?

I used to love these playpens but they're supposed to be psychologically damaging.

It would be if you put them in at eight o'clock in the morning and left them there till half past six. I never thought of doing that.

Barbara's in the Meadowbank Village now.

Yes, I haven't left Meadowbank Road yet.

They knocked down the big centre that Mother was in.

It's all new.

They're with Oceana.

Oceania. Oceania is the name of the owners. They bought all the Presbyterian Trust ones throughout New Zealand. Oceania did get the top award for all retirement villages in New Zealand.

Yes, I know that. Yes.

Is Mallory's full?

Oh yes. There's I forget how many people waiting.

My sister's gone to a Mallory's one in Chapel Road, and my brother, but they both say that my apartment's got better appointments.

Well this was one of the first ones. It's the staff of course.

There's so many people now living in places like this. We're all living so much longer. All us grey-haired widows.

Are you looking for a man so you won't be a widow?

No no, no thank you, I'm fine. I could always dye my hair.

I better go and sign out.

No, they're doing that for you—I told them.

See, I don't have to do anything.

What were you going to do?

Sign out. We have to sign out. So they know I haven't run away.

All the things one carries around.

Barbara just about fell off her chair when I said we lived in Ngāruawāhia.

That folder said Bowel Charts.

8

The new arrive women's autumn winter fashion vintage asymmetric embroidery cape woollen outerwear coat new fashion 2013.

**fabric the larceny shameful**: 30% wool 50% polyester fiber 20% wire

**washing the larceny shameful**: clothes, must have a good attend

different material of nursing please reference shop

more skirt please click here

more maxi dress please click here

more runway dress please click here

go store homepage please click here

**measurement the larceny shameful**: (unit cm, measurement the larceny shameful random decimation measurement, plus clothes ductibility, allow have the 2–4cm error.)

the above is the real pictures of the dress

you see what you get

Subject: It's so erotic

Hi!

Maybe somewhere, there is a person who will be perfect life partner for me. By nature I am a calm, open-minded and warm-hearted woman. And I would be really happy to meet a smart and cheerful man who wants to create a family. My heart is full of warm feelings and I want to give all of my tenderness to my special man. I have a lot of friends, because I know how to listen the people. My friends tell me that I'm very attractive. I need a honest man with serious intentions who will appreciate me, who respects me and has his own opinion. I'd like to start our acquaintance! Let's chat!

Regards, Nadezda.


The greatest destroyer of the glass eye is the salt in the tears.

9

Sally Field Is Gone! Today we say goodbye to Sally Field.

IT'S THE 9TH OF JANUARY.
Yeah, what happened to Valentine's Day?
I ask myself that every year . . .
And it's not even Lent yet.
Well you need to have something to give up in the first place I suppose.
I saw hot cross buns at Countdown last week.
I blamed my wife for our messy house, I was wrong for many reasons.
Scientists tell you why making your bed is disgusting. A weighted blanket moulds to your body like a warm hug.

Hurry up and cross. The freakin' cars aren't stopping for you, did you notice? Man you guys are eggs. Now get to that toy department.
You don't know about falling, do you? I don't want her to go through life with facial scars.
No, but I also don't want her to learn to be scared of the world.
Tina struggles with reality, and Dev gets his birthday wish.

Sister Julienne receives a phone call from Holloway Prison where the Salvation Army, who normally provide midwifery for female inmates, have been struck down with influenza. Two young girls who happen to look identical decide to swap households so they can play matchmaker to their single parents. A thief falls for an heiress as she dies in his arms. When he learns that he has the gift of reincarnation, he sets out to save her. An elderly lord abdicates to his three sons, but two of them become corrupt and turn against him. Dominic endures the scorching heat of the vast Australian Outback to locate one of the rarest bats on the planet—the ghost bat. Doris has been buying and selling vintage clothing for over thirty years, and has built her magnificent obsession into a high-end boutique store in LA. Old hand Stuart shows his skills handling dangerous eagles, but just how good is he? Lisa is called to a horse in trouble, and an adorable puppy melts hearts on its way to Florida. A body is discovered lying beneath a Jaguar Mark 2. In the movies they're sultry seductresses; cunning liars manipulating men with lustful acts.

The only witness to the conversation was Hitler's Alsatian. This is awkward.

## 10

When someone you love is in heaven, there's a little bit of heaven in your home. Right now murder is hot. That's what everyone wants, that's what the competition wants. A must-watch video about monthly periods. Take note of the male who thinks periods are brought on by stress.

I am on a garlic-roasting mission over here! I just pulled these bad boys out of the oven! I also have bread going into the oven right now! Woot! Home-made gnocchi, home-grown lettuce, peas, tomatoes and basil! Espresso machine ready!

He may look like a normal pup. But wait till you see WHAT he does with THIS paintbrush. WOW!

I NEVER knew sleeping on your left side can do THIS to your body. Did YOU know about this?

Do you have a novel inside of you? Stop reading this. Start writing. James Patterson Writing MasterClass. Author of nineteen consecutive bestsellers reveals his tricks of the trade. I have started but have no clue where to go from here. I even have a second book in mind for my character. I picture myself in front of a fireplace in a mountain cabin writing an insightful novel. My whole life is an interesting novel. I just lack the focus to write it all down. I write a chapter a day, on my eleventh book, love writing, don't know what to do with myself without writing and face book, poet on my page and have lots of readers also post on another page from where I grew up. I finished writing my manuscript, but don't have a clue on how to get it published? There are uncountable numbers of self-publishers around now . . . and many are on FB. Mom and I recently had a book published. All I can say is DO YOUR RESEARCH! This is a wonderful bargain. But . . . James Patterson doesn't even write his own books any more. You get popular then hire other writers. For the underemployed that isn't cheap. Make it cheaper. It is the best look inside the mind of the best author of our time. Afterlife + Angels + Love + mind + soul + murder mystery + time travel. Im in the process of finishing my first book but I have almost every James Patterson book he ever wrote. I was hooked on James Patterson for years and even Introduced some of my co-workers to his books too. Is there anyway to figure out if you have enough material in your head to do this? It's a lot of money for me, and I don't want to waste it. I've almost finished mine lol

I want this! It would be perfect for my needs. All I would need then is a small electric motor. I have got to get this!

## 11

Woke up this morning not quite awake and half in dreams. Would you survive in a horror movie? Why do so many people hate America? What is the saddest truth about life? If it's true that God made man in his image, then why are we not invisible too? Which language do you love? What keeps you from giving up on life? Are we the same person from birth to death? What colour looks best on you? Is everyone addicted to at least one thing? Is feminism a hate group? Are you afraid of bees or wasps? Do the people of North Korea like North Korea? Do you believe Donald Trump can make America great again? Can I have sex with any guy I like once I'm legal? When can babies eat eggs? If you were a bird what kind would you be? What should I name my book? Is there a chance my cat has mental problems? What is love? Do you have enemies? Do you have frozen meat in the freezer? If you knew your husband was cheating, would you contact the other woman? Is a person who's had homosexual sex a homosexual? How do I help my daughter not be attracted to demonic things? Do you like Sundays? If mathematics is so useful how come people barely even use it? Does vanilla matter? When you brush your teeth, do you look at the mirror while brushing? Why don't you go out for a little walk? Is there a website where I can get paid cash to answer questions?

## 12

No, Tuesday would be the first appointment. I'll let her know you're here. David Bowie passed away yesterday. He wasn't that old, either—but I suppose lifestyle. When you're dealing with plants that have been in a hothouse, what do you need to know in order to take them outside? I'll never give up, I admit that loud and clear, but I'll certainly cut down. I bought 30 grams and it cost me fifty-two dollars, up from forty-three. They can't say it stunts the growth of babies, look at Angela—she smoked all the way through Cody and he was nine one. So there goes that fucken theory. All you need to do is stretch out your arms and legs as far as they will go, and then relax. Stay afloat, stay alive. For now, it is appropriate to cry.

## 13

I've taken the dive. If you're uncomfortable, just let me know. It feels like your skin's popped. I've got you. This is the solution for you. If it's too much, just let me know. You may get a little tender. You may get a bruising feeling. If it's unbearable, tell me to stop. You're not alone.

I don't think I want to watch Real Housewives of Melbourne; it makes me feel bad about myself.

Well, how many of them have had a book accepted by Chatto & Windus?

I used to be a runner. I'm a mess. I get home, I sit on my couch. You feel like you have to keep control. Shall we have some courgette? You hold it. You don't have to get dressed. They're never little long enough. Good girl. Bite. Good girl.

This is your last chance. You can feel all the muscles in your body contracting. This is the solution for you: a little gentle manipulation.

I was the blinded doctor. I felt it in my core. Spiders. Rats. Men standing in the corner. Don't ask. It probably feels strange, but it'll help. Is that you? What are you waiting for?

## 14

I played the baby her own heartbeat. A lot of people use cotton buds, but they can turn their head, and bingo, they can't hear any more. I keep wondering what she's going to look like as a person. If I took a daguerreotype of her she'd need to be asleep, but it could look like a post-mortem. In baby photos of me, you don't see my face. I'm just talking, but apparently I'm boring you. It's a stock image deliberately chosen to be empty.

I'll have to check out the back. My hips are my biggest nightmare. I wore it twice and it all unravelled. Do you want another one? I don't think so; it's soulless and horrible. It's been too long, eh—we're in January. See if there's another large, Rose-Marie. Did that go all right? What about the red cardigan, no good? It was a *large*, Rose-Marie. It's been really hard saying goodbye to one in particular. Is this how we get out? What have I done to deserve this? She kept saying I'm healthy, there are worse-off people than me. And she's, like, towering. Are you happy there? Are you all right?

## 15

There might be a label on the shelf but that doesn't mean we carry it. We might have had it, at one time, and it didn't sell and didn't sell and sat there for ages. There's very little call for something like that in Hamilton. Did you get a name when you rang? I'll give you the speech I give everyone: you must always get a name. Otherwise they'll just tell you yes, we'll be getting some more in next week, goodbye, hang up. They don't care. There's no customer service these days. I tell you what, if I had a name I'd tear strips off that person. I'd hang them out to dry.

Watch your step as we go in, and try not to hang on to anything. It will be noisy at times—I'll get the guys to stop using the saws, I don't want to upset the ears. Steps are a big thing. And lots of leads, so be aware of tripping. If something does happen—if we have to evacuate the site—not that I think we will have to—just go to the end of the driveway, and if something does happen there's a first-aid kit in that red box. Now I just need you guys just to sign, just to say that we've talked about the very simple hazards, just to protect me, if anything does happen.

I always tell people, the first person you want to go and see is the builder. Go and see the builder, and then go and see the architect. And the reason I say that is that we'll give you good practical advice—an architect will give you wow, we can do this and we can do that. Nothing against them, but they don't necessarily always understand the implications. And so what they did was the architect arranged it all with the earth-moving guy, before we came on the scene, and got them to cut that there and then push it all out here. They could have pushed back quite nicely . . . but they didn't. They got it wrong, and I said that's a massive drop going down there. I think the house should have been where the shed is. It wasn't my problem, because we came along once it was done.

So we've started doing some of the fancy stuff—the finials and the fancy barges. We've got the fretwork to do, between the posts and the beams. He put a lot of detail into stuff like that. Typical architect though, we had a lot of detail that we didn't need, and no detail where we needed detail. We've had to make it work. He sort of shows it, but he doesn't tell us how it's going to work. There was a lot more head-scratching here than there needed to be. They're using an original front door—it's not quite right, because obviously it's come out of a different building and different width jambs and what have you. They've got ceiling roses as well. When I show you the plan you'll be blown away when you see what *would've* happened with the ceilings. The client didn't realise that they were going to be having what the architect drew, until I pointed it out.

Typical villa—a lot of what I would call wasted space, with the hallways. There were going to be arches going in, but the cost factor to get them curved—we were kissing goodbye to another $10,000. I was a little bit afraid where the cost was going. There's just so many unknowns.

Now you've got to let your eyes adjust a little bit. You definitely don't get this in an original villa—this is the media room. There's no light whatsoever in here. This had to be as dark as we could make it. It's killing the size of some of the other rooms. The bedrooms I think are actually quite small. I would do it different.

It's going to be the good old authentic-looking kitchen. They're not putting in a coal range though—it's more like, they want that look—that there might have been a coal range at some stage. Can you go somewhere else, mate? Go do something else? We were going to have balustrading round here—we've just talked them out of that. You couldn't look through, you'd lose the view, because by the time we'd come down five hundred from the top and we'd come up a metre high across the bottom, you end up with a tiny gap. And you're looking out and you're thinking, I'm in jail. As I said to them, it's all right if you're looking straight out through that gap, but every time you turn onto the angle, it suddenly becomes a solid wall. I said to them, it'll be like going back to pre-school, because you're going to be in this little playpen. And we're having to get them up here and say hey, there's no detail, there should be detail, what do you want? We'll raise things with you, like that out there, and say hey, we think this is going to look ridiculous, how do you want us to do it? And then what they think is in it isn't there, and then when we go and do something that's according to the plan—we didn't know, we don't like that. Well it's on the plan. Oh well we didn't ask for that. Unfortunately when it gets to the plan stage, for us as builders, we're taking it that you've signed everything off. They wanted a wood burner, and then they couldn't decide what they wanted, and then they decided they didn't want it, they wanted something a little bit different and a little bit bigger. We can't change that structure now, we have to go with what's here. So they've gone with the gas, which will look good, because they've got a massive big mantel. There's a few things, like they've got a four-poster bed that has to fit the bedroom, and this mantel has to fit. It's just making sure that we're understanding each other. We're governed by the likes of yourself and the architect. We don't really have a lot of say. They turn up every day. And I love that with clients, but sometimes I think—can you actually see anything? There are days like today where you'll look and you'll think, what have they done? But I guarantee we've been there.

You see what I mean about the corridor. That's at least five square metres, so between that and the front entrance, there's another bedroom that's disappeared, and by the time you go down the other corridor, you've almost lost two. That's why I was a little bit . . . with the architect. I don't think there's been a lot of actual thought. It's about getting the outside looking great, absolutely, but the inside's got to work too. And if you can't get it to work right, then it doesn't. The thing with us, we do pretty much anything. We're the old-fashioned builders, we're not like a housing company. The housing companies these days, they don't really employ builders as such, because the builders just stand frames and put trusses on and that's it. They don't do gib board, they don't put the windows in, they don't do the roof work—they're not builders. It's a little bit different with us, we're the good old-fashioned guys. You're welcome to come back and have another look if you want, once it gets further on. Because at the moment you can see it, but you can't see it. Give me a call though, because I'm a shocker.

I've got a nephew down at Massey doing political science—I wish I'd never liked him on Facebook. Everything's political. I don't mind, but talk about a subject that gets people going. And my other nephew's going down to uni in Otago, to be a doctor. It's a place I never got to. It's funny isn't it, you play to your strengths. My dad always said to me—I come from a family of four boys—you're not going to be a labourer, you're not going to sell stuff. You've got to get something behind you. You're either going to get a trade, or you're going to university. There's nothing else.

*

He was nice, actually.

He was. I wondered if he reminded you of your dad.

He did a bit. How do we get to the other one?

It's an eye-catching sort of home, isn't it, really. Are you guys looking to build?

We're just starting to think about it.

Would you be in Cambridge?

We're in Hamilton.

It's been very popular. Absolutely insane. People want something that's a bit more than the cookie-cutter. We do design and build, we design per site per client. It's light and airy. It's wonderful.

Here he is. That's my husband. She just had to finish her bottle.

Ohhhh . . . so cute. How old?

Seven months. All right, we'll just have a wee look around.

Alice, come and see. Don't poo on the shagpile. Oh my God, look at that chair.

A window seat . . . I'd love a window seat. Um, we live in Hamilton.

Eh?

We live in Hamilton. Not Ngāruawāhia.

Okay . . .

This is what I would rather, than the other one. It's more realistic.

The other one's imposing.

I like this carpet. It's a shade darker than ours.

It'd be nice having the TV set out of the way like that.

It's quite high. I suppose you'd get used to it. I find that quite high.

I want this chair. I want this chair.

I bought you a recliner.

And it didn't fit.

And we had to sell it to the lady with cancer. These are the kinds of drapes I want, with that pleat. Not stupid bunchy ones. This is nice.

This is very nice. I really like this.

This is so much nicer than our grotty deck. Our on-the-cheap deck.

Let's not talk about our house for a while.

Okay. There are no architraves. The granite's brilliant. Isn't it. Oh, it's got a chip on the edge there.

Amazing how you can do that.

All right, we better get her to Nana's.

Are you off, little one? Well you know where we are.

I was just wondering why they didn't have architraves, if they're going for the villa look. I mean I quite like it.

They wanted more contemporary on the inside but definitely villa replica on the outside.

I mean it still works.

She's adorable. I would spoil her rotten. That's why we have them, isn't it.

### 16

Look at this lawn. I have lawn envy.

This is the Burt Reynolds' moustache of lawns.

Why don't we have lawn like this?

Because we were sold bullshit.

It didn't say bullshit on the bag.

No, but we were sold bullshit from a bullshit artist.

What would be an alternative to lawn? Why do we have to have grass? It's just a convention. Astroturf?

Gravel?

Velvet?

I like that letterbox.

I don't. It's rustic.

It's a bit unrealistic. If you were afraid, you'd turn on all the lights.

Maybe you don't want to alert the killer to your presence.

Stop thinking so loudly, I need my own thoughts.

She's got a new hairdo.

It doesn't look very professional, does it. She looks like a bit of a bimbo. Murder–suicide?

I like her new hair. Is he the killer? That's the new Leo, I take it.

She had breast implants—they have serial numbers.

Do we know she had implants?

We just saw them.

That's the fake sister.

Who was the first guy they showed?

Just then?

Yeah.

It was the same guy, they just turned him over. It's Mossad, doing it all.

Is this your theory?

Yes.

You're all right, bubba. You're okay.

Tear some more hairs out of Daddy's leg.

Her hair's straighter there than it was in the last scene, but she's wearing the same outfit. So now that the other guy who wasn't Leo isn't in it any more, they have to sex it up with her and the new guy.

Did we see him leave or die or whatever?

No. We must have missed something. We didn't see Leo going either.

I meant Leo.

Murr-durr.

Thurr's bin a murr-durr. Again.

Was she a Mossad agent too? The nanny?

Maybe.

She's got the cord again! Cords and shoes!

It's coiling around her foot like a tourniquet. We put you in there to be safe. Not for you to garrotte yourself.

The chick in the wheelchair doesn't get to be much more than a token character.

She's developed.

But we don't see her back story or love life or house or anything.

She probably just goes home and plugs in and charges up for the next day. It's a very limited color palette in this. It's all greys and blues. It's desaturated.

What was that?

I'm lost.

Nathan, the little boy who died. He's his nephew. The guy who was shot through the ear.

Who's he?

The manager guy.

What does that mean?

I don't know.

Okay, I think it's bedtime.

Where's my sweet? Where's my sweet little strawberry? Give Mummy a kiss.

Oh, *he's* the nephew.

Yeah. They collected his DNA.

I thought it was the little boy. So they were double-crossing him?

No, they're Mossad. He's a terrorist. They're Secret Service.

So they were helping?

Although they don't have the bag.

I always reach a point in this show where I completely lose the thread.

They found the evidence on the corpse from the ferry. That's where the ransom was originally. She'll be drugged. Now I'm confused. I don't know who that was that's dead. I'm short of a character.

Bubba's MIA. She's working on the camera again. Crossing wires over, making a bomb.

## 18

Many people are shamans—healers who have access to the spirit world—and don't know it. Are you a shaman and you don't know it? Here are some telltale signs. I can relate! I'm Christian and I have been feeling better lately as I have been answering God's calling on my life! Wow! Natural therapists and psychologists have always told me I'm super empathetic and that's the cause of most of my illnesses, because I literally feel the pain and suffering of the earth and animals, so I can definitely relate to this. Funny this pops up and I have been really drawn to aromatherapy lately! I have desperately tried to be a shaman and help others in their afflictions but it seems that most only want to whine and complain and not do anything about it . . . I printed out all kinds of information and even gave them medicine to take and they don't do anything but go back to the doctors and get some more poison. I can relate to all of the listed, and especially the stealth shaman. I do have physic feelings and have seen my guardian angels. I have no memory of this. I was bullied, lied to, verbally assaulted, not invited to Christmas.

## 19

Placed in the right spot, shimmer is not just for teenagers. Do you really think gravitas is a key attribute for women? It pays to plan your wardrobe like you plan your life. You're probably not going to fix the heart.

Dark lips and dark lids are no longer taboo. This season you need to commit. If he's smoking five cigarettes a week, it's ten cigarettes too many. The fact is he's got one foot in the grave and a gentle gust of wind is going to blow him in there.

Wearing a smoky eye and bold plum lip has never been so exciting. He's walking a tightrope for his heart. The subconscious is just a bunch of programmes of all your life experiences; it's just an operating system.

I will die or I will live.

## 20

I thought I might take some DVDs to the beach. I've got Triumph of the Will and The Goodies.

Oh my God, it's a two-headed cow. Wait, it's two cows standing end to end.

## 21

The students could just stick a synonym in here and there and it won't catch it. You'd think they'd do that, but they don't. They just don't. Because if they were clever enough to think of doing that, they'd be clever enough to write their own freaking work. They're pretty dumb when it comes to that kind of stuff. If you ping somebody for plagiarism you have to get them into your office and make them cry. Now she's trying to come back and do further papers and waive pre-reqs because of special consideration. It was all a bit ridiculous. She hadn't been to any classes—obviously bad stuff was happening in her life, but bad stuff happens in our lives all the bloody time. Bad stuff happens in my life and I don't just not turn up to lectures for three weeks. I lost a baby and I wasn't like, I don't think I'll come in and teach you guys because I'm a bit sad now.

The people who were in our house were professionals. They were in and out like that. They only took stuff they could sell, they didn't trash the place, but they tipped out drawers that might have had cash in them. They'd been watching. I kind of didn't want the stuff back after they'd had their grotty little hands all over it. Even when the X-Box came back, I said to Sahaj, disinfect the whole thing. I had this whole big long narrative about how I was hanging around with horrible people when I was sixteen and did some real dumbass things, and at some point you have to make a decision to stop doing that because it never ends well. If you keep doing that stuff, it never ends well. And lots of people I knew then are dead, and is that how you want to end up, because you very nearly did in my car—you were lucky you didn't kill yourself or somebody else, which would've been worse, and really, sort yourself out. He cried a bit and I ended up hugging him, and he hugged me back—he didn't back off and he wasn't like, weird middle-class white lady. And I think it was good for Caleb to see that he needs to behave himself as well so he doesn't end up there in a few years. A lot of people I knew, friends of mine, who were children of nice very well-off Remuera families, ended up doing some really stupid things and are dead now. Wealth and privilege don't protect you.

Instead of the only option being to kill people, you can polish their stuff, motivate their people, *or* you can kill them. You build an empire—you research new technologies and you make houses for people. And then you kill them.

And your worlds get deleted.

### 22

How do you see this working?

I don't know, I'm an artist. Don't question me. If you choose to take in the views, listen to the melodic ramblings of a tūī, or examine the flower of a pūriri, then the walk may take longer.

### 23

Their daylight path followed the flight of the shining cuckoo, and relied on their knowledge of wind, waves, clouds, birds, and drifting seaweed. Expect the unexpected. Where you look is where you'll go.

Life's too short to live in a shithole like Hamilton.

We don't live in Hamilton.

Haere Mai Ki Ngaruawahia.

## 24

Apparently we're not to look disappointed if she says her first word and then won't repeat it, because that might harm her self-esteem. So when she does say fuck for the first time, we're to let her get around to saying it again on her own.

## 25

I'm the winner anyway because if you aren't smart enough to debate and your only real response is to delete me then I could care less. You are obviously a closed minded person out there dogging something because YOU COULDNT DO IT! I have not cursed anyone on here as that is just replacement for a person that has a limited dictionary. This is an extremely weird and toxic conversation.

## 26

Meryl Streep Is Gone. BREAKING NEWS. We will miss you Meryl Streep.

And how are you?

Just back from a holiday at the beach. Alan wants to move to Coromandel, he's decided.

He obviously hasn't spent enough time there.

Small.

Miles away.

He wants to make daguerreotypes there. I did point out to him that it would be quite a long commute for me to work, to earn some money, so we can afford to live.

Flying cars are not far away. Surely in another couple of years—we must be getting them soon, surely. So how did your body react to having time off?

I've been feeling better in there, but it's kind of all moved up. But that's more to do with sitting on the laptop. On the couch.

On the couch.

I know.

So do you think you'd move?

I had the idea that I could run very expensive, very exclusive creative writing workshops for wealthy tourists. But I'd have to look at a lot of shit writing.

Lots of Americans having mid-life crises. You need Disney to buy one of your books.

I don't think I really write Disney books.

I am so happy to hear that.

The Holocaust on ice.

Is that too much, or is that okay?

It's okay.

Not really. It's a weakness in your pattern. Between now and when I see you next, have a serious think about patterns. And if you can, take a mental Polaroid every hour, to see what you're doing.


Turn left at the roundabout, taking the first exit. Prepare to go over the roundabout after 970 metres. Prepare to go over the roundabout after 300 metres, taking the second exit. After 100 metres, go over the roundabout, taking the second exit. Recalculating route. Drive for 1.4 kilometres. Prepare to turn sharp left after 280 metres.

It's Where Your Pets Would Shop. Biologically Appropriate™ Dog & Cat Food. Inspiring Excellence in Fish Care! Enriching Environments for Feathered Friends!

I think it's the Grasslands that we get, but can you just check on our card? It's normally my husband who comes.

Course I can. What's your last name?

I think it's under Chidgey. C-H-I-D-G-E-Y.

Is it Cat A?

Is it what sorry?

It's for cat, isn't it?

Oh yes, it's cat, sorry.

I think it is . . . I don't know if it is, eh.

Maybe it's under Bekhuis. B-E . . .

No no no, it's under your name, you've told me the right name, but I can't remember . . . was it Pacifica? Catherine? No, it's Wild Prairie.

Oh is it? Did we used to get the Grasslands?

Yes you did. Did you want to go back the Grasslands? You've been getting the Wild Prairie.

I'll get the Wild Prairie then. Is Ginger Boy hanging out on the concrete where it's cooler?

Yeah. It's real hot, eh.

Not nice to be a cat today.

Recalculating route. Take the next left. Then, turn left at the roundabout. After 50 metres, turn left at the roundabout, taking the first exit. Prepare to turn left after 460 metres. Take the next left. Take the second left. Then, go over the roundabout. Recalculating route. Fuck. Prepare to turn left after 610 metres. Prepare to turn left after 300 metres. After 100 metres, turn left. Recalculating route. Prepare to turn right after 410 metres. Prepare to turn right after 280 metres. After 100 metres, turn right. Prepare to turn left after 400 metres. Take the next left. Prepare to turn right at the roundabout after 550 metres. After 100 metres, turn right at the roundabout, taking the third exit. Take the third exit. Then, turn left at the roundabout. After 70 metres, turn left at the roundabout, taking the first exit. Prepare to go over the roundabout after 430 metres, taking the second exit. After 100 metres, go over the roundabout, taking the second exit. Prepare to turn right at the roundabout after 770 metres. Prepare to turn right at the roundabout after 300 metres, taking the second exit. After 100 metres, turn right at the roundabout, taking the second exit. Take the second exit. Prepare to go over the roundabout after 490 metres, taking the second exit. After 100 metres, go over the roundabout, taking the second exit. You're over the speed limit. Recalculating route. Fuck. Prepare to turn back at the roundabout after 250 metres, taking the third exit. After 100 metres, turn back at the roundabout, taking the third exit. Take the third exit. Prepare to turn back at the roundabout after 340 metres, taking the fourth exit. After 100 metres, turn back at the roundabout, taking the fourth exit. Take the fourth exit. Drive for 12 kilometres. You're over the speed limit. The police are investigating threats made against a woman who filmed herself sexually abusing her one-year-old son for $300. You're over the speed limit. A woman has died while diving in a bay on Wellington's south coast. Islamic State militants have set up a specialist command to plot attacks against Europe. The signs are that Paris was not an isolated attack. The coroner says the driving of two Korean tourists prior to a fatal crash on the West Coast was so poor that witnesses photographed it. The deaths are another example of tourists needing to drive more responsibly. A woman injured by a car in a Whāngārei cake shop is now in a stable condition in hospital. Recalculating route. Motherfucker. Prepare to turn left after 490 metres. Take the next left, pinning her and her daughter against the counter. The Ford Motor Company is pulling out of Japan. Prepare to turn left after 290 metres, focusing its attention instead on China. Take the next right. Drive for 4.3 kilometres. You're over the speed limit. Shut up. You're over the speed limit. Prepare to turn left after 800 metres. What is the appeal of that kind of cricket at the Basin, do you think? I think it's just sitting on the grass and watching cricket. Prepare to turn left after 300 metres, when you've got two great teams going at it on a sunny day. Take the next left, then, take the next right. Take the next right, then, take the next left. You feel like you're part of something. Take the next left. Prepare to arrive at your destination after 240 metres. No. Arrive at your destination after 100 metres. No. You have reached your destination. No I haven't.

## 27

I still don't know what I'm meant to be doing.

## 28

On an exhale, release the heart.

## 29

Work-Integrated Learning Seminars: The Curriculum Enhancement Programme's (CEP) Curriculum Design Framework addresses increasing employer demand for 'work-ready graduates' by incorporating industry and community engagement into curricula. To assist in developing a sound strategy

## 30

We often wonder if the earth beneath our feet could swallow us up.

## 31

I don't get over very often and today was a free day and I thought shit, I'll come over. I've been driving a truck for this guy—I've been halfway round the bloody globe. Timaru and back twice, Christchurch and back, way up north . . . I run a trailer down to Christchurch for him and I charged him seven hundred and fifty bucks. Just a figure that came out of my head. And he up and paid it.

Who's Erin engaged to?

Some untidy-looking coot from Timaru. He's got the biggest beard you ever did see. The first thing I said to him was, you got a job? He goes yep, I work for Fulton Hogan. Then I said, have you been in jail? And he goes no, not yet. I said, have you got any money? No. Have you got a house? No. You're not much bloody good to me then.

You'll have to have a cuddle with Honorary Grandad Brian, bub. You'll have to get used to him. We don't have any other grandads for you. It's all right. It's all right.

Look at the mouth.

I've stopped getting old. I've just stopped having birthdays.

That'll save me buying the cards and birthday presents that I used to.

And that ten shillings that Johnny Burrows used to give me, and you never ever did. Johnny Burrows always gave me ten shillings for my birthday and I waited for Aunty Pat and it never ever turned up.

Who's Johnny Burrows?

The old dude next door. There was Tom, Bob, Terry and Johnny. Four brothers.

My godfather.

Who was your godfather?

Johnny Burrows.

He was mine too.

I know.

Were they all bachelors?

Yes.

And Miss Gallagher. Miss Gallagher lived there—there were five of them in the house. And the funny part about it, I was at Mum's graveside just the other day, and two of the Burrows boys were fat guys, and they both died at sixty-four, and the two other guys were skinny and they died at seventy-four. Ten years apart, they all died.

Flat white?

41

Yes please, love. You're a good girl. Thank you. All my pilot mates have lost their licences with cholesterol. If they have a heart attack while they're flying. One time he took my heart and it was a smidgen under what it should be. Doctor Somas— he's been there for a hundred years. He's from one of those funny countries. They play cricket there.

Johnny was my godfather. When I was little he used to buy me a pair of shoes every birthday. My father used to buy us a drink at the Halswell Hotel. What was it? Sarsaparilla, that was it. After the Wednesday sales at Addington they all used to go to the Halswell pub, and I'd be sitting out in the car and Dad would bring me out a sarsaparilla. I don't even know if you can get sarsaparilla now.

Yep, you still can. I'm sure it doesn't taste the same as what it used to, though.

It tastes like toothpaste to me, whenever I've had it.

That's it. So have you read the books on those murders in Picton, have you? Gone out and bought those new books about Scott Watson?

Don't upset her.

No, no I haven't. Have you?

No I haven't, but I'll have to get them and read them. I like that sort of thing.

Yes, I was thinking about reading them. Very interesting, isn't it. I think there's a lot hasn't come out.

They're saying now in one of the books, they're saying there was a drug deal.

Yes.

They took one off the market, but it's back on today.

Have you got the books?

No. No. They took it off the market Wednesday or Thursday, and Whitcoulls have got it back on the market today.

Have they got it back again?

Yeah.

Have you got any of the books?

No. No.

No, I'd quite like to read them.

It does sound interesting.

Don't let her get upset.

Do you know those writer guys?

I know of them. I don't know them.

How would he get all this inside information?

He said he'd sifted through the police files.

Well how'd he get the police files?

I don't know.

It's never quite said about that, has it.

No. But this witness that he says he interviewed says he saw someone fitting Scott Watson's description getting rid of two bundles that looked like bodies.

That's interesting isn't it.

And that they might be buried on land, not disposed of at sea.

Yes.

Mm.

There's still something queer about the whole thing.

I think that he definitely did it.

Oh yes.

I don't know. That Scott Watson, he lived next door, and when he was born we'd push him round in the pram. And his mother was Beverly Boone who lived where we used to park the bikes to go to school in the bus. We weren't really associated with Beverly Boone, because she was bad. She went to Halswell Primary, you see. And *her* mother, Mrs Boone, she was on our party line when I was a kid, but she was bad too. She always had a new boyfriend. Always on the line talking to a new man.

I had no idea. I didn't know that.

There's lots of things.

I'm too far away.

# [ FEBRUARY ]

## 1

I googled a lost love's name and found his obituary.

## 2

Good to see you after all this time.

I didn't want to come to New Zealand and not say hello. I thought it would be weird—I mean everyone would see Facebook photos, and not saying I was here is a bit funny. Sorry about being so un-German about times and dates. This is an age where they keep banging their head, isn't it.

She needs to explore the world, she's going to hurt herself now and then.

That's the good thing with Luisa—because we've seen it twice, we just don't care. And I know it's bad. With Johanna we were really strict—I think the first five minutes of television she ever had in her life was when she was three, and the first ice creams or chocolate . . . whereas with Luisa, she'll scream for chocolate and we'll just look at each other and go, I can't be arsed to fight, here you go. Johanna is still really well-behaved, so it was easy to give her away and not be embarrassed by how she's going to behave this year. I'm not sure about the two others.

So is Johanna's English pretty good?

She's had English at school for six years, and she can

44

understand most of what people are saying. She's really shy about speaking, but that will have to change now. The Asian students who come and who don't speak a word of English, that must be so hard. The family, they had another student before Johanna—she was Japanese, and she didn't know any English, so she had an interpreter with her, an electronic thing. They don't speak any German. He can say 'I am a mushroom'.

I think you're getting tired. Are you getting tired? The most common population in the world to have coeliac disease is the Irish, and I'm three-quarters Irish by blood. I don't know if something weird happened to Irish genes during the potato famine. The first time we gave her meat her eyes got really big and she was just grabbing for the bowl.

Do you want to see photos of babies, Alice? Don't put in the wrong code, because I don't know how to undo it. Let's see if I can show you a baby photo. Do you like baby photos? Do you want to touch that? Go on then. Don't delete them all. Oops. Don't delete them. Hang on. How do I undo it?

Did she delete one? Let me have a look. Shall I just have a look.

I don't think there are any really embarrassing photos in there, apart from us having a shower under the waterfall. This is Hamburg, and they have built this opera house and there has been a lot of debate about it. It's just one of those major disasters in Hamburg. It became more expensive the longer it took to build. I think it doubled in price. The population wasn't happy about that, saying, well, we need money for education, for childcare, for all that, and there's never any money, and you're putting it all into this ugly building. A bit like the Sydney Opera House. It's a major landmark and it's in the harbour so it's the first thing you see when you arrive by sea. Car keys! And there's a torch, look!

These are some test ones. Test daguerreotypes. The images are really fragile. You could just wipe them off with your finger.

I've never been to Mount Taranaki before, so she sent me on a walk where you get really nice views up . . . are they called Pukaiki, the range?

Punakaiki?

Not Punakaiki, but something like Pu . . . oh these names, Catherine, I just can't! They all start with a P. They are very similar and I'm not very good at it because I don't know what it means—there's Māori meanings, isn't there. So I don't know whether there's syllables that mean house, mountain, lake . . .

Sometimes we know what it means.

3

We'll be a Pacific underclass ruled by US corporates. This is the end of our sovereignty, and they're just blithely telling journalists what they need to be focusing on. And they'll have a referendum on a shitty tea-towel flag but nothing on the end of our sovereignty. It's just so appalling. The US is trying to escalate things by telling its citizens here not to attend any protests—stay out of Auckland tomorrow. And police are preparing their tasers, and the whole thing is designed to escalate into a law and order issue. It makes me feel sick.

I once got a taxi, the driver was from India and had been here for one and a half weeks. I asked if he had a NZ driver's licence and his reply was 'actually this is my brother's business'. He couldn't drive at all. The amount of times people from other cultures have almost caused accidents in front of me on the motorway and were completely unaware amazes me. Not being racist, it's just an observation.

That is the same situation with my friend Ben, he live over in Massey. He got in the taxi from Lynn Mall to his place and the driver he's a Indian, he hardly speak English, all he said thirty-five dollars, Ben said to him I won't pay you, if you want me to pay you, it better you call the police, that the end, because he have any licences at all.

Hey, any progress with the cage? We need to try and trap the mother.

## 4

Tired of stressful news? Yes, I want uplifting and inspirational news. No, I don't want positive news.

## 5

Pick up the parsnip. Here it is. Pick up the parsnip. Here. Pick up the parsnip. Bubba. Pick up the parsnip. Here it is. Pick up the parsnip. There it is. Pick it up. Pick up the parsnip. Here it is. Pick up the parsnip. Here. Pick it up. Pick it up. Pick up the parsnip. Come on. Pick up the parsnip. Yes. Pick up the parsnip. Here it is. You like it. You like parsnip. Here it is. Pick it up. Pick it up. Where's your hand. Pick it up. Here. Bub bub. Bub bub. Come on. Pick up the parsnip. Here we are. Good girl. Good girl. Pick it up. Do you want the parsnip? Want the parsnip? No.

## 6

Maybe I should include some lines of me whingeing about Creative New Zealand's funding application process, and then include that section as my writing sample in my application to Creative New Zealand for funding to write the book.

So please, don't leave your child or animal unattended in the car. With the weather getting warmer, we at The Warehouse want to ensure that every member of your family has a safe and enjoyable summer.

How's Karen doing?

She come back home, yeah, she come back last year. She's working at New World.

Back at New World? Good on her. She was there for a long time.

Yeah, so she come back home last year.

I don't think it's all painted up quite what they say it is.

Yeah, nah nah nah, she come back home. You can't beat your home.

Is he still over there?

No, he come back too.

So is he with you?

No no no no no, got none at home. I don't think so!

We used to give her cheek about hey Karen, when you going to start your family?

When you see her, it's not that—it's too much eating.

Especially over there, eh. I know Talia put on a fair bit. She's been getting into exercising. She goes walking up the top of the Hakarimatas. She said to me, don't you say you're gonna come, Mum, because you won't make it, and I says how do you know? Wayne said to them you gotta be careful going up there, not only of humans, but wild pigs. Because they come out on the tracks. It takes them about three and a half hours.

So how many Kieran's got?

Two. Calais is coming up ten and Denzel's seven. Which one keeps dyeing his hair blond?

Michael.

He always talks to me and I'm like now which one are you?

That's the chatty one. That's the yakkity yakkity yakkity one, that one. I have to pull him away, he's talking to anybody. Never stops.

I'm home by myself today, so I thought I'd just come and do what I want to do. I'm getting close to proper retirement age.

You don't look it.

I'm sixty-four.

You don't even look—when's your birthday? Or has it gone past? Or coming up?

I've got one coming up.

True? You don't even look it.

My mother didn't look her age either when she died.

True? You don't even look—you don't.

Some days I can feel pretty old. I've got more grey hair than what my mother did when she died at seventy-eight.

Still, gee, I can't get over—you don't even look it.

Time doesn't stop for anybody. Some people look at Wayne when he says how old he is and they go, you don't look that old.

How old is he?

He's seventy-six. He's older than me.

Yeah but you don't even look it.

Some days I feel ancient.

Actually you don't.

I better let you go.

7

I took exception to Mum pointing out twice now what different colours the kittens are. Implying that Jasmine's been whoring around the neighbourhood with different fathers.

Mum's apocalyptic comment about the cat was she might have AIDS. She might have cat AIDS and give it to the other cats.

Is it your birthday today? Did I get him a card or something?

We're going to the movies on you.

That's good of me.

I've got little scratches all over me from the kittens and little bruises all over me from the baby. I'm feeling quite brutalised.

You can't do that to Mummy. I don't think you do, I think Mummy's making it up. Yes I do. Show Nana how you can stand up. I don't think you can, I think Daddy's telling lies. Yes he is. You don't want to stand up, do you? Oh, clever girl!

That doesn't count. Come on. You don't get praise just for

doing that. That's not how children learn to be independent.

You didn't stand up on your own, I know. I'm not going to say it again until you do it properly. Is it really hot out? I love this room because in the winter it doesn't matter and in the summer I have those trees shading it. You don't really want the sun pouring in in the summer. Gwen's room gets so hot.

It's not very clear, but that's the little white kitten Baz—short for Basmati—and his tortoiseshell sister.

They're quite different, aren't they?

We might keep the mother cat, but at the moment she's terrified. Not that we need another one. We're just fostering the kittens—we're not keeping them. When they're old enough we'll find homes for them. Tell Mum what she did last night, Alan. Alan managed to trap her, finally, in a cage.

We got her to our place, and put her in the bathroom with the kittens. After a while I thought I better go and check on her—make sure she's not doing anything to the kittens, given that she's a bit feral, and she hadn't seen them in a week.

It wasn't a week—just a couple of days.

So I opened up the bathroom door and I looked around, stuck my head in, and I couldn't see her anywhere. It's not a very big bathroom.

No.

So I kept on looking around, wondering where she's hiding. I had my dressing gown on the back of the door, and she was hanging on top of that the whole time—she'd climbed all the way up to the top, and I was opening the door and swinging it back and forth, and she was hanging there.

Like a ninja.

Not making a peep. And then when the door opened up wide enough, she jumped over the top, past me and out into the hall.

And down through our bedroom and into the en suite.

Since then we've been a bit wary of her.

She's been wild for months. We haven't let Alice loose on the kittens. She gets a bit over-excited. They're so tiny, they can sit in my hand, like that.

She's very observant for her age. I can't believe it.

Right, we'd better dash.

Wave madly. Turn around and wave madly again across the bowling green. She's still waving. Oh God.

I thought I could make each month progressively shorter, so it simulates time speeding up. That could be quite interesting.

I've got a whitetail under a glass in here. I didn't really think this through.

## 8

That's too much like the fucking Luminaries, though.

## 9

If they can trust what they read, that's great. They will either incentivise or sanction us. It's all about the end product. It's about both absolute and relative measures. What is your purpose? What's working? What's not? How do you know? How robust is the evidence? Are any changes leading to worthwhile improvements? What's the difference between Not Yet Confident and Not Confident? Do we have significant gaps or weaknesses? Do we want to say that we do? Too much for a Tuesday morning?

Here's your organisational rubric for self-assessment. If you can read it. Self-assessment should be continuous. Every time you do something, you should be reflecting.

When we're telling the story amongst ourselves, can we talk about lack of understanding rather than lack of support? Can anyone speak to that?

Students become really clever at disguising and hiding.

Students disappeared. They just disappeared.

I came here to do art, not write.

## 10

If she could not be tattooed in her ear, because she's white and it's really obvious on white cats.

It's meant to be obvious. That's the point of them. So they don't get trapped twice and desexed twice. If you'd just sign down the bottom there.

The SPCA said it was okay.

So we'll give you a call when she's awake from surgery and ready to go.

Can you make a note wherever possible about the no tattooing? We really really don't want the tattoo.

I've crossed it out on the form, and it's also written there with asterixes around it, so . . .

Will it need to be written on the form as well?

It is written on the form. I've crossed it out, and that's where we look, on every single surgery that we do.

So we don't need to write it on there as well?

I can put a bigger scribble through it.

## 11

I've decided that the landlady doesn't wear a glass eye herself; she was married to an optometrist and has a cabinet of antique glass eyes.

There were two other babies in the class and they were about eighteen months old. Alice doesn't mind having her ears in the water, it doesn't distress her, but the other two don't like it, they haven't reached that stage yet. The instructor holds her, and we go one, two, three, and then we throw her under the water. She said it's not really important to reach any sort of goals, it's just so she has a fun experience, and that's all she needs to remember from it. And if she picks up some skills along the way then that's all good and fine.

But she will get a certificate? We must have the certificate. We must have the qualification.

She was moving really well today. She doesn't cry and complain like the other babies.

She's much better than the other babies.

She didn't really cry about anything till I had to go back to the changing room and was trying to get her out of her swimsuit on a hard wooden seat with slats. And she peed on the towel and was crying and I had to get her out of the wet swimsuit and she didn't want that and then she had a really wet nappy—some of that must have been in the pool. In the changing room, I have to look and see if there are any naked men around. I have to pull the sun shade up on the pram. There's always some strange man standing down the back in the nud, just staring into nowhere.

The same one?

No, it was an Indian man this week, and last week it was a Chinese man. Saying nothing, just standing there waiting to dry or something. I don't know what they're doing.

Seeing a dong is not going to traumatise her.

## 12

How's your mood at the moment?

It's all right. It's the same old thing—if I stay on this really restrictive diet, then it's reasonable, but as soon as I try and reintroduce anything, it all comes crashing down.

Your white cell count's always running a bit low. I might just repeat it. Getting back into your writing again?

Yeah . . . fitting it around the baby is . . .

What's your next book about?

I haven't decided yet.

Anything you find inspirational at the moment?

No.

I think a child in the house brings a different kind of joy, doesn't it.

### 13

They could eavesdrop on the violence of the universe; their calculations told them how stars perish.

Jane Fonda Is Gone! WE WILL MISS YOU JANE FONDA.

### 14

Ladies don't sit with their feet up in the air. No. What's that on the front of your top? Is it anything?

It's a lion.

Eh?

A lion. Or a cat.

Oh. It's lovely. Now I can see. Mmm. It's lovely. The colours are lovely.

Bubba, put your legs down.

I was just telling her before it was not ladylike. But she didn't take any notice. You don't see Mummy doing that, or Nana. Put your hair back, I want to see your earrings. Oh, beautiful. Diamonds?

Yeah. My Katherine Mansfield Award earrings.

Not make-believe. Isn't it funny, people think they can wear a bit of glass and it looks like a diamond. Ladies don't shout like that. No. No they don't. No. No. She's quite amazing for her age, I hope you realise that. Have you got any secret Valentine's cards? I've got one from Jiffy.

Alan got one very similar to yours. I also put it on Facebook. He's got quite a following, Jiffy. The cats have their own Facebook page—Mintie and Solly and Lily and now Jasmine, as well as Jiff. They've got 2059 people who follow them.

You're joking!

Yep. All over the world. They've got a fan in Syria.

Helen's just been to Syria, hasn't she.

No . . .

Wasn't it Syria Helen went to?

No. They're on their way to Finland.

But I got a card from her.

I'm pretty sure you don't go to Syria on holiday.

I'll have to read it again. Did I buy anything? I haven't got a parcel.

## 15

Some people's author photos are just ridiculous, eh. Taken thirty years ago, and totally unrecognisable. This bloody photographer that's taking a photo of me—she wants me lying on the ground with my head surrounded by fruit and flowers. Some kind of dusky maiden thing. She wanted to do it at the beach, and I thought, I don't want my hair blowing in the wind at the beach. I said why don't we do it in Ōtara—I work here, I live here. I thought it'd be a bit more real. But she said she's not very good at capturing life. I haven't been able to answer her. I lose words, and sometimes I don't find them for a couple of weeks.

I was an in-between person. I bought a damaged house. Everything crashed and fell. A lot of things broke, very important things to me broke. Sinkholes opened up. I'm realising that the safety I thought I had doesn't really exist. Nobody came outside. The trucks came, the little diggers came and filled in the holes. It was just so completely unexpected. We've moved on, and got on with our lives; set out our precious things. Ask me a question, because my mind is empty.

## 16

I've scribbled all the way through it. Eighty percent of my

notes are *brilliant, yeah, this really works now, perfect!* Most of the marks I've made are tiny things. There are a couple of things we had talked about before which I feel are still a little bit there for me. I still feel that some of those early sections could be just a little bit tauter. But I wondered what you felt about that, because I know that was something that I asked you to do. This is not radical. It's a tiny degree. It's not even particularly about content, it's more just about pace. I think that you've definitely done a lot to move it in that direction, I just think we could push it a little bit more, just to make it a little bit more urgent. But why don't I have a look? I've got lots of notes on the manuscript already, so I will go through and check and see if there are obvious places. Because even again this morning, I was looking at it and there were little things that I saw. There was just a tiny thing this morning as I was reading—and I mean it's a tiny, tiny, tiny thing, I mean literally we just cut one sentence. Two sentences. There are a few places like that where I feel maybe you need to be a little bit brutal. I can go through and see if there are sections that I feel could be shorter. I don't know how you feel about that. I know that this isn't a new point that I'm making. I just feel like we could do a little bit to push that tiny bit further.

What I might do in the light of this conversation is go through and find some of those places where I think maybe we could cut. A paragraph, two paragraphs. Maybe I'll put a few notes just to explain. I think sometimes you are a bit too clever for your reader. There's a risk that you're doing something that's much more interesting than a reader would necessarily realise. Sometimes things are so subtle that they might not realise. You need to make sure that they're still on board. Even if it feels like a signal, it's not. I mean it's a signal, but it's still quite a subtle one. That was my only thought. It was just literally a thought I had this morning. I don't know whether it's worth your having a bit of a think about it.

Let's see how long you think you need. I don't want to rush you. Obviously I'm really happy to keep discussing things if you don't agree, or if there are places where I've suggested things you aren't sure of. It tends to be about tightening, or being brutal and cutting a section out completely. Hopefully it will be clear from my notes what I mean. I think the work you did last year has made an enormous difference; if we can just push it that tiny bit more. But I think it's really nearly there. It's not much, at all. I think it is about just being able to step back and being a little bit brutal.

## 17

We'll never know whether a crime never happens or not.

## 18

Have you heard of yoni eggs? And yoni steams? I think a Mayan womb massage could help too. You can heal yourself. I was surprised to learn that the majority of women are walking around with a prolapsed uterus and don't even know it.

## 19

My initial reaction is that this would be too much change and undo too much of the sophisticated and extremely rewarding patterning that shapes the book. I especially like the gradual slide into horror, and the avoidance of a conventional romance plot—because of course it isn't, and I wonder about negative reactions if the book raised expectations that it is.

## 20

I think about ultimately where we'd like to live, and where we'd be happy. If it's not here—and I don't really think it is—where is it? And I think about moving back to Wellington. Back to the enclosed hills. It's a mental barrier, to get over those hills, and away to somewhere. You can never go back. I do feel we are very fortunate for what we have. We're on the periphery, but that's okay. We're a bit more fluid. I don't want to be anywhere to do with Auckland. Up in Northland, it's too hot, isolated—and anywhere south of here, like Whanganui—I just don't feel the pull, the draw of somewhere like that. Napier's too isolated as well, so is New Plymouth—although I've never been there. The Manawatu, Palmerston North is probably even more of a grey death than Hamilton. So where is it? Recently I was thinking about Nelson, but it's too cliquey there.

Too tie-dyed.

Part of it is, and part of it's quite elitist. And it can be tie-dyed and elitist at the same time. But there's the Abel Tasman National Park, and the West Coast—amazing places to visit. I was reading something recently—no, it was a YouTube video, about living in New York. It's the most cunning of prisons, because the prisoners are their own warders. They commit themselves to their internment. They convince themselves that this is the place to be and they put up their own walls—a prison to keep them from leaving. That's what big cities are. People sit in the subway and crammed in traffic, ignoring the very reasons they should be getting out, living somewhere else. I just don't know. I go back and forth. Recently I was thinking if Margherita and John decided to put lifestyle blocks in next to the paper road, you could put a driveway in off the cul-de-sac, going past that big tree, going back and over the bridge they have there, and then those paddocks at the back could be this amazing lifestyle block that's away from the road and away from people, and you could regenerate it with native plants. But it'd be a chunk of change to buy that size land, and in the end you'd still be in Ngāruawāhia. But is it a bad place, really, in the end? Look where we were at Sycamore Lane. It was very highfalutin, but the people there had a Jurassic-sized carrot up their arse. I don't want to be associated with white privilege. For me, being next to the manufacturing base at Te Rapa—

there are some advantages there, for what I want to do with the daguerreotypes. And we can holiday in the Coromandel. It's not such a bad life. I feel if we went back to Wellington, we'd just be getting caught up in the rat race, and we'd be crammed in somewhere, enormous cost, high debt, and be forced to earn a really high income just to get by. If we can both do our own thing it's so much more empowering, and in a way opens up many more options that will make us happy. Because we're both introverted. I think about this. I go round in circles on it all the time.

## 21

Is there a picture of her on the back?

There is on her website.

I never thought about that. I do want to see a picture of her now.

Is there one of Vahid?

I googled, and I was trying to find him, and I couldn't find a picture of him, and I was very disappointed.

It's quite nice that they've managed to keep their privacy in this day and age.

But we're all poking and prying and trying to find out.

It's a very intimate book. I mean if she's laying it out there . . .

She goes to book clubs in the UK. She's been to about twenty or thirty book club meetings. Unfortunately I couldn't find any book club questions for us online.

We were saying before, we wondered about the speed with which she fell in love and how she went from being, like, he's a bit of a pain but I'll use him to get to his mother because I want to cook, to all of a sudden falling for him.

I didn't see the falling in love part. I'm confused. You didn't like him and now you do.

Especially because of some of the things he said to her about her appearance.

You're dirty.

Part of that's got to be the environment they're in though. It's like all the reality TV programmes. The Bachelor and whatever. They fall in love instantly. It's that enclosed circle where you don't see that person out of their comfort zone. It's very intense.

Amazing then that it's lasted.

I wasn't expecting that. At all. I thought at the airport, she's going to break his heart.

The fact that he followed her—Tehran, and then on to Istanbul and then London.

And left the family, which must have been a huge deal.

For that culture.

Mmmm.

I was kind of surprised that it ended with them being together, because when they were first becoming involved with each other I did find myself thinking this feels quite exploitative, and I wonder if he knows that she's writing this book. I mean obviously he must, now, but I wondered about the writing process. Because it did feel all quite immediate—how could she have remembered conversations to that degree if she wasn't writing it as she was going? And if she was writing it as she was going then it did feel like she was using him for a story, to make this something more than just a recipe book.

They ended up not having that many recipes in it at all. I thought there were going to be more.

And who was the author she was having an affair with? Did anybody google? With the wife in France?

I did try but I couldn't figure it out.

I thought ooh, I wonder who that is.

I bet we could find out.

And the instant conversion to Islam that she didn't realise was happening. She was just repeating these foreign words. Does that mean she is now a Muslim? I mean, does that stick?

I wonder how her parents feel about the way she wrote about them.

I kept thinking that too, but that's the nature of memoir, isn't it.

You've got to hurt somebody.

## 22

We have walls full of nail holes. People just walked out and left the remnants. Nobody says, hey guys, we need to take some responsibility for this. There's chips, there's bones. It's filthy. It just sits there and rots. They smear chicken fat all over the screens.

We can get spray bottles, we can have them there.

I did that, and they nicked the spray.

Maybe if staff members can have their own spray bottle.

I don't want you to do it, I want the students to do it. It's about respecting each other, it's about respecting the building. It can be quite frustrating. You get an email saying this job has been logged, and there's still a hole in the ceiling where the tile fell out. Expecting something to happen tomorrow is a false hope. What if a student cuts themselves? Look for hazards. The new guidelines lift the definition from hazard to risk. Someone runs a cord across the room—you need to be thinking about that risk. Once a risk is turned into an incident, we can then look at how we can prevent this happening again. You don't want someone falling over, having a diabetic incident. Please don't wedge doors open. If a door's wedged open, anyone can walk in and anything can happen. Saying I didn't know about today's meeting means you haven't been reading your email. Because that's how we communicate it to you.

## 23

I've only got five likes. Maybe the world's not ready for your head superimposed onto Patrick Swayze's shirtless body.

It's still early.

## 24

You have a unique code.

## 25

She prayed at the tomb of Rachel, who also suffered infertility. She even drank crushed red rubies. Watch thy houre cometh.

## 26

With the eyebrows, can I have them not so skinny this time?
So just a tidy-up with the little loose ones at the bottom?
A bit of an arch but not skinny-skinny.
Do you know what colour you're wanting for tinting?
Medium brown.
Sure. You can close your eyes.

She did them really dark again.
Good Lord.
I know. I'll have to soap them. Say something.
. . . The shape looks nice.
It's a strange feeling, lying there not being able to see anything, and a stranger wiping your eyes for you.

## 27

We contacted the brick people about this and they said it's probably coming from the inside, from a shower or something. But it happens all over the house.
Does it happen when it's wet or dry?
When the weather's wet.
And then the weather fines up, but there's certain areas where the moisture will just hang round.
And it's always from the bottom up.

Yeah, on the photos, I could see. I can tell you now, it's nothing to do with what we put around the windows. What we've got is we've got building paper on, and then we've got all the flashing tape, and then once we put the windows in we put the black CPC, and that's folded up and around the windows—

I've got photos.

It's not gonna get into the house, no way. I spoke to a few people where we have a couple of beers and there's a couple of bricklayers there and they said clay bricks do absorb moisture, but it shouldn't be like that. We've been building a few houses for Jennian Homes, and they've had major troubles with the bricks.

What sort of problems?

The bricks were nowhere near straight and the bricklayer never picked up on them until he laid them, and then he stood back. And Monier said they're within the regulations. So they had the big engineers come down and they said nah, it's not straight, so the bricks had to come off two whole houses. And Monier just walked away from it. Not our problem.

In their email, they immediately said it's a house problem.

But it's not just behind wet areas like she was saying.

So it's everywhere?

It's worse on the south side. Our neighbours over there first saw it, we hadn't really noticed it but they saw it.

Because they drive in and out of their driveway, they were noticing that half the house is a different colour. It's the moisture that I worry about, if it comes through.

Yeah well it would take a lot—a *lot*—to get through to the house. You've got all the holes between the bricks down the bottom. That's what the bricklayer said, just make sure you've still got all your weepholes and that. Only thing I can do mate is just go away and talk to a couple of bricklayers.

But maybe talk to Monier.

Yeah. Yep. Yep. Yep. I'll give them a call. I'll go back to the guys who laid the bricks and see if someone's ever come across it before.

I did a google search for this particular brick and an old Trade Me listing popped up from a guy who was selling some leftover bricks from their house-build, and it was the same brick, and their house was built four years ago, so a year newer than our place, so I emailed him, and he said they didn't have a problem at all.

I can tell you now, Monier are just gonna wash their hands of it. They're just gonna keep walking away. The thing is, the Council would never have signed it off if all the things behind the bricks weren't there. If I could get the bricklayer here and Monier here . . .

She was going to be passing through on Tuesday, that woman I emailed.

Yeah we need to probably go higher than her. She's just a sales rep.

It's just a worry that if it is getting in, in a couple of years all the gib will turn mouldy and—

I can tell you that's never gonna happen.

It's also thinking about when we come to sell the house, we don't want someone coming round on a wet day and saying what's wrong with that.

If you don't disclose a problem, and they come back later on—

Yeah, nah, we'll get it sorted. We'll definitely get it sorted. We might have to seal the bricks. But I can assure you it won't be getting wet on the inside. Because between the bricks and the wall, you've got a 50-mil gap as well. So if any water does get in there, all it's gonna do is drip down the bricks and come out the weepholes. That's why these weepholes are here.

Mm.

And you've got all the building paper, and you can actually squirt building paper with a hose, and the water still doesn't come through. But I can see entirely what you guys are talking about.

But how can Monier walk away? I mean there's the Consumer Guarantees Act.

They just do mate. Like Jennian's is quite a big company, and they said to them get stuffed. And they said we've got all these reports, from these proper engineers, saying your bricks are crap, and they were horrible. Obviously it's not gonna happen overnight but I'm not gonna tell you guys to get stuffed. We will get it sorted. We'll just have to make a time where we can get the bricklayers back, get someone higher up from Monier, and we'll just all come on site and we'll just nut it out. We can see what you did just with the hose mate. I can already tell you, Monier are just gonna walk away. But we'll try and get them here, we'll go higher than her. We'll just say look, we need to get this bloody sorted out. I'll keep in contact with you guys and we'll just go from there. We'll get it sorted for yous.

How much do you think it would cost, to do a topical coating? Maybe that's the solution.

Not much mate. You wouldn't even be talking a thousand dollars.

Does it change the colour?

It makes it look like it's wet.

## 28

The climate change show last night was in the Victorian greenhouse. It was a really nice venue, especially with the rain pattering down on the glass roof. On the way in I'd seen these perfectly acceptable seats about four rows back, on the aisle, and they would have been good, but—typical Cath manoeuvre—I thought no, we'll take the ones in the front row. I said to Tracey shall we go sit in the front row, so she said okay, so we went up there and then we realised there was a guy who'd be sitting directly in front of us, filming the show, and he said to us a couple of people have already moved from those seats because the view won't be very good. So then when we turned round, someone else was just going into the first seats, so we had to go way way further down the back. And then these tall obnoxious hipsters came in after the show had started and sat in front of us. He put his arm around her and she had her head on his shoulder and they were kissing and they were completely obscuring our view of important climate change theatre. The tickets were free, but still.

Sometimes you do make a rod for your own back.

## 29

So you know how you forgot our wedding anniversary, when I made you a thoughtful bespoke special card, and—

I'm not liking where this is going.

—and so you were going to pick a bunch of hydrangeas for me, but you forgot to do that too?

Well, you told me that I was going to. And I forgot.

I thought you could do that today. To make up for it. Because today's an extra day. A bonus day.

# [ MARCH ]

## 1

Terse little note from above.

I wasn't quite ready for the full locust.

The most common piece of graffiti is 'I was here', isn't it. And I think that's what creative writing is too—if we could stay off our phones in class, please? No phones on in class?—I think that's what creative writing is too: a desire to leave behind some trace of ourselves, some evidence that we were here, that we existed. Of course the context of a story matters as well. If we think about those three words, 'I was here'—think about different contexts, different settings for them. So for instance, how would the story change if you saw those words written deep underwater? How would it change if you saw them in footage of the moon? Do you want to come up with some ways the story 'I was here' would change in different settings? Have a think.

If you got out of the shower, and you'd never written it on the condensation. You'd be like, what?

Or if you found it in a sealed underground cave.

With a tally next to it.

Or Tutankhamun. If it was there, eh. Tutankhamun's tomb.

I saw one online. It probably isn't real but there was a place in I think it was Greece or somewhere. It was an old church and there was like scratchings on the floor, and no one really knew what it was. And apparently it was left by a group of people that were loosely related to the Vikings. And it literally said something like 'Erik was here'.

They've reportedly found like things off Portuguese ships in Raglan Harbour. Hundreds of years old. Predating Cook.

What if it was written in blood? That would change the story too, wouldn't it?

On your bathroom mirror.

Or if it was written on death row, or if it was written on a school desk that once belonged to a famous writer—that tells another story, doesn't it. Maybe it's written on the sand where it'll be washed away in an hour's time. Or on a stretch of fresh concrete.

On a pub table.

On a drunk person.

On the eastern side of the Berlin Wall. In letters so huge that it's not visible at ground level but is visible from the air. This is all by way of getting you to think about context in story, and who your audience might be. And sometimes that can be—

I just want to ask a question. You talk about us, while we're writing the story, having an idea of our audience, but like obviously our audience at the moment is people in our class. But like how do you think of an audience?

I'm glad you mentioned that, because I do think we have to tread a fine line between being aware that our stories are going to be put out there, but also not locking ourselves into a particular audience so tightly that we paralyse ourselves. We'll talk more about that later. We can think of stories as an attempt to give structure—beginning, middle and end—to the daily chaos surrounding us. Because as people living in the twenty-first century, we are bombarded by information, day in, day out. We are bombarded by different stories, and we have to choose what to pay attention to and what to ignore.

Some authors, you'll be reading them, and it's like, the narrative is so boring, it's like, just this incidental detail, and then suddenly—like that novel The Outsider, by Camus, like it's really boring, and then suddenly he's on a beach and having a fight with this guy and he picks up a gun and shoots him. And then that's the whole story.

I went to Shakespeare last night. It was just appalling.

Which one did you see?

Henry V.

Oh Henry V is quite boring.

Why did they choose that?

They wanted to do one with all women. But no one needs to see fifteen blond women on stage.

There weren't even diverse women?

I went with someone who asked people at the interval if it was finished. It was really embarrassing. I said no there's usually a bit of a like meltdown towards the end. But I was with her in some ways.

If someone else is moved by our story—if we are able to reach an audience—then it gives meaning and significance to what we've produced. It proves that someone's noticed our little scratch on the wall.

The woman who gave us the milk today, her baby's fifteen weeks old and can't digest fats because she has a liver condition where she doesn't produce enough bile. They figured it out on the third day, that she couldn't digest the milk. When she was still in utero they said that she had this serious condition and would probably only live a few days, but then when she was born they said oh, actually it's not that, it's this instead, this liver condition, but it does mean she'll probably need a transplant. I felt a bit bad saying thanks for the milk that your baby can't have, it'll mean Alice won't get eczema.

Shh, shut the door.

## 2

I must say, it's supremely easy working in the garage now. If I want to get the drill out, it's there. Sprocket set is there. I've got more storage space. It seems like I've got less stuff. It'll make the daguerreotypes much easier.

I'm so tired of wrestling the baby. We were reading that Peter Rabbit puppet book, and I had my hand up Peter's butt, and she decided to bite one of his paws, and bit into my finger.

What'll we do with Baz? The people who answered my ad . . .

There's crazy Angela. There's the man or the woman—we don't even know—who lives on a farm, offered us fifty dollars for him, kept texting, wouldn't ring and hasn't rung but then wanted to come round today and pick him up. There's the woman who wanted him for her grandchildren and offered us forty dollars and lives on a busy road. There's Kylie, who has a fully fenced property, which means nothing with a cat. She apparently can't ring us, and just expects us to do it all by email. Who are these people? And there was Debbie, who has a three-year-old ginger cat called Milo, and she said that text is best. I told her we need to *talk* to her. I'd rather keep him.

The Indian couple, I think.

It's just they live in such a busy area.

They'll really love him.

I know they'll really love him.

## 3

Was Dorothy's death notice in the Waikato Times?

No.

I saw it online in the New Zealand Herald, but I don't think it was in the Waikato Times.

No, no it wasn't. I love those earrings. Are they proper diamonds?

Yes, these are my Katherine Mansfield Award earrings. Why wouldn't they put it in the Waikato Times?

I have no idea. I was sure it'd be in this morning's paper.

Do all her children live in Auckland or something?

Yes.

You'd think they'd put it in her local paper, though.

Well I thought it was amazing.

I hope they get a good turnout, because people might not know.

No, I wondered about that. And she wasn't a great mixer, because she never kept good health.

What exactly was wrong with her?

Something with her spine. She had cancer in the spine quite a few years ago.

Did you know her before then?

Oh yes, we went to school together. And then I hadn't seen her for years and years because I moved away from Christchurch. She was a class behind me. She's actually older than me, but I was in Form Two at eleven—I was so clever—so she was a year behind me. And in those days you really didn't talk to the kids that were in Standard Five. But I always sort of knew her because she lived next door to a friend of mine called Thelma Murnane, and often I used to go and play with Thelma, and Dorothy would come over because she lived next door. And then time went by, and I went to college, and work—we drifted apart. Now and again I'd see her at a dance and we'd have a bit of a chat. And then she came to live here.

Why did she come to Hamilton?

Because she has family. She married one of the Pooles from Christchurch, who were very wealthy. I don't think she's got much money now—he divorced her. No, she probably divorced him, because he had about ten flings. He was awful to her. He was always at the dances, before she was even going out with him. He danced with all the girls and when he danced with you his hand went down your back and he'd touch your bottom—you know the sort of person? You know the sort of man I mean? I hated him, but he had pots of money and so the Pooles were always popular. They did a lot for the convent and the church and everything, but I always got the impression they did it for show rather than to give the nuns a loaf of bread. It was always made known. My father kept the convent in potatoes for as long as I can remember, and I never heard anybody saying Mr McGough gave the potatoes. But Dorothy wasn't a show-off. I don't know that she was all that happy with her husband. Because she divorced him. Then she met this man she was working with—her family had grown up, and she went back to an office job—and she married him. I didn't really know him because he died just when I came up here. I heard that from Theresa.

Here we are. Plenty of parks.

Where are we—oh. I was just going to say something absolutely stupid.

Where are we going?

Yes. Coming in here, I don't know where I thought I was going to go.

We're quite early. I suppose it's better to be early than late. Have you been here before?

I don't think I have.

I better take my glasses in case they have a slide show.

I've had a really sore back lately. I said to the nurse about it, and she said well, you're eighty-five.

Except you're eighty-four.

Do we go in? That's a recent photo of her. And that one's a while ago—she's a lot younger there. But that's how I knew her first. She was always pretty. We were jealous of her—she had lovely hair. I'm not sure if that's her father or her husband, because I never knew her husband.

Husband, I would say—the tie looks quite modern. Where do you want to sit?

I don't mind. Not too near the front. I haven't been to this church. Is this a Catholic church?

No, it's just a funeral chapel. The undertaker's chapel.

I'm not questioning her religion.

Why are they playing Mary Poppins?

I don't know. I wouldn't have had quite that tune.

It's an interesting choice. Maybe she liked musicals, did she?

Yes, she did. She didn't like classical music and she didn't like modern music. She couldn't believe that I liked classical music. We always used to have jokes about it. She used to reckon it was always out of tune.

Do you know anyone?

No. But my cousin Theresa might be here. It was her that rung and told me Dorothy had died. Her father and my mother were brother and sister. She never said, but I think she had a pretty tough time with her first husband.

Dorothy?

Mm. I think he careered around a bit. But I never met her second husband. When I came up here, he had just died.

Hello ladies, how are you?

I'm fine thank you.

Do you know who that is?

No. I think it's the undertaker woman.

I don't know if that was all family out there.

Yes, I don't know.

It's one thirteen.

And what's the time of the—thing?

One thirty. We are still quite early. Hello.

I'm Dorothy's son Mike.

I'm Pat Chidgey. We used to go to school together. I shifted away from Christchurch years ago and we lost contact.

It's nice of you to turn up.

Well no. We made contact again when I came here. My cousin, Theresa Gill she was, she's Theresa Allsop now, I don't know whether you know her or not—

Allsop? It rings a bell.

Yes, it probably does—and she told me that Dorothy lived here. I can't remember whether Dorothy rung me or I rung her now, but we kept in touch up here.

In some ways I sort of feel bad because I don't feel too much remorse about all this. I think it's probably good, the poor thing.

I don't know how she used to keep smiling.

What was it, last week I was down here? Or the week before? Last week, I think, and I was trying to remember the way to the Assisi place, and I got lost and was halfway to Morrinsville or somewhere, I don't know where it was. So I do a U-turn and come back thinking I can find another way, but I can't find it, so in the end I just drive home. And unfortunately . . .

I was talking to her on the phone not that long ago. So I'm quite glad.

Do you live in Hamilton?

Yes, I live in Sunset Court, a retirement village. I like it. We're treated really well. It's a little bit more expensive than the others, but we can go and make fifteen cups of coffee if we want to, where at other places people have to put in a dollar. I'm well looked after, aren't I?

Mm.

You'll be hanging in there for another ten years.

I'd be ninety-five then. I'm trying to get a letter from the Queen. No, I'm pretty good for my age, but when I do get old, my other daughter's a doctor, and I always tell her she's got to send me a pill. I don't think she will.

I don't know that it'd get through customs. She's in England.

She could put it in a cake. But I'm aiming for the Queen's letter, you see.

You're going to hang in regardless.

I think they'll be wanting to get rid of me before then.

I went back to Australia two weeks ago because my wife's father passed away. He was almost ninety-four. But he was in a demented state—in the same sort of retirement home—and he just gave up the ghost and that was it.

Old age gets us, doesn't it.

Well eventually. I reckon eighty-five, that'd be it. Give me a bottle of whisky and a rowboat and I'll just disappear.

How do we get out of here? Feet first?

It's quite funny that Theresa wasn't there. I'll give her a ring. Whereabouts in Auckland does she live?

I'm not quite sure. I've never really been to her house. I've forgotten. I have known her address.

What are they doing? Idiot! They didn't even indicate! Are there any pieces of music or readings that you'd like, when the time comes? I know it's not a very nice conversation to have.

No, it's fine. I was thinking about that. I'm hoping it'll be a long time.

Well it's nice to know, rather than choosing something that didn't mean anything.

I'll have a think about it. Les had one. Now what was that . . .

Panis Angelicus.

Yes. That'd be fine. I haven't been round this way for ages. That's quite a pink sign.

I guess they want you to see it.

Oh, it's Wet Floor. Cleaning in Process. I don't think Hamilton's an exciting town, is it.

Why have I driven all the way down here? Oh well. I'll get there eventually.

I can't even think how you get to my place now. You just get me there. I used to love the shops on Alexandra Street. Best Buy Beds. I don't know any of those shops.

So the guy with the long hair was one of her sons?

Yes. Dorothy was always a bit concerned about him. I think he'd been a pretty odd guy all his life. Just from various things she said over the years. I don't think he was a burglar or anything but I think he had weird women . . . you know. She never really said much. Are you sick of hearing about the new flag? Do you really care what colour it's going to be? What are they doing it for? That pool's still open, that swimming pool there. I used to take you and Helen there when you were little.

No you didn't, because we lived in Lower Hutt.

Oh. Oh, well they've shifted it up here.

The Naenae baths?

Yes. That's them there. You didn't know that, did you.

No. I didn't know there was a pool in there.

I thought I knew.

Do I go round there? I'm completely confused now.

We don't know how to get home.

I find Hamilton very confusing.

I used to when I was driving. And I drove for years. Is that antique shop still there? And those two chairs are still out the front. They've been there for years.

I think it's because there are no hills to orientate yourself by, like there are in Wellington.

And the streets all look the same. Have you got a clock in here?

Two fifty-two.

Is that all it is? I thought it was about five o'clock.

I think there would have been more people there today if they'd put it in the Waikato Times. I can't understand why they didn't.

No, I can't either. She knew quite a few people here.

That sounded like a dashing first date, to be taken up in a Tiger Moth above Christchurch.

She was always very glamorous, particularly once she started going out with What's-his-name Poole, because they had lots of money. Her family didn't, they were quite working class. She used to be just in funny old clothes, and when she started going round nicely dressed she was a completely different person. Some people didn't think she should do that. But she was going out with and then married What's-his-name Poole. I'm not criticising her.

Here we are. Who's that?

I don't know, but she lives here. I reckon I see her every time I come out here, and she waves. I don't think she knows who I am and I don't know who she is.

What does Molly call this place?

The Home for the Bewildered.

I cried, of course. But it felt like I was crying for something still to come.

### 4

Did I dream that the baby said Jesus?

### 5

There's a theory that depression could be the result of an infection. This Danish study of three million people found that being hospitalised with an infection was associated with a much greater chance of developing depression. And autoimmune activity seems to be involved too, where the body attacks itself. No one's ever been able to say why my white blood cell count is always low, why I'm always strongly positive for antinuclear antibodies. Oh, sometimes that occurs in healthy populations. Remember that osteopath in Auckland who got me to think about white potatoes? He got me to hold the image of a white potato in my mind and think about how it made me feel. It didn't make me feel very good to know that I was paying him a hundred and fifty bucks to contemplate vegetables.

6

I've still got that thing on my eyelid. A small hard lump.
There's probably something under there.
Hatching?
No, like a bit of grit or something.
Hatching.
Yes. Hatching. That's what I thought.


And there's an argument that depression should be thought of as an infectious disease.

Person-to-person infectious?

No, as a result of infection in the body that leads to inflammation. And it does have physical symptoms—extreme tiredness, leaden limbs, change of appetite, not wanting to get out of bed.


It's beginning to feel like autumn.

7

8

I need to get going. It's yoga class again tonight. I don't really feel like it but it might help.

You should go.

I don't know. I don't really feel like it.

That's what you always say before something like that.

I don't want her to think I didn't enjoy it last time. So I should go.

You should go.

An asteroid may have just gone past. Predicting where it's going to be is a very uncertain business. It probably flew past, although nobody's actually seen it. So how do we know? How do we know it's gone past if we haven't seen it? There are uncertainties.

Underneath it all I'm very grey.

9

It's just on ten, so we'll make a start. Don't be terrified, it's completely painless, I promise. Take two of these slips of paper each—take two each—and write two lines. One of them needs to be a voice and one of them needs to be an image. You don't have to make them self-consciously literary or poetic. The voice could be something you remember overhearing today: Careful crossing the road! Or it might be a voice you remember from childhood: Don't forget to brush your teeth. It might be an internal voice—something that's churning and turning around in your head: I don't know why I'm doing this course. I bet everyone else in the room is better than me. Why did I wear these shoes? The other slip of paper is for your image, and on that I want you to write a line that contains something concrete, something that you can see, and touch, and feel. Clean sheets on the washing line, for instance, or the rusted-shut shed door.

Don't fret too much about it, just jot something down.

Now what we'll do is edit. So, take your strips of paper and lay them down the length of one of the tables, like this. Any old order, to start with. Just lay them out. And then I'll tell you the next step. You do have to get up from your seats. Okay. I want you as a group to look at them, and shuffle and rearrange them into what you think might work as a poem. Is there something that presents itself as an obvious first line, or an obvious last line? That might be a good place to start. Then have a look at the guts of the poem, what's left on the table, and start shuffling and rearranging those lines. You might want to see if there are some that seem to belong together, or that spark off each other because they're different.

Are we happy with the final layout? It's always interesting, this exercise, and I think the craft of it lies in that editing process, looking at it with an analytical eye and seeing how you can rearrange the raw material to come up with something original. I always say it's very difficult to edit a blank page. If you've got that raw material to start fiddling with, then you might surprise yourselves. Art is there for the taking; ideas are there for the taking, all around you, all the time.

It's just on ten past four, so we'll make a start. Don't be terrified, it's completely painless. Take two of these slips of paper each and write two lines. One of them should be a voice and one of them should be an image. You don't have to make them self-consciously literary or poetic. The voice might be something you overheard today: Have you got the time? Or it could be a voice you remember from childhood: Don't forget to brush your teeth. It might be an internal voice—something that's churning and turning around in your head: I don't know why I'm doing this course. I bet everyone else in the room is better than me. Why did I wear these jeans? The other slip of paper is for your image, and on that you need to write a line that contains something concrete, something that you can see, and touch, and feel. Clean washing on the line, for instance, or the rusted-shut letterbox. Just jot something down.

Now we'll edit. Take your strips of paper and lay them down the length of one of the tables, in any order. Writing side up, so you can read them. I want you as a group to look at them, and shuffle and rearrange them into what you think might work as a poem. Is there something that presents itself as an obvious first line, or an obvious last line? That's a good place to start. Then have a look at what's left, the guts of the poem, and start shuffling and rearranging that. You might want to see if there are lines that belong together, or that spark off each other because they're different.

I always say it's very difficult to edit a blank page. If you've got that raw material to start fiddling with, then you might surprise yourselves. Art is there for the taking; new ideas are there for the taking, all around you. It's always interesting, this exercise, and I think the craft of it lies in the editing process, looking at it with an analytical eye and seeing how you can rearrange the raw material to come up with something original.

### 10

Flip flops have lots of xenoestrogens and get in your body through your feet! Sad, but true!

### 11

History is silent to us. The vast majority of the past is gone. A team of researchers set out to map the acoustic fingerprint; it seems pitch black. You cross the threshold and have to adjust. You notice saints, who are your size, staring at you. You're in this world of myrrh. Have you ever longed for a different life, or tried to make one? You've got to live with yourself wherever you go. How long are you missing before you are declared dead? The frequencies go back and forth; the sound of angels' wings.

What is a vertical burial and would you consider having one? They used to do that to hanged men. Those who committed a heinous crime weren't to rest in peace; they were left standing for eternity. Auckland is running out of space to bury its dead. I want to have a little bit of me sprinkled on my enemy's grave.

## 12

Is it religion?
It's actually about Jesus's death and remembering—
Not for us, thanks. Have a good day.

I should have said can't stop to talk, the baby's currently channelling Satan. Do you know anyone who could do a good exorcism?

## 13

There's an open day today. They're showing people round.
Has someone died? Is there a free room?
Yes, that's what it is. People come and put their name down. There's always people waiting. I might have told you that Mallory's won the whole of New Zealand, of all the rest homes. They're very good. There's just one staff member nobody likes. She thinks we're all stupid. That's a friend of mine going off in the ambulance.
Has she got a sore leg?
Yes.
Was that the one you patted her on?
We have a joke about her leg.
Do you pull her leg?
Yes.
Even though she's in extreme pain.
Well it's not her leg, it's a . . . made-up one. And we have a bit of a joke sometimes. She just had a joke with me then.
You mean it's a fake leg?

Yes.

What's she off to hospital for?

She said she's going to get makeup on it. She said I'm just going to get some new makeup on my leg.

What's her name? Is she called Peggy?

I don't know. I can't remember. There aren't many in the lounge.

I'm not sure if the ones who are there are still with us or not. They're not moving much.

Did I tell you I had a nice card from . . . I can't remember her name. I've forgotten.

Can you give us a clue?

Someone. She lives in Hamilton. Her husband ran away with his . . . with his secretary. I don't know where I've put the card. Oh, here. Oh no, that's Joy and Don. I haven't heard from them for ages. They used to live next door in . . . in . . .

Stokes Valley.

Yes. What lovely news I read in the paper on Saturday. I'm sure you are very thrilled at the arrival of your granddaughter Alice. It is great that Catherine and Alan are so close to you and you'll be able to watch her grow. We are getting older and slower. We hope you are keeping well at this exciting time. We pray for blessings for Catherine, Alan, Alice and for you, our good friend Pat. Love from Joy and Don. That's lovely. Lovely people. I thought I had something I was going to ask you, and I can't remember what it was. Oh, yes—I was going to ask you to wash that. I can't imagine what they'd do to the beads here.

You should change into something else as well and I'll take that home because you've got some coffee on there.

You're going to take this home, are you?

Yes, it's got some coffee on it.

I got a card from Helen and I can't see it at the moment.

This one?

Yes!

Oh no, that's an old one from France. We got one from Finland, or wherever they've been. Is that it there, with the reindeer?

Yes!

Those are dogs.

Where's that from?

Lapland.

Yes! That's it. I had a feeling I had something here to show you or give you or something. Have you picked the flag?

We're sticking with the current flag because we hate the whole process.

Yes, it's stupid, isn't it. Ninety-five percent of us here have said the same thing. How ridiculous.

Do you need your form to be posted back?

Yes. It's quite ridiculous. What a waste of money. Everyone here's going mad about it.

Have you posted yours back, or do you need us to post it back?

No. We're doing them all here and sending them all back together. The management are going to put a note on the top to say we're all against it.

Grubby monkey, grubby monkey. Yes you are. You're a grubby monkey.

You are not, you're beautiful. I don't know what you're going to be like when you're three. You know too much now. Yes you do. You're a lucky little thing. Mummy and Daddy look after you. There was an awful piece in the paper the other day—some mother had not fed the kid for three days or something or other and she'd been getting boozed up.

Did the baby die?

No, but they took it off her.

Did you watch that new Father Brown thing on Prime? With a vicar. Set in the 1950s.

Don't talk about it. I wanted to watch it and Myrna came

just when it was starting. I said I was going to look at that, and she said I don't want to see that silly old thing.

Just say to her, I'm going to watch this, maybe we can catch up later.

Well I thought about that after she went and I thought if she comes again I'm going to do exactly that. I've known her for about thirty years and she's very odd. She doesn't get on very well with anybody else and she's rude to the staff, I can't believe it. They like us all to be up by nine thirty—well that's not early. She won't get up till ten. So that means the person who cleans the bathrooms has to wait to clean hers. I have my shower at about half past eight. We have breakfast at eight, and then I get up and have my shower. And that's what most of us do. No wonder she had three husbands. Divorced two, and then the third one was killed in a car accident. When I was at a party one night, not long after it happened, one of the guys there said I bet he ran into something. I sometimes hide in the bathroom.

There aren't many places to hide here. Not many options.

Well no.

Right. Let's try and get a coffee.

Can you get the seat belt?

Oh thank you! Alice has just given me her cuddly. What does she call it?

Not much at this stage, because she doesn't talk.

Dadadadadadada.

She's starting to, isn't she. Why do they always say Dada before Mama? She's getting so interesting. Aren't you. You're going to be very cute. You're going to be very bright. You know too much for your age. I don't know what you're going to be like when you're three. They're Nana's rings. You might get one one day. Are we getting out here? Oh, I know where we're going.

Shall I put her in the playpen? It's exactly the same as our one.

I don't know . . . other babies have been in there.

The floor looks a bit hard.

And, faecal matter.

Is she allowed to have some marshmallows?

Ahhh . . . no. Thank you, though.

Wasn't that nice of him?

Now I feel horrible. She hasn't had anything like that ever.

There's a time for it. Plenty of time for her to have those things. That's your sock. Yes it is. Bunny's falling out. Bunny's falling out. There he is. That's a nice little biscuit.

I thought it was a fortune cookie. It's just biscuit inside, no fortune.

Did I put sugar in that?

Do you want sugar? Is that Equal?

Yes, Equal.

Do you want sugar?

Equal's all right. I never know the difference. She's very responsive, I can't believe it. Babies at ten months normally just sit there and look at you.

She's only nine and a bit.

That's right, she is. You're showing off. I don't know what you're going to be like when you're five. You're going to start school at three. You'll be reading at two. No, not nice to eat. No. No. No, don't put it in your mouth. Give it back to Nana.

I suppose she can have my keys.

And poke herself in the eye.

Oh!

Oh dear. I'll have to pay for a glass. Or shall I run away?

Careful. Careful. Careful, you're standing on it. No, you've dropped it. No, no, give me the bunny. Give me the bunny. Pat, give me the bunny.

I'm just going to wipe a piece off him.

No, you're putting glass in the pram.

Shall we move to a different table? I think we'll move to a

different table so she can sweep up.

It just shattered.

She might need a nappy change. She's started flopping round lately. Not helpful.

It's a darn nuisance when they won't just lie there.

Alice. Alice. What are you doing?

The flopping haddock.

I could do with some help.

I gave her the keys.

Well can you hold on to her? Hold on to her arms. Just pin her down.

I better take that shirt too, you've got coffee on there as well. You need a new pedal bin.

Don't talk about the pedal bin.

Have you told them?

Yes, I told somebody the other day and they didn't take any notice. I haven't got the part—she threw it away, obviously. Silly woman. Have you got my address book?

No. You have your address book.

I must have put it somewhere. I didn't really look, I just opened the drawer and it wasn't there. What are you looking for?

Your address book.

It's over there. In the drawer.

There's the black one . . .

No, that's my phone book. What are we wanting it for?

You've got a stash of knives down there.

Oh yes. They're to give back. Somebody came in this morning, to do the cleaning, and she must have had those and she left them here. So I'm going to take them down tonight when I go to tea. I don't know what she was walking round with all those knives for. I didn't work that out.

Right then, we should make a move. See you Thursday for swimming if you're up to it.

I don't need to swim, do I.

Not unless you want to.

I can't.

No.

I'll walk out with you. They keep it nice here, don't they. It's always tidy. I'm about the only person who ever sits over there. I often sit there in the morning. It's lovely. I'm amazed at the people who never go out of their room.


That was the usual catalogue of disaster.

She's still standing there. Wave! Wave across the bowling green. What was with all the knives? There were half a dozen knives stashed next to her bed, and there was another one over by her La-Z-Boy.

Maybe she feels she needs protection.

They were just table knives. Maybe that's all you need to fend off the residents.

Maybe she's gone klepto.

I don't have her address book. I've never had the fucking address book. I don't know where she's stashed it, I can't find it. As for the café . . .

She picked up the rabbit, which had glass on it, and then shook the rabbit over the seat of the pram, and I saw these bits go in, and then I cut my hand. I tried to pick it up and it was jammed into the side of the seat and I pushed my finger onto it. I tried to get it off her and she whisked it away and held it over the pram and it was dropping glass. The baby sits in that.

They must have been thrilled with us.

It was a fucking disaster.

It was really. It's like she attracts it.

You can see what she's going to do wrong and in some way you psychopathically transmit that to her mind and it becomes this suggestion.

What, I do?

No, one does. It feels like that. It feels like there's a mental communication going on: oh my God, don't do that, and she goes, oh, I better do that. Telepathically, not psychopathically. Although probably a bit of that as well.

Pretty sure I saw a used condom by the bowling green when we were leaving Sunset Court.

You are a deeply disturbing person.

Might have been an ice-cream wrapper.

Just pretend it never happened.

## 14

I'm still getting the headaches right in there. And between the shoulder blades has flared up again.

Are you going to be comfortable lying face down? Is that sore there? When someone's listening to a book, does that mean they're reading it? Or not really? I'm listening to a book.

Is it abridged?

No.

That's all right then.

One Hundred Years of Solitude. That's quite a book, isn't it. It made me realise I'm not vaguely clever enough to catch on to a lot of what they're talking about. The symbolism. It's huge.

I think there's an argument for just letting it wash over you, though, and immersing yourself in the beauty of the language.

I was given the gift of knowing that I'm rubbish at that sort of thing pretty early on. When I was young I read The Master and Margarita, and about two months later one of my mates said you know that's all totally about the Communist Party. Can I get you to turn over? How's term going?

Sometimes I'll be sitting there talking and I have the feeling: I've already said this.

It is a bit tight.

One girl said to me I've had a really happy childhood, I've got nothing to write about.

I wish I'd had more trauma in my life! I read that the more stressful your environment, the more cultured your people are. They reckon that if you live in a very easy environment, you have relatively simple god structures and legends, whereas the harder your environment, the more complicated your god structures and versions of heaven and hell. I can't even remember where I read it. It was in a book. I mean it sounds like total racism coming out of my mouth—the idea that early technology came from Nordic areas, where life was pretty rough. The idea that if you live on an island and you can walk out, grab a fish, come back, eat, die, then there's a god of the sea, a god of the sky, and that's about it. Sorry about that. Sorry if I've beaten you up too much today. Is that okay?

The beauty salon's gone.

Eh?

The beauty salon's gone.

Where was it?

There. Next to the water shop. It's completely bricked up. Am I imagining things?

I think you are. It's been like that for a long time.

That's where the hairdressing salon used to be. Sheree's salon.

Are you sure it wasn't on the corner? By the physiotherapy? It's not round the other side?

No. No.

But that looks ancient.

There was a window there. A hairdressing salon, with a window.

Well, the drugs are working.

I'll have to text Sheree.

Ask her if she's bricked up inside.

I'm not imagining things.

What about that roller door?
Ah.

I may have been nabbed by a red-light camera today. It was orange orange orange and then went red just as I was through— but I'd already been past it.

### 15

We are mainly other things, it seems, and many millions of them.

### 16

I've still got that splinter of glass in the bottom of my foot. I can't even see it.

It'll have to work its way out.

That's what I thought, but it's been a couple of weeks now. And I was reading online that I may have to have my foot amputated.

### 17

Top o' the mornin' to you. I've photographed Jiffy as a potato. It's his punishment for keeping us awake.

Why is it that people in early childhood care are all in their twenties and shrill?

Because they're used to being JOLLY JOLLY JOLLY all day.

It makes me want to slap them. It's not normal.

### 18

Stop! Stop! Stop! Stop! Mistakes happen. Expect trains.

### 19

It wanted me to go left off Great South Road down Waingaro Road, and along Regent Street, and then back out onto Great

South Road somewhere further down the line. It was stupid. So I ignored it. But it doesn't correct itself, the way my old one did. It doesn't say recalculating route.

Who has travelled overseas with a baby? And who has left them behind?

Growing up I thought, when you're happy or sad, you sing. Her soulful voice took the world by storm; we'd be crying because it was so good. But success was overshadowed by addiction, disturbed behaviours, sense of rejection. Uncover startling revelations; did alcohol kill her? And was it the only factor in her death? Autopsy: Amy Winehouse. What is she doing here? Go on, that's it, hop it, love. What? You're not welcome. And what's with the bag? I was going away. Right, well go on then, shoo. Don't stand there gawping. You'll have your turn one day. It's coming closer, the flames are now licking my body. Won't you help me, I feel like I'm slipping away. It's hard to breathe, my chest is just heaving. Lord have mercy, I'm burning a hole where I lay. Your kisses lift me this Easter, every night is a treat. Wow! I'm bringing the party to you, and this Easter Saturday, December 7th, 1941, the United States of America was suddenly and deliberately attacked. I think World War Two just hit us. We will not give up or give in, Ben Affleck and Kate Beckinsale. Victory belongs to those that believe in resetting the sensors to respond to a lighter load. How do you feel about forty kilos, Miss Hall? Perfect. Shall we? Miss Hall? Haven't you forgotten something? What are you trying to do, señorita? Rob me? The thought had crossed my mind. I'm missing something here. Coming up . . . are you the master of this game? Richard gets the royal treatment; I think it's time to get rid of King Richard. He needs to be knocked off his pedestal. You can lift me. Do I look like a criminal? Well you have a tattoo. Stop and see if you're all right. Apparently we're neighbours—my house is two blocks from yours in Montreal. Cabot, north of Laurier. Bonjour. Bonjour. For you—I'd like to take credit for it, but it's from Mary. My name is David Caravaggio but nobody ever called me David; Caravaggio they find too absurd to miss out on. Son, and wife . . . it's a nice picture. It's charming, it's commercial, it's saleable—I love it. I was surprised about the Victorian glass—that was very disappointing—but the painting and the actual Ming vase have exceeded what I expected. I've now got a figure in my head. I'll go back to the office and discuss it with James and see where we are per litre on your next fuel top-up! That's right, forty cents per litre! Move, you dogs! Faster, faster! Load them all! Greetings, Panda. Tell me what happened that night. What night? That night. Ah, that night. Yes! We're talking about the same night, right? Yes, I was there. Yes. I watched as your parents abandoned you. It's a terrible thing. I believe it went something like this. You didn't storm out of the room, things would have got five times worse. I am not going home. I don't believe it's being a selfish mother. I don't want to be here in the house. Mum wants to stay, but I just need to see how the next couple of days are going to go. Miss Carter! What's he going to do to us? Not us, me. What? I took the mission, I'll take the consequences. You wait upstairs, and when they worshipped their gods, they put on equally elaborate ceremonies. I've come to the Instituto de Cultura Puertorriqueña in San Juan to see an artefact that was part throne, part seat, and part time machine.

## 20

She's not doing that wheezing any more—she's doing new sounds.

Just trying out noises.

I think that's all it was.

Not bronchial asthma, then.

She likes it when I roll them down the tray to her.

So I'm supposed to stand here and roll blueberries one by one. I feel so fulfilled as a mother.

I had a dream last night that I was in a Wellington café and it was all glittering. Far from the Waikato. Are you having fun?

One of us is.

21

Und now, za baby und I vill vatch Das Boot.

Was there anything else?

Yes, I think I've got a piece of glass stuck in my foot. You can't even see it. Alan broke a wine glass and I cleaned the floor twice, so it's tiny.

I can't see anything. And I can't feel anything.

No, it's microscopic.

You might want to make an appointment with Dhanesh and he can have a rummage round. Or he might refer you, but I doubt if the ultrasound would even pick it up. I suppose it's more of a nuisance than anything.

Well it does hurt.

It's a shame the way you feel about Adam and Dunedin, because it would be a cheaper version of Wellington. It's a city we know and love, and if we sold here and moved to Dunedin we could have quite a nice place.

I was thinking about that the other day, and then I heard a news story: house prices in Dunedin booming! Because it's cheaper than everywhere else in the country.

Well there's a bubble, and that will deflate. And then Dunedin will still be where it is.

It's not just Adam, it's Sean as well.

But if you could get over all of that, we could have somewhere that we—

Just get over a huge life trauma.

I know, I know, but it would be a place that we would find interesting to live in and feel engaged about. I could make some great daguerreotypes.

It's fucking freezing, and Tracey's not there, and I don't have a job there.

I'm speaking in a theoretical way.

And Cindy and Jo aren't there any more.

I know all this, but on the weekends, when we want to go somewhere and do something to get out of the house, what is there to do in Hamilton? Where would you want to go? Unless you go to a mall, there's nothing. Or the gardens. Those are basically the two places of interest.

I do like Dunedin, I do have an affection for it. But there's the Mum question as well.

I'm thinking . . . beyond that.

I would consider it. I don't know about the weather. And the cats would need a very quiet road. I can't go through what we went through with Daisy again.

If we lived in a new, insulated home I think it might be a different experience, especially if we lived in a sunny location as well.

She keeps knocking down my block towers. She's very destructive.

I have to have all the wooden jigsaw pieces on the board. If I distract her enough I get them all in, but then she immediately pulls them out.

I can't even get to two blocks high and she's whacking it over and laughing. She's so sweaty.

I know. It worries me.

It is quite hot in here.

I used to feel interested and inspired and sparked living in Dunedin. I made the daguerreotype of Larnach's tomb, and the grave hands. There's nothing really wrong about the Waikato, it's just uninspiring. I feel like a consumer living in a consumer society, and there's no point to it. Are you getting tired? We've got to go out.

What time is it? She's rubbing her ear.

Come on bub. Sweaty, sweaty.

Are you saying sweetie or sweaty?

Sweaty. Sweetie. Sweetie sweaty. Sweaty sweetie.

Now I can finish my block tower.

Kriechbaum, make a note for the war diary.

Aye aye, Captain.

22

I'm feeling quite confused with the hypnotherapy. She doesn't make it clear. I'm meant to come up with an anchor or a trigger to help me relax, but I don't know if I should be picturing the calm dial turning down, or the German meadow of wildflowers, or the blue of the sky sinking through my body.

23

I'm signed up to a few sites that donate to boob jobs. Men who like boobs. I'm at an advantage because I already have big boobs. A lot of men like to see boobs grow.

And anyway, if the calm dial is turning down, doesn't that make me less calm?

24

For my birthday I want the carpet shampooer and the bilingual Proust.

25

I've got this thing on my arm. It started last night—I don't know what it is.

It looks like a rash. A reaction. Maybe an insect bite.

Is it leprosy?

Yes. That's what it is. Your arm will fall off.

You've grown, Alice! So much! And you're so fair. She doesn't look that fair in the photos.

She's been grotty today. We gave her an egg yesterday and we're trying to figure out if there's a pattern.

Look, Alice. A little tiny bubba. That's Tilly. That's your . . . cousin. Or sister? What are we going to call them?

I'm easy.

Sperm donor cousin? No. Hello Tilly! Hello sweetie! You're so tiny!

They only look like newborns for a matter of weeks.

Or Alice not at all.

Alice was never this tiny.

Who's that nasty man?

You can pick her up. If she pukes on you I take no responsibility—she's very spilly. She's mainly on formula. I'm going to try and get my milk up to try and give her at least a couple of bottles a day. The birth was quite awful. I had to be repaired, and then she was on oxygen, and when I finally got to hold her my midwife Sarah had been there all night and she wanted to go home, so she said I'll leave you in Jennifer's hands. Because Jen still had two hours of shift left. And as she walked out she said to Jen, Donna's got formula and bottles in her bag. I'd already said to her, Jen's going to have a fit when you tell her I'm formula feeding. Because I have to go back to work. Jen came over and put her straight on my breast and fed her. And then afterwards, when she had to go back onto oxygen, Jen said I'm going to express colostrum off you. So while I was lying there she did, she expressed colostrum, and I was going ow! I'd just been through an awful birth—no, she insisted on getting a full syringe. Then she was happy.

She milked you.

Yes. She milked me. And then she goes oh well, if you won't feed her, I will. But Sarah must have had a word to her, because when she called in on Tuesday for a visit, she never said anything, never said anything, never said anything. And then I said she farts a lot, and Jen goes, it's all that formula.

Gentle. Gentle. Don't be doing that! That's not for you. That's for the other bubba. She's got such dark hair, like Alice did when she was born. You really don't get a sense in the photos of how tiny she is. Is this a formula bottle, or breast milk?

Formula.

It always confuses me. It's counterintuitive. Formula is thinner? No. Breast milk is thinner.

When I gave her a bottle of expressed milk yesterday she was spouting it out. And I was going, do you know how long it took me to get that?

She is so tiny.

She's teeny. A teeny bub.

She's got big hands. Like Alan. Look.

Everyone says that. I think all newborns have big hands and feet. You didn't have to bring presents. I think you gave me enough, don't you? Oh, an Easter bunny! Did you make it?

No.

I remember buying a little girl a tea set a couple of years ago. I set it all up for her, I had the cups on the saucers. She takes them all off, and then she's playing with it, and then I put them back on. I couldn't figure out why she was taking the cups off. Then she told me food goes on the plates. She'd never seen teacups and saucers, just mugs. We're so old. Do you think she looks like Alice?

Yeah she does, I think. A little bit.

She's definitely got Alan's chin. That triangle chin.

Well the Bekhuis chin is quite pronounced. I had jaw surgery to reduce mine.

Oh really?

We won't dwell on that though, will we. We don't want to scare Donna.

That's all right.

I see you more than me. I see much more of you. She's such a little darling. She's so light.

She's a featherweight. Oh, what's up, Alice? What's happened?

Daddy's holding another bubba. You don't like this, do you?

Gentle, gentle. No, not gentle with me—gentle with Tilly, your cousin. Sister. Half-sister. No no no, don't grab.

Are you talking, Alice? Are you talking?

She's babbling.

Dadadadada.

Mama as well?

No. I'm way down the pecking order.

It seems like a lifetime ago that she wasn't around.

And they just—they grow up too quickly. They're not like that for long. I want her to stay like that.

This is the only turn we're going to get.

I hurt Tilly's finger trying to get her in the car seat, and then I bumped her head on the mobile putting her in the bassinet. I was like, I've broken my baby. Trying to dress them, you're scared you're going to break their arm.

They've got such soft skin.

It's all starting to peel off.

Alice's did that too. Didn't you? You peeled like a banana.

How's your mum doing?

She's all right. I think she's a bit confused between you and Leila. Because I told her we were coming up to visit you today, and she said oh, she's such a lovely person, isn't she. Yes she is, but you haven't met her. Sometimes she still doesn't understand the whole surrogacy thing with Leila. She thinks we just adopted Alice. A couple of times, when Leila was pregnant, she asked if they knew who the father was. I really didn't want to have to explain about Alan and a jam jar again.

She's not getting worse?

Well . . . if you met her and talked to her for fifteen minutes you probably wouldn't notice anything was wrong.

It doesn't sound like it's moving too quickly.

Mm. She'll be eighty-five in May.

There's different levels, isn't there. I've got two oldies from church that I get along really well with—they're both around eighty-five. One of them you would swear was fifteen years younger than the other. She still goes out all the time. She's got all her marbles, goes to movies with her friends. The other one's quite elderly—I worry about her. I hold on to her all the time.

Mum's got very elderly in the last couple of years. She used to be very social. Apart from the memory loss and the confusion, her life really changed when she had to stop driving. Suddenly her world just shrank. And now Alan's mum's turning eighty in July.

And she's going into a retirement home?

She needs to. He wants to move back down south, to Dunedin . . . but there's Mum. I don't know. My best friend lives in Cambridge and it would be very hard leaving her behind.

But Dunedin, you get a lot of bang for your buck if you move from up here.

But then you can never come back.

Exactly.


So how did it feel, meeting Tilly?

I don't have any issues. I don't have any pangs or regrets or anything. It's not my baby. Having said that, I'd be happy if she was my baby—she's gorgeous. But we were just visiting someone else.

I didn't have any pangs either. I thought I might be weepy

and feel inadequate and weird—Donna had a baby with my husband, and I couldn't. But I didn't at all.

It seemed very natural. I keep thinking, should I be feeling something? But it's just resoundingly no. I'm fine with it.

It's a good thing that we've done. I'm glad we did it. That was interesting what she said about Jennifer. Milking her.

Waffen-SS, really.

I'm wondering if they should be sisters, rather than cousins. If we should call them sisters. I kind of like that idea. Do you?

Both come with complications—trying to explain to others.

I don't care about other people. The only thing I'd wonder about is would Leila feel put out about Poppy and Freya. But I don't mind if we change them to Alice's sisters too.

Leila came up with cousins.

No, I did.

Donna doesn't seem fussed either way. And she's very obviously so grateful, calling us her donor family. Are you resigning yourself to living in Dunedin now?

No. And it is mainly because of leaving Tracey behind. I've never been a person who makes friends easily, and I don't click with many people—hardly anyone—and to have a friendship with someone like I have with Tracey is so rare.

I know. I don't have that with anyone. Haven't had for decades.

And also the weather. I hate the cold. I absolutely hate the cold. It gets me very down.

How do you feel about staying in Hamilton ad infinitum?

The other day when we were talking about leaving I felt like it'd be good to get out. There's nothing cultural going on here, and I saw some photos of a book launch at the University Book Shop in Dunedin, and Emma Neale was there, and Pamela was there, and I thought it'd be really nice to be part of that scene again. But the next day, when I was in my office and I was looking out of my window, I was thinking it does feel like we've put roots down here, and although there are aspects about the place that I don't love, there are things that make it seem like home too. Our house, and where we are, and the little niche that we've carved out for ourselves. And my job, I suppose. And our routine. We're lucky to have the house that we have, and all that space.

I do think it's a finite situation with that new housing development. Where we are is going to get built out.

## 26

Don't make me go out there again. The shops are closed for one day and people panic that they won't have enough instant noodles and Mountain Dew to last them till Easter Monday. I did see some men digging a grave down at the cemetery, though, so that partly made up for it.

Steve's spraying the wasps' nest. Is it Steve? Next door? Is that his name?

It could be tricky. They could be right underneath the tiles—a whole big nest in the roof.

## 27

I can't have the same fight over and over and over. Every time, a little bit more is chipped away. A little bit more breaks. You have no idea what you've undone. You can't unsay it. Why don't you go to Dunedin on your own? I have that same sick feeling. It's too broken.

Can somebody come? I can't get out.

I'll get you out. Mind the seatbelt—don't get your foot caught. Come in away from the sun, eh Aunty Pat?

Here you go, Brian. We brought you some raspberry slice.

I'll hide it. Did you know there's two models of that? Very very similar, but the things go the other way.

The wiggles on the icing?

Yeah. And I got the dud one last time.

You're a connoisseur.

Does it taste better when the wiggles go that way rather than that way?

Yeah. Yeah. Made by a different place. At the grocer shop that one's standing up on the corner, and the other one's in the cake and biscuit rack. They're different models. And the one I didn't buy was the nice one.

That's always the way.

Do you want to sit down? How's life? I haven't been in to see you for a while. I've been working every day. Same silly job, driving the same silly truck.

Do you not mind early starts?

If you want a job with this guy, that's just the deal. Simple as that. And I got a pay rise, I don't know if I told you.

You must have been a good boy.

I don't know about that, but I got sick of asking him. He promised me back in November but they always forget. It come round to February and I says to the son, tell your old man he's promised me a pay rise—and the old man was sitting right beside him. I didn't ask any more and I got it, so I was stoked. There's a tractor for sale just round the corner, which I'd like to get, but it's got basically no seat on it for a start, the clutch doesn't work, it's got no brakes, and the radiator's full of oil. It's good right where it is, I think. Nothing from our friend in Whanganui?

No, she hasn't even read the message yet, so I think we might just have to leave it. This is a woman who's got a whole lot of breast milk she was going to donate to us, Mum. It was for her son who had a birth defect and he died. She'd amassed this whole freezer full of milk and she offered it to us, and Brian was going to try to call in some trucking favours and get it brought up here, but she's fallen off the radar. When she offered it to us it was only a week since her son had died, so I think she's just not coping.

She's growing so quickly.

I had some photos on my phone of baby Tilly—Matilda—who we went to see, but I transferred them to my laptop this morning and didn't keep them on my phone.

So when they come off your phone, onto the computer, do they not stay on your phone?

You can either check the box to delete off the phone or not.

Who's Matilda?

We were sperm donor to our friend Donna in Auckland, remember.

Oh yes.

So that's a half-sister?

That's Alice's half-sister, yes. We went up to visit her on Friday.

Oh yes, a half-sister, that's right.

Are you saying hello to Charlie? Are you saying hello to Charlie? You're his somethingth cousin. You've got two cousin Charlies.

I think Aunty Pat worked it out, didn't you? Told us what she is.

Yes. But I've forgotten how I worked it out now. Is the family all good? What are they doing?

Erin's engaged. She's going to be married.

Oh yes, when's that happening?

I never knew that.

December.

Who's she engaged to, Lin?

A guy called Reese. He works for Fulton Hogan.

Are you pleased?

Yes. Yes.

She'll be walking soon. Helen taught you to walk. She was really funny, she used to pull you up and make you walk. How are all the brothers?

Good. Fighting fit. Terence is out today doing pine cones. Remember we used to go to Owen Ruddy's and get pine cones?

Yes.

What, for firewood?

Yeah. Owen Ruddy had them down the back of the place he had on Ledleys Road. Dad cut our trees down, but Owen Ruddy still had his.

I used to get Owen Ruddy's when I was a kid. He was Dad's cousin, you knew that.

Yeah. Yeah. Well no, I didn't really.

Didn't you? Owen Ruddy and Pat Ruddy came out from Ireland. And their mother and Dad's mother were sisters.

Who was the guy that lived in the whare? Went back to Ireland. Who was that?

That was Owen Ruddy.

Uncle Owen.

Uncle Owen. And Pat Ruddy was my godfather.

I thought Johnny Burrows was your godfather?

Yes, Johnny Burrows. He was my godfather.

He was my godfather too.

You'll have to dust off the suit come December, Brian.

Brian's really looking forward to it, Catherine, as you can see.

What's in December?

Erin's wedding.

Brian's about the only person I know in the world who doesn't look forward to a wedding.

You'll have to make a speech and everything—father of the bride.

Oh my God.

Have you got a collar and tie?

In fact, I was at a funeral the other day, and I seen a guy— he's older than dirt—with a Saint Bede's Old Boys' tie on, so I went and talked to him. I said where'd you get your tie from? He said I got it at Saint Bede's about forty years ago. I get a letter from the Saint Bede's Old Boys' Association about every five hundred years, an email, so I looked down the bottom, and sure enough, ties, thirty-five dollars. So I bought one and it arrived in the mail and I wore it out to a wedding I did in the Buick. Had a white shirt with the Saint Bede's tie. Nobody knew what it was, like. It's got SBCOB in very very fine print in the middle of the tie.

They had the same tie when I was a girl. They've never changed it.

So I put it back in the plastic bag, and I'll probably only wear it once again.

Is Grandad Brian eating your grapes?

We pick them straight from the vine, don't we?

Yes, they're from our garden.

Can you eat one all by yourself? Can you eat one all by yourself?

Feed me, slave.

Where did the grapes come from?

Our garden, Mum.

Oh, they're home-grown.

It's the one thing we've managed not to kill. You have an actual *camera* camera, Lin. I can't remember the last time I saw someone taking a photo on an actual camera.

Well my phone's just for texting and listening. And phone calls.

I don't take photos now because we've got I don't know how many, and everyone's over one side. And there's a big gap in the middle. Everyone's on one side, and then there's the trees or garden.

And sometimes we don't have heads. There was always something weird about your perception, Mum, because when you were learning to drive, remember, you felt like you needed to be sitting in the middle of the car, otherwise you couldn't tell where you were on the road.

Yes. In the end the driving instructor made me drive with one hand. I think there's something wrong with my eyes, because I do mad photos.

At least with these you can delete them.

You used to know somebody I knew. Who was that?

Um . . .

Years ago. A man.

A man that you knew?

Yes. I worked with him.

McKenzie?

Yes!

How did you know that?

The one who gave me away?

Yes.

How did you know that, from that tiny amount of information?

Because I knew that she worked with Mac McKenzie, who gave me away. That's how I knew.

I couldn't have remembered his name. He was a lovely man.

He died, some years ago. He died quite young. After my dad, but not much after. He must have been mid fifties.

I used to really annoy him, because if you were writing there, I could stand over there and add up back to front. He used to get furious, because he could only do it on the adding machine. I could do it back to front. I used to only do it to annoy him.

He was one of Dad's best friends.

I got on very well with him. I was years younger than him, but we used to have morning tea together. He was lovely, always showing me something about accounting if I didn't quite understand it. Sometimes you don't quite understand something, and I'd just go into his office and ask. He wasn't very popular.

Oh, wasn't he?

I think he was such a pleasant, quiet man, and insurance men are always big and rude.

They're probably a bit better now than they used to be.

I suppose they are.

They wouldn't get any clients if they behaved like they used to.

They used to be terrible. We had one agent, and I don't know what religion he was, but an unusual religion, and he used to tell us God was up in that corner, and that corner, and we had to look up and say hello to God.

Did he say hello back?

He used to say now Pat's going to say hello to God, and I'd say hello God. He was really weird. But if you didn't say hello to God he'd keep on.

### 28

The Vengabus is coming. And everybody's jumping. New York to San Francisco. An intercity disco.

### 29

The Vengabus is coming. And everybody's jumping. New York to San Francisco. An intercity disco.

### 30

The Vengabus is coming. And everybody's jumping. New York to San Francisco. An intercity disco.

### 31

Who am I speaking with? We can cancel and reschedule. What a beautiful smile. How's your uncle in Aussie? He's going to move out soon. I should have warned you. She sells out pretty fast. Yeah, nah, she's still at the market. She does raranga on a Thursday at the wānanga. The other one's boring—all the palagis. I was choking too much, I don't think anyone would appreciate that—I better stay away. Stay in your seat, mister. He's gotta know everything, that one. That's how you learn, eh baby. Marie, please? Marie? Marie? It's bad news up there now. A friend of mine on the long weekend, they said if you don't go to work on Saturday there's no point coming back Monday. That's wrong, they shouldn't be allowed to do that. That's Talley's, eh. The only thing they've kept is the Affco name, but it's a dirty name now. It has dirtied Affco's name. It used to be good up there, everybody enjoyed going to work. They don't now. If Affco had kept their percentage instead of selling it off, it would have been all right. They don't have much say now. Heinz own Wattie's now too, not Wattie's. When I was over the Hawke's Bay about six months ago I seen all the Aussie products in the shops over there, and I thought oh shit, they'll slowly creep into Hamilton. I was quite shocked when I saw that. I'll see you later. Say hello to your mother. So you've got your birth certificate— that's this. This is you? That is you, isn't it. Yes, that's you.

Catherine, hi. Come through. I tried calling the other day but I think you were having a relaxation session.

Yes, I've been doing this recorded hypnotherapy. I've been following a woman who has had similar food intolerance issues to me, and she's now recovered, and part of that has been working with a London hypnotherapist, and she's put together this four-week course to try and—

Is your diet still quite restrictive?

Very. Very. And she was down to eating four or five things as well, but through a combination of supplements and looking at hormone levels, and hypnotherapy was part of it too, she's managed to recover.

So do you find that this relaxation technique has helped you? In terms of sleep, et cetera?

It's too soon to tell, really, because I've only been doing it for a couple of weeks. And it's a four-week—

Do you go into a quiet room and do it?

I try to find—

Is it a bit like meditation?

Kind of. It's—

Have you tried meditation before as well?

I can't sit still.

No.

I find it much easier to have a voice guiding—

I don't think I'll ever be able to do meditation. Maybe when I'm older. We'll check your white cell count again. Do you know what age your mum reached menopause?

I think late forties, but I can't really ask her, because she won't remember reliably. The thing I wanted to ask you about—I think I've been bitten. It's about four weeks ago now, but it hasn't really gone away.

You see that tracking up your arm? You've got an infection. It's ascending lymphangitis.

Say that again?

Ascending lymphangitis. Your lymphatic system is draining, which is what you can see there.

It has gone down.

It's still warm, though.

There was an itchy, itchy lump there for a couple of weeks, which is now gone.

You'll need antibiotics for that.

Really?

Mm.

Is there any way of avoiding those, given I'm trying to heal my gut?

I'll give you some topical treatment.

What do you think it is?

You obviously got an insect bite. See that streaking up there? I'll just have a little feel in here if you don't mind. No pain in there? You might have developed a local reaction to it, but that track up there is definitely ascending lymphangitis. We'll just make an ACC claim, in case it gets worse. So when would this have happened?

Um . . . it's a few weeks ago . . . probably four weeks ago?

What day was it?

Um . . . I know it was a weekend . . .

We'll make it a Saturday. At home?

Well, I noticed it in the morning.

Let's say ten.

While you're doing that, I also stood on a piece of glass, again about four weeks ago. I talked to Ngaire about it last time I had a B12 injection, and she said I should come and see you. Because it is still in there, but it's absolutely microscopic. Alan broke a wine glass. I washed the floor twice, with a wet cloth, and I thought I'd got it all up. Hang on . . . if I just press on it . . . it's somewhere in under there, but there's really nothing to see.

Is that where it is?

It's a bit lower than that . . . it's right in there.

There is a little puncture wound in there. It's very tiny though. What will happen usually with those things is the piece of glass might pop out over the next few weeks or months. I'll document that as well, and if anything does happen—if you get a severe infection or something—we have that on record. I remember one guy had a car accident, and he got glass into his thumb. He came in with severe pain, and just pushing on it, a big piece of glass popped out. And this was about six or eight months later. The body gets rid of foreign bodies. When would this have happened?

It was about a month ago. It was around the same day as the bite.

We'll say Sunday. Morning or afternoon?

Ah . . . afternoon.

Say, six p.m.?

Okay. Also, do you have any tips for getting rid of an earworm? I don't know how it got there in the first place.

Ear *worm*?

Not a real worm. You know—like a song that you can't get out of your head.

I can't think of anything. How often does it happen?

Almost every night. For about a year. Sometimes it's worse than others.

Have you tried listening to different types of music?

Yeah. It's a stupid pop song, as well—not something I normally listen to. I don't know why my earworms can't be Mozart arias, or Gregorian chants.

It's not the Spice Girls, is it?

No, it's the Vengaboys.

Oh my God.

I know.

The Vengaboys.

Yeah. The Vengabus is coming. And everybody's—

You can go and have your bloods now.

Clench your hand.

What do you feel for, when you do that?

It feels like a sponge. It bounces back.

And that's the vein?

That's the vein. Because sometimes you can't see—you can see a little bit on yours, but sometimes you can't see at all. But as soon as you put your finger on it, it bounces back.

People never go for that bulgy one.

Everyone has three choices on their arm. The middle is our first choice—usually it's bigger. You can go here too, but I would rather go here. Because sometimes they give up, and you have to go in again.

So just because you can see more of that one, doesn't mean it's bigger.

Yes. Are you all right?
Yep.
Open your hand.

How's your recording project going? Your quoting—your snapshot of life project?

I gave a chunk of it to my publisher to read and he didn't say this is a big chaotic mess. He thinks it's cutting-edge. I think if it is published it won't have a terribly wide appeal, unless the ladies who lunch—who are the ones who go to book festivals and buy books and have book groups—unless they decide it's the next hot thing, and they have to have read it so that they also can be cutting-edge.

You want to be avant-garde but not very. Is it a year-long project?

Mmhm. So today I am a quarter of the way through.

Don't say that. I know what that means.

What does that mean?

That we're a quarter of the way through the year.

I had Dhanesh look at that thing on my arm, and it's not leprosy. It's ascending lymphangitis, probably from a bite. And the old term for ascending lymphangitis is blood poisoning. And complications can include septicaemia, tissue necrosis, gangrene, amputation of the affected limb, and death. So who's laughing now, eh?

# [ APRIL ]

## 1

Good Lord.

What?

There's an email from Caroline saying her rights team have had interest from Hollywood in my book.

Ah.

What?

Ah.

Is that all you have to say?

Um . . . are you ready to accept the Academy Award?

No. Because it's April Fool's Day.

Oh.

I'm going to ring Mum and tell her Fred's been tipped for a knighthood because of his cancer research.

You're a horrible person.

Hello, just me. Sorry for ringing so early. I'm about to jump in the car and head for work, but I thought I'd let you know I had an email from Helen, and Fred's been tipped for a knighthood because of his cancer research.

Oh for goodness' sake! I didn't even know he was doing cancer research, did you?

Yeah, he's been doing it for quite a few years.

Did you know he was?

Yeah, I did.

I never knew. Well I might have been told and I forgot, of course.

Mm. It's going to be awarded in exactly a year, so it'll be next April Fool's Day.

Isn't that lovely.

Except it's an April Fool's Day joke, Mum.

Oh, I hadn't realised that. You naughty girl.

Sorry about that.

I didn't even realise it was April Fool's Day. Now we can have a proper conversation.

I told Alan that my novel's been bought by a Hollywood producer.

Who was?

I told Alan that my novel's been bought by a Hollywood producer.

Oh, well we'll see it on the screen.

Maybe Sir Fred can come to the premiere.

Will I be allowed to go?

Hmm, I don't know.

Silly old lady—probably not.

Anyway, I better jump in the car—I've got to go to Auckland.

Okay darling.


I am a horrible person.

It's because people trust you.

They do. I know.

And you abuse the trust.

Yep. I'm going to say to my students that in the first hour, as per the course outline, we'll be doing our in-class exam.

Hah! That's good.

So it's all right for them to be duped.

Oh yeah.

I'm disappointed you weren't more surprised about my Hollywood deal.

It just goes to show that I believe in you.

Even though I'm a horrible person.

Yes.

## 2

With your eyes closed, just begin by thinking about your breathing, noticing the gentle movement of your chest and stomach. And with every breath just recognising how your body can release, relax, soften. All that you're doing is communicating with yourself. Sending and receiving important messages. You can breathe out those areas of tension from your body. Your body can heal. It's growing cells, repairing itself, becoming better, stronger. Purely because the Vengabus is coming. And everybody's jumping. Just trust in your body to follow your gentle guidance, to recover your vitality and your health. And the more you can relax, the more space you can create for all the natural, automatic healing functions of the unconscious mind, perhaps even visualising what that space might look like, sound like, feel like to inhabit. New York to San Francisco. An intercity disco. Just like watching a bruise fading with time, you could find yourself noticing a gradual change in your physical condition. And many people find that when they really listen, the Vengabus is coming. Smiling from time to time to recognise that other regenerative activities are becoming habitual. And all because a little part of your mind can remain focused on this, and everybody's jumping. We have no control. The truth is that nobody can make you have a good day. Some people engage in a process like this thinking that it will make life easier, but that's like taking sailing lessons and hoping the sea will stay calm. And everybody's jumping, just imagining what that would look like. An intercity disco, guiding and directing your mind, even if you forget to remember.

What ten o'clock is that?

The actual ten o'clock. So really eleven o'clock.

So ten o'clock.

I held off putting her down for her nap until it was eight thirty, but really nine thirty, but really eight thirty.

It was never going to be easy.

The time changes between two and three a.m.—just before three o'clock, you put the clock back to two. So you get that hour over again. But what happens if someone wants their astrological star chart done, and they're born in that hour? When do they say they're born?

I don't know. I think it's unnatural. You should just cope with the fact that the day shifts. The seasons shift.

It's a strange term, anyway. There's no more daylight—you don't get any more daylight.

It's all about electricity. You use less electricity because you're asleep and not turning on the lights.

You would think that the power companies would be trying to discourage daylight saving then, wouldn't you.

It's a government thing. Always has been.

But the government used to own the power company.

Mm.

If you committed a crime in that hour, and the police wired you up to the lie detector and said where were you at 2:43 a.m., you could honestly say I was at home in bed. If you got home after having committed the crime, in that second bonus hour. That would be the ideal time to knock over a bank.

Mm.

I'm a criminal mastermind.

Aha.

I think that's a cat poo skidmark on the duvet. I suspect Mintie. I can no longer ignore it.

4

I was supposed to sign something to say I'm happy, but they couldn't find it.

5

A narrow escape. He shows them mercury; they think he has caught the moon.

6

It's my nana's birthday today. Nana Chidgey. She must have died when I was about eight or nine. I can remember her. I can remember her floral nylon frocks—

Osti frocks.

Osti frocks. And the cordial, the raspberry cordial, that horrible nasty bright red stuff. That syrupy stuff you used to dilute with water. She always gave us that.

What was it called? Not Raro—the stuff in bottles.

Yes. And we had it in floral glasses—their special floral glasses. She was always working—always baking, making sure guests had something to eat and drink.

I don't think those women exist any more. They've died out. And I'm glad they don't exist any more, but the reality is I miss my nana more than any other human being. I have a sense of homesickness for her. And I dream of her more than of anyone else. Often in dreams I smell her—that baking smell, and the feel of flour on her forearms. I hate cooking, I never go in the kitchen now, but whenever I was with her I was always standing on a stool, digging into a bowl of whatever she was making. I can smell that nearness to her.

I can't remember the smell of Nana but I remember the feel of her skin. It was so soft. The wattle under her chin and her seventies glasses and her pure white hair. I remember that. And the bosom that came down to the waist of the Osti frock. She was all bosom up the top.

So was my grandmother. It started just under the chin, and it was only the belt of the frock that defined where it ended. And she was only four foot ten.

That's two feet of bosom.

She was round. She was a little dumpling, which she hated. And the weird thing was she was always baking but always restricting her diet.

Is that where your mum got it from?

Mm. They both had a religious approach to calorie counting.

I remember we got a few bits and pieces that had been Nana's, and the one thing that I must still have somewhere, I wouldn't have thrown it out, was a flattened large tin can. It was for cocoa or something, and she'd hammered it into a kind of metal envelope, and she'd hidden money in it. And she had these all over the house—stashes that she'd kept from her housekeeping that Grandad didn't know about.

When my grandfather died, my grandmother didn't know how to sign a cheque. She had absolutely no clue about finances—other than the few coins in her purse to trot down to the dairy, she had no grasp at all. She was terrifyingly childlike in so many ways—maybe that's why I miss her so much. It was like having a playmate.

When Nana turned sixty, Grandad's present to her was a bike—a pushbike—so that she wouldn't have to walk to the shops to get the groceries and walk back. She could go on the bike. But he had a car—they did have a car.

Lucky old duck.

Chidgey men are known for their romantic side. I remember we always used to make them presents for birthday and Christmas, and I remember—I feel terrible about this—I knitted her a cotton dishcloth. This little square dishcloth. Isn't that tragic.

That is tragic. She would have loved it though. She probably never ever used it. Folded it up in her hanky drawer. Hankies don't exist any more either. God, that reminds me of those little old ladies who wander into hospitals. When I was in there you always had a troupe of old ladies who would bring you soaps wrapped in crochet-edged flannels. And if those ladies don't exist any more, where will those people be? Who are we going to be, when we're nanas? Not like that. We never were. We'll probably be even more jealous of our time than we are now.

Maybe we will have run away somewhere by then.

Mm.

I had an email from my sister Helen the other day saying that they were watching a documentary about W.B. Yeats, and Fred's mother Elizabeth was there with them, and she happened to mention in passing that oh yes, he's related to us.

Whoa.

I know. On our honeymoon in Ireland we went to Sligo and visited his grave, and visited Ben Bulben and picked up fossils that we brought home with us, and did a boat trip and saw what may or may not be the Lake Isle of Innisfree. And we went to . . . um . . . great windows open to the south . . . the house . . . the stately home . . . begins with an L . . . Lissadell! Which he writes about in a poem . . . is it just called Lissadell? Two women, both something, one a gazelle. Anyway—we went to Lissadell House. And we saw the great windows open to the south. I said to Helen, you have to find out. She said oh, she just mentioned it in passing. But then she talked to Elizabeth and Elizabeth said it's through the maternal line, and she's pretty sure that her grandmother was Yeats's mother's sister. So my brother-in-law's great grandmother—

Okay, I'm mentally growing a tree. Her grandmother was Yeats's mother's—

Yeats's aunt. Fred's great grandmother . . . wait, have I got that right? Yes. Fred's great grandmother—she was Yeats's aunt. She used to go and stay with them. And Elizabeth said they were all very worried about the children when he went bohemian.

Oh that's a lovely little sound bite.

But isn't it amazing?

It is insane. I can't believe no one's ever thought you might like a whiff of that information. There might have been an interesting little trail you could have scurried along.

Last night I was googling pictures of W.B. and looking at pictures of my nephews and thinking hmmm, perhaps Harry . . . ? But they all look like Helen. Anyway—I'm related by marriage to Yeats.

Yes. You can milk that.

I do want Helen to find out the exact connection. She said it's the Pollfexen . . . I think the maternal name was Pollfexen. Pollexfen. Pollfexen.

I love that book George's Ghosts, about his wife and all her spiritual dealings.

They were nuts. Quite bonkers.

She was more of a genius, really—convincing him that she was channelling the dead. It'd be fascinating if some previously undreamt-of fragment fell into your lap down strange little back roads of the family. If they've forgotten that he's significant enough to mention to someone like you, maybe they have little titbits, scraps of stuff that have been tucked away, that they've forgotten to pass on.

It's such a shame Elizabeth didn't mention this while her mother was still alive. Both of Fred's grandmothers lived till well over a hundred—one of them had entirely lost the plot, but the other one was sharp right up till the end. It would have been amazing to talk to her, if she was the one whose mother was Yeats's aunt.

Yeah.

Yeah.

You're related to all the good people.

Who've you got, then?

I can't think of a single human being of note. I don't think my tree grows those interesting branches.

I was almost related to Fleur Adcock and Alistair Campbell.

Oh yes. Yes, you've slept with better people too.

I will arise and go now.

## 7

Happy birthday.

Thanks, but it's not till tomorrow.

Oh. Forget that then, and I'll ring you in the morning. You never know what day it is in here, you see. How are you?

Still forty-five.

## 8

Oh, the bilingual Proust! Thank you, Alice. . . . It's quite long, isn't it.

Hello, just me. I'm ringing to wish myself a happy birthday.
Pardon?

I'm ringing to wish myself a happy birthday.

I thought I'd rung.

You did, but I'd already left for work.

Oh yes. Well that's lovely—I'm glad you wished yourself a happy birthday.

It was nice of me, wasn't it?

Yes. Did you send yourself a card? Or give yourself a present?

I did actually. I did give myself a present.

What did you give yourself?

I gave myself a ring that I've had for years and years and never worn. I decided I needed an eternity ring for my birthday so I gave myself that.

That was a very expensive present. What does it look like?

It's a diamond trilogy—art deco. I thought it could stand for me, Alan and Alice.

And do you feel any older?

I feel about ten years older.

What's done that?

Alan and Alice.

Oh I see.

And Jiffy's been contributing. The cat situation's been contributing.

You can't put him in the car and drop him off somewhere?

Poor Jiff!

I know, he's lovely.

Three a.m. in the morning he doesn't seem that lovely. Alan's been shutting him in the cat cage, in desperation. When he starts up, Alan goes into the garage and shoves him into the cage and covers it up with a blanket like a budgie. And that kind of works . . . but then yesterday Alan realised that someone had pooed in the cage. He was making his feelings known. Jiffy, not Alan.

I've given you something for your birthday, haven't I?

Yes, you're giving me some money for a massage. Which is very thoughtful of you.

Oh that's right. Remember when I used to go down to you in . . . was it Dunedin? And I went and had a massage there.

Ana. She was lovely.

Yes, that was the name, wasn't it. I've never had one since.


Happy birthday—Facebook tells me it's tomorrow, but it probably already is tomorrow with you. But you don't think of it as tomorrow—it's just that our today is your yesterday, and your today is our tomorrow. Many happy returns nonetheless! Every day you sparkle, but today you rule!


Longtemps, je me suis couché de bonne heure. Parfois, à peine ma bougie éteinte, mes yeux se fermaient si vite que je n'avais pas le temps de me dire:

## 9

Happy birthday Catherine Chidgey! HAPPY BIRTHDAY Catherine with a cherry on top (painting by yours truly, I guess I should note). Happy birthday from Denmark! Happy Birthday Catherine! Have a fabulous day! I would like to propose a toast! I think I missed it.

## 10

I'm meant to be imagining my healthy future self, and listening out for a message from her, but when I picture her she's sitting in the German field of flowers, which is the same as my past self, so that can't be right. Plus, she's eating chocolate.

Happy birthday to my favourite Kiwi author!

## 11

I just got progesterone cream on the cat. I'm not sure what this means.

## 12

I got a skip today to go outside the house. It's been worth it I guess, coming down, but it's kind of frustrating, because so far I'm just having to throw stuff out. I haven't made a hell of a lot of progress because of the bub—looking after her all the time. I just can't get round to dealing with the rest. I found a daycare place and she's going there tomorrow so I can get the things onto a pallet to be sent up. How are you?

I'm really tired. It was a long day. I was meant to start week four of my hypnotherapy on Sunday and I haven't even looked at it—I just have not had time. Jiffy's ripping shit out of the couch. I think we should get some antimacassars—some sleeves made for the arms. It's probably too late. He's destroying it. I haven't been hearing him at night, though.

Maybe I'll just ignore him—but when I do, you say you can

hear him and he wakes you up.

Maybe it's when you're here that he's more of a pain. And Solly hasn't been asking to go outside at night either. He knows you're not here and it won't work. He knows.

So it's a destructive relationship I have with him.

Yeah. You're codependent with the cat. And I'm top bitch.

We'll have to go into therapy. Have an intervention.

If they haven't finished the kibble, do you just throw it away and put fresh stuff down?

Yes, because they goob all over it and it gets soft and they don't eat it. That's why you've got to be careful not to put too much in their dishes. But then with Solly it's a problem because he runs out—it's a constant to and fro. I do end up throwing out kibble.

That's a shame . . . it's so expensive. And I'm so tired. I'm working my arse off and we're not even treading water—we're going backwards.

Well if it's any consolation, I'm having a hellish time.

Where are you?

Eh?

Are you down in the bedroom?

No. Nowhere. Little bits chipped away here and there.

I said where are you—are you down in the bedroom?

I thought you meant in terms of progress with Mum's house. Because Ian's demanding progress reports.

Tell him to fuck himself.

I'm in the spare bedroom. They can't hear.

So will that mean it's all going to be your fault that it hasn't been done properly?

No, he'll be gleeful about it, because he'll just throw everything out.

Well make sure you do get the things that you want to keep.

I'm trying to get the metronome. There's just too much to go through. These little things . . . today I took the back off the radiogram to see if it had bulbs inside—tubes that might break in transit—and no, it's all transistors. But there was a layer of dust in there, and an opening at either end of it, rectangular, about an inch by about five inches, and inside were these feathers. Because in Ōtautau, from about 1975, we had a budgie who used to go out and fly around the living room, and perch on top of the curtain rail. And he must have got inside the radiogram once and bashed himself against the transistors and lost a few feathers, and went out down the other end.

There weren't any tiny little bird bones in there? A little bird skull?

No no no no, we had Billy until well into the 1980s—he lived for a very long time—but they're Billy feathers.

Have you kept them?

That same green that I remember.

Have you kept them?

I've put them in a little frame. But it's nearly forty years. And I took off the back, and it's obvious I'm the only one who's ever taken off the back of the radiogram, which is not surprising really, and it's like seeing Billy again after forty years. It's very weird. It's a weird perspective, seeing stuff from my formative years, and having Alice here, and she looks like me as a baby. It's hard to make head or tail of it. And at the same time it's all slipping away. The hours are counting down to when it's going to go, and all I can do is look at it. Even if I wanted—even if there was a possibility—I can't keep everything. And the menace of Ian is coming, and it's all going to go, and I'm just getting a little portion away. But also, being in Te Anau, I have these memories of growing up and going to school here, and I doubt whether I'll ever come here again. It is quite a strange experience.

How's your mum coping with throwing stuff out?

It's taxing on her. Yesterday she got me to throw out Dad's shoes and trousers. I cleaned out a suitcase and I got those two dresses of hers I told you about, and the one I thought had peacock feathers didn't have peacock feathers at all, it has peacock colours. I got them for Alice—they're coming back up on the plane. But I took a photograph of my feet next to Dad's shoes and they're so much longer.

Of your feet, did you say?

Yeah, next to Dad's shoes. They're so much longer. And his trousers are so much longer and so much bigger. I feel like a little kid in my dad's clothes.

You're six foot four.

And at the same time Alice is a little version of me. It feels like all the gossamer threads to my growing up are just withering in front of me and everything's disappearing and in a day and a half I'll be gone and then that'll be it.

Is your mum happy about the retirement village she's chosen?

She's very apprehensive and scared about it. To be unshackled from the house, though—I can't help but think it will be good for her not to have the burden of the house. She had the new owners come through and that made her happy because the woman was ecstatic about the garden. I was talking to her out the front on her own, the woman, and I said you'll probably hack quite a bit back. And they might, but the bones of it will stay. The trees. There are four cats here, buried in the garden. All these things. Suki came in at an early hour this morning but Mum couldn't keep her in—she was bashing to get outside and Mum let her back out. I don't know if we're going to see her again before we go. And I'm supposed to be taking her down to the cattery in Invercargill. And then over the weekend Ian and Ross will be around and she won't come in.

No, she won't.

So I guess we'll tell the neighbours, and I'll tell the vet, but I don't know if we're going to be able to catch her. She's getting feral.

You're not tempted to take the enormous boulder in the garden, from the farm? No, wait—where's it from?

It's limestone. Not something you'd get on farmland. No, you couldn't move it. I'm trying to concentrate on the photo collection—I'm trying to take all the photos up until 1984, and Mum can keep the albums beyond that, and I'll get them another time. I don't know. I'm going to bring my bike back, from when I was ten, but I've put a whole lot of other stuff in the skip—the rocking horse, and the little scooter that was mine.

Did you take photos?

Not really. I've taken some.

You should get photos of Alice on those things.

Some of it's going onto the pallet to be sent up. I'll probably have to get the piano stool and the little chair sent via a freight company, but it might get banged about a bit. I've only got tomorrow—only really tomorrow morning, so it's very difficult for what I want to achieve.

What did you say? It's very difficult . . .

Yeah. For what I want to achieve and what I'm going to be able to achieve—there's a huge gap. Anyway, my dinner's in the microwave—I have to go have something to eat. I'm so hungry.

I haven't rung Mum—I'm feeling bad about that. But on the up side, we did get a flyer from Mallory's inviting us to a talk on living with dementia.

Oh.

I'm sorry I didn't get to say hello to bub bub before she went to bed. I miss her.

She misses you. She's been saying mamamama. And she's said Oma, but every time she's said it, Mum's not been listening. But if you've seen the video, there's been quite a bit of coercion.

Quite a bit of what?

Coercion.

What day is she actually leaving the house?

She's supposed to go on Sunday down to Noeline's. Ian's forcing her out. And then they'll do the shift on Tuesday.

Ian's whatting her out?

Forcing her out.

Oh, forcing her out.

To go and stay with Noeline while they throw everything out of the house.

It is sad. It is. But like I said to her on the phone, it's well documented that a person going into a retirement village gets a new lease on life. I've seen it happen with Mum. Tracey said that Paul's grandmother was the same.

It's just the here and now. At the moment Mum says she feels like she's already dead and she's watching everyone mop up afterwards.

It is sad. It's hard.

For the second time in her life, she feels like she's dead.

When was the other time?

Back in the eighties when we were at Centre Hill, and she was clinically depressed.

Mm. It's rubbish day here tomorrow, isn't it? But the bag's only a third full, so I won't put it out.

Yes you will.

Why?

Yes you will. Tie it off and put it out.

Why?

Because there's another one in the bin next to it that's already tied off. Put them both out, because we have an overrun situation most of the time, and you're only allowed two per week, and when bub comes back there'll be nappies again. Tie it off and get them both out there.

Do I need to do it tonight, or is the morning all right?

Do it in the morning. They never come till nine o'clock.

I'll be leaving at eight anyway.

If you do it at night dogs go through them to get the cat

poo, so it's best to put it out in the morning. Whatever's in the recycling bin, put that out—but don't put out any cardboard or paper, because I put that out around the corner. It's the only way it gets recycled.

I've already done the cardboard and paper.

That will go into the compacter. It will get trashed.

At this stage I kind of don't care. I'm so tired.

Bring it in when you take the bags out and just throw it in the garage, anywhere on the floor, and I'll deal with it when I get back.

Okay. I miss you. It's lonely here.

I miss you too. I'm going to go have my dinner.

Love you.

Love you.

Bye.

Bye.

Bye.


You're running out of time to die young.

## 13

Hello, just me. Sorry to ring so early. I was hoping I could FaceTime with Alice before I go to work. Will you ring me? I'll just nip down to the study.

Okay. Bye.

Bye.

Hello. Oh. Hello?

Hello?

Hello.

Hello? Can you hear me?

I can hear you, but there's quite a lot of rustling.

Can you see me?

I'll just shift the . . . right, can you see her?

I can see bubba. Hi Alice! Can she see me?

Yep.

You sound tired.

Sorry?

You sound tired.

That's good. I'm sorry. I don't know.

Pardon?

I can't really talk. There's so much to do.

Sorry, what's that?

There's so much to do—I'll be up all night I think.

You could really do with another day, couldn't you.

Another week.

You've only got so much time.

I'm just going to leave you to talk to her for a sec—I've got to go do something.

Ah—okay . . . hello sweetie! Hi darling!

I'm here.

Oh, hi Oma! How's it going?

What?

Hello!

Where's Mummy? That's Mummy.

It's very early, isn't it bub. Hi sweetie!

It's a bit early in the morning.

It is. I don't think bubba's quite awake yet.

She's been eating. Haven't you?

What have you been having for breakfast, bub bub?

She says it's that nice stuff—that yummy stuff.

What's that?

It's that, ah, ah, green thing, you know?

Avocado?

That's      fella. She likes that.

Yes, she does like it. Yeah.

She's      to stick on it now. She's not                carrots.

I might just go down to the living room—a bit closer to the router. The sound is coming and going here. Hang on—I'll

131

just go on a little walk. There's cats everywhere underfoot this morning.

That's where Alan is at the moment. We've shut Suki in my en suite.

Oh you did get her. That's good.

I wish I'd never had her. I wish she'd go        I wish, I wish.

You wish she'd go what, sorry?

Get lost.

Poor Suki.

Oh she's a        There you are,        Mum. Where's Mummy?

The sound is—the sound is still coming and going. I'm dropping a word here and there.

Alan        back in a minute.

How's the packing up going?

There's boxes everywhere. There's still a hell of a lot to do. But        a skip, so that's where the rubbish can go. Here's Alan. I'll leave you to it.

Hey bub bub. How's my sweetie pie? How's my sweetie pie? Alice!

This morning I had her on the single bed, nappy off, and I got        and everything, and then I was looking for a pair of trousers, and I heard a rustle and then a bang. I        around, and she was down on the floor, her arm was up at a funny angle, and her        motionless. She had this puzzled look on her face, trying to work out where she was.        crying started. She's okay. But oh my God, I still feel sick.

Bad Daddy.

Yeah.

The sound is cutting in and out. Am I losing words? Can you hear me okay?

        can hear you okay.

I keep missing words. Oh, nostril-cam.

I don't know if that's any better. I think it's picking up the noise of the floorboards when I'm moving, and cutting out.

That seems better. So I did put one rubbish bag out last night, because I just wanted to—

Can I say something? I've got to talk. She's going to daycare today, from eight till one, so we've got twenty-three minutes to get her there.

Okay. I need to go soon anyway. But last night I put the rubbish bag out that you'd already tied off, and then I went out this morning—

Last night?

Yes, I put it out last night. It was fine. No dogs got to it. I just wanted to be organised, so I could make a quick getaway this morning, because I've got lots of stuff to read before class. But I went out this morning to tie the other one off once I'd put all the cat poo and cat litter in, and there was another bag. Someone had put another bag there. And I looked at it and it was tied with red cord, and I looked over the road and there were three sitting outside Margherita and John's that were also tied with red cord, so Hannah had dumped all her party crap outside our house. So I took it back. I took it back over the road and put ours out.

Definitely. They wouldn't have had any recycling out, would they?

No. No. Why?

Because she wouldn't. She throws everything in the rubbish. I'm sorry you're feeling tired.

Pardon?

Sorry you're feeling tired.

Am I feeling tired?

No, I said I'm sorry you're feeling tired!

Oh. I said you sound tired before.

Oh is that what you said. I don't know.

You can only do what you can do.

I'm going to have to go—

Can I just quickly tell you how I saved Solly from a white-tail?

She's got to have her milk.

I'll just quickly tell you—Solly was nosing at something on the carpet last night, and I thought it was a bug, but then I looked closer and I saw it was a white-tail spider, and so I heroically got a glass, and trapped the white-tail underneath the glass, and then got a piece of cardboard and slid that under the glass, and took the white-tail outside. And then I couldn't bear to just put it down, so I threw the glass onto the lawn and ran away, and then went and got the glass this morning.

Of course you did. All right, she's going to have to—

But I saved Solly! And I have not put the recycling out, because I wasn't sure where you put it when you take it round the corner because of your conspiracy theory that the rubbish men are not recycling the recycling but putting it in the main rubbish compacter, so I've just left that for you to deal with once you're home.

She's got to have her milk and I've got to go now. I've got to get out the door.

I'll let you go.

## 14

So.

So it's been feeling okay. The left shoulder has been quite sore again, but that's because I've been sitting on the couch with the laptop. I know, I know, but it's weather-related! In our living room our couch is in quite a cold spot in winter, and so I shift it over to underneath the window so it gets the sun, and it's much more pleasant to sit there than in my cold, south-facing office in the mornings. It's a design flaw.

Totally understandable. I don't suppose there's a way round that, either.

Short of shifting the house, not really. No, I just need to bite the bullet and put the heater back in my office and let the power bills go sky high.

It's so depressing, that. And do you get a term break coming up?

I do, but I'm up at MIT as well, and their terms aren't the same.

Oh come on. How frustrating. And they weren't going to change it for you?

No.

How selfish!

I know.

Hmm. Well there's some areas moving better and some still a wee bit stubborn. Have you been to see Hunt for the Wilderpeople yet?

Yes. Yes.

Did you enjoy it?

I did . . . as a vegetarian I found some of the dead animal scenes a bit hard to take. I had to close my eyes.

I think as a human you find them quite hard to take. They're pretty rough. But that speaks to a story of New Zealand, to an extent.

It does. We went on my birthday—it was the first movie we'd been to in months and months. Our neighbours looked after Alice and we went.

Oh how exciting.

It was tragically exciting. We were out of the house for probably two and a half hours total. Did you like it?

I really enjoyed it. I really really really enjoyed it. It was very imaginatively filmed and the acting was very clever.

And the music was surprising.

Absolutely.

I hadn't realised that it's based on a Barry Crump book.

He's quite a weird man, isn't he.

I used to live with—as in my partner was—the son of a poet

who was married very briefly to Barry Crump. He beat her up.

I've heard he was quite horrible to several of his partners, and certainly wasn't averse to drinking.

I think he was a troubled man.

But from that came something quite amazing. In the same way I think Robbie Burns was an alcoholic misogynistic tax man, but he did produce some of the most beautiful writing. I've treated a number of pig hunters and because they've got nothing to do but read books, they are so well versed in literature. When I first arrived here I went with this guy into the bush, this pig hunter—his language was pretty colourful, but he could quote Shakespeare, and he could talk to you about all the different classic books. Because in a lot of the pig-hunting huts, they just leave hundreds and hundreds of books. They're in the bush for three months at a time, and they are either hunting or reading. He had a phenomenal grasp of deeper meanings of books—and killed things for a living. Which I think takes a wee bit of your soul away. It changes something somewhere.

I don't understand it. So these men do it for a living? Do they sell the meat?

No no no, they're paid by DOC. And they go into the bush, and they live in the bush—they're helicoptered in, often, to places you couldn't dream of walking to, with three months' supply and five dogs. And they go and they live in the hut for three months, killing as many goats and possums and everything as they can—it's how they controlled all that for a long time, but DOC's funding is now so dried up and there are very few of them left. Basically they lived off what they caught, and they'd fish. I think vegetables were a pretty low priority— cans of baked beans, maybe. They spent a lot of time on their own. Which can be quite good for people.

With no internet connection.

Not even a phone. There's no nothing. And they are so horrendous to animals. The stories that come out of it . . . did you ever hear a Crump story about a hawk? One of his mates said let's strap some dynamite to it and shoo it away. And of course it flew back into their hut and attacked them, and caused untold damage, and then obviously it blew up. But that sort of thing is commonplace. This guy's stories were peppered with craziness like that.

I don't want to know. Our neighbours who built behind us on a small lifestyle block—he's a hunter and they've got hunting dogs, and I have to draw the curtains when I see him coming home with his mate in the ute and unloading whatever it is they're unloading. I just can't look. I don't understand it. I don't understand doing it for sport.

New Zealand's got this really hard question, doesn't it—how does one maintain the place as it is when all these things are killing it? My problem with hunting is that they'll catch and kill all the big boars, these guys—I mean the luxury hunters, the leisure hunters, not the ones who work for DOC—but they'll let pregnant sows go. Because then they've got more hunting. And they populate deer into areas and then go and shoot them, which I don't understand. One of my friends invited me to this deer range where you can go and shoot deer. Would I do that? I certainly wouldn't pull the trigger. I love tramping. I love going into the bush and walking. But I wouldn't shoot a deer, not ever. At this place, you drop food in the morning, go back in the afternoon and shoot whatever's eating it. That isn't hunting, and that's not fair. When I first arrived and that guy took me out pig hunting, I wasn't very good at saying no. He handed me the smallest knife I've ever seen in my life and pointed to this boar head on his wall. And I said what am I going to do to that with this? But at least there's a fairness to it. That I can almost understand. And he is getting rid of them—he gets phone calls from farmers and so on and goes and gets rid of them. And I guess it's man testing himself against the elements or whatever.

Why do you get so many pig hunters to treat? Is it because

of the weight of carrying the animals?

Yes. And because often ex-pig hunters are now shearers or some other thing that wrecks their body. I'm very lucky with my job—I see everybody. Most of society.

I remember when I was doing online dating—back in the wilderness years—and I had on my profile that I was a strict vegetarian. It was obvious to anyone who read it. And this guy sent me a message, and his profile photo was him carrying a dead pig strapped across his back. How does he think that's going to work?

Maybe someone should talk to him about his profile photo, because you're narrowing your field of interest quite largely. Maybe if you introduce yourself, and maybe after a wee while you bring up the killing . . . I grew up in a hunting area. It was so important as far as income and also eating went.

Where was that?

Up in the highlands of Scotland. I was brought up on game.

Did that include all the gross bits?

Well Mum had done cordon bleu—they were both chefs, and Mum was trained in France, so they cooked with everything. And I do come from Scotland, where our national dish is haggis, so the chances are quite high that there's a lot of gross bits. But it couldn't get more organic, or happy. You know—the animal's happy walking along, and then suddenly it's not. I have much less problem with that than I do with factory farming or carting cows around and then sticking a bolt through their head.

I don't want to know.

I think people need to eat a lot less meat. Not for ethical reasons. Environmental reasons, health reasons—meat has just gone crazy. Especially with this paleo diet where you've got to have a steak every day. No caveman ever had that. Maybe the king of the cavemen had that. You've got to take into account that they fasted—they didn't eat for long periods. They didn't eat bacon and eggs for breakfast and a steak for dinner. It's funny though—being in Britain, my exposure to New Zealand was a couple of snowboarding films and Once Were Warriors. And now Lord of the Rings. That's what people see New Zealand as. Mind you, I suppose everyone sees Scotland as haggis and kilts and Braveheart, whereas it's mostly slums and poverty.

Do you go back there much?

My folks live in France now. I never go back to the village I came from because almost everyone's moved out. Was it the pig-hunting neighbour that you left your daughter with when you went to the movie?

No.

The guy I went pig hunting with, he would do things like hang the pig—

I don't want to know.

Anyway, his kids were very comfortable with it, let's put it that way. It was eighteen years ago—I'd love to know how that turned out.

Dad's family, and Dad, were very much into their hunting and fishing, and that's probably why I became vegetarian—lots of people who eat meat never see the actual process.

They see cling film. So have you got any exciting plans for the dying days of summer? I know it's supposed to be autumn, but I can't quite get the word out.

Not really. Marking.

When I was down in Wellington a couple of weekends ago I went to the Gallipoli exhibition at Te Papa. Have you been to it?

No. I can't imagine it. I look at my students who are nineteen, twenty, twenty-one and I just can't imagine them going off to fight.

When I was younger I got drafted for the first Gulf War.

Really?

I got the letter from the Ministry of Defence drafting me. It's the first time I ever swore in front of my mother. I was so angry and upset and worried about it . . . but as it turned out, it was my uncle sending me a hoax. If you read to the end of it, it said due to military cutbacks, can you please provide your own Sherman tank.

What a hilarious uncle.

He was such a funny man. In retrospect it was actually quite funny, but at the time—I can't imagine, I can't imagine how horrible it would have been if it was real.

How old were you?

Seventeen.

What about your mother—did she think it was real too?

No. She was the one who kept saying that's awful, but why don't you read to the end. I said some words I regretted afterwards.

That's mean.

It felt quite mean. I'm not sure I'd do that to someone else. My mum won't even set foot in the war museum, because of what it did to her family. Her uncle got the VC, and everyone was in the RAF. And none of them were the same.

Did they ever talk about it?

No. My gran was in Coventry when it was bombed and she was driving lorries with the headlights off—driving Spitfires around to confuse the enemy. They used to move them from airfield to airfield, so it confused the spies as to how many planes were where. The only thing Mum knows is that she saw people burning to death in the streets. She didn't stop. She saw people burning in the streets, either side of her and underneath her. And she never was the same. Who was the author—who wrote The Jungle Book?

Kipling.

Kipling. He was a pro-war correspondent—he was the war office's . . . whatever it is you're called when you write positive stuff about the war. World War One. Very very pro-war. King and Country. He did all this amazing writing for the . . . what's the word . . . not propaganda, but not far off propaganda. It *was* propaganda, World War One propaganda—there's a word for the office that did that. Until his son got sent off. There's quite an interesting movie and book about it, called My Son Jake or James or something, where Daniel Radcliffe plays the son. And you can see his heart break.

I like Daniel Radcliffe. He's done such a good job of not remaining typecast.

He has, hasn't he. And quite quickly as well. And that is a huge typecast to break.

I got Alan to give me a back rub the other night, and he said my shoulders—just above where you are—felt like rocks.

I can believe that. But your body's doing well. I mean I know there's still the rocks in the shoulders and so on, but I think that will lessen as everything else starts to move more. It really is starting to move more. So you're dealing with patterns now, historic patterns, more than you are acute injury.

I missed you.

It feels like I'm walking into a palace. The creaking floor, the dust.

Oh the dust. That house feels like it's built from dust.

## 15

I got a voucher for a dozen eggs. I emailed to complain that they have tiny tiny little sparrow-sized eggs in each box now—always two, on the left-hand end—and I'm sure they know it, but I had two emails back basically not responding to the complaint at all. Thanks for getting in touch! Thanks so much for your feedback! We always have a range of sizes in our dozens, and some will always be a little bit smaller than others! I said that's not the point, the point is that it's *changed* recently. I know that some are always slightly smaller, but these are tiny.

And they're always together, on the end.

Yes. But I've noticed the ones that I just bought the other day aren't like that. And I had a look through the other ones on the shelf—I opened them up and checked them—and they're not like that any more either. So I think they must have had a flood of complaints.

They tried it, and it didn't work, so they've given up on it.

They probably sell the runt ones to pavlova makers. By the way, Mum rang me yesterday, and she wasn't overtly tearful but I could just hear that it was lurking there in her voice. No, bubba. No—oh God. And we did the how are you, blah de blah—bubba, you're going to get stuck in there, aren't you. And you're going to scratch the wall as well. Anyway, after a couple of minutes of chatting she said I just wanted to talk to you about when you're going overseas. And I said I'm not going overseas. And she said you and Alan—I thought you were going overseas. And I said no, no—well not until next year, when my book comes out. I might go over for a couple of weeks then. Oh no, not that—no, I know about that. But it sounded like she meant that we were going over there to live. For good. That we're moving overseas. And then she said just ignore me—obviously I've got it wrong. Maybe I dreamt it. Yes, I must have dreamt it, because I was thinking about it when I woke up first thing this morning, that you're going overseas. So then the lurking tearfulness dissipated immediately. But where on earth she got that idea from—

I think I told her that when your book comes out Alice is going to go over with us.

Dada! Mamama!

Oh. Well clearly we can never move away.

Unknown. The system cannot provide the required information because it has expired or does not exist.

## 16

Thanks for your order, Catherine! Your order is confirmed and we'll let you know when your Emoji Poo Shaped Stuffed Plush Pillow Cushion Smiley Face Sofa Toy Doll has been marked as shipped.

Hi Patricia Chidgey,
On Monday we sent out the April/May edition of the SuperSeniors e-Newsletter. Unfortunately there was an inaccuracy in the dementia-friendly living story around the correct temperature for storing hot water. We have sought expert advice from the Ministry of Health and have been advised that hot water should be stored at 60 degrees in the hot water cylinder. As a result of that advice, we have revised the newsletter and the amended version follows.

Do you want to watch Jamie Oliver getting all preachy and righteous about sugar?
Not really.

## 17

I hate to mention it, but we need to have a huge clear-out here too. I've started going through the cupboard in my study but I'm barely scratching the surface . . . basically I need to go through every cupboard and every drawer in the house. It's all getting on top of me. I have to start somewhere. University notes and books I'll never open again and clothes that don't fit. How many paperclips do I really need? And how many measuring tapes? And you know when you buy a new piece of clothing and you get a spare button with it—I have a whole box. I don't even know which garment most of them came from.
Get rid of them.
But we might need them one day, if we lose a button.
We might not. We might never lose a button.

I've found these drawing instruments of Dad's—I'll keep some of those, I think.

I like the closure on that case—the little pins on the end. You should keep that.

You pull out the pins to open it.

It's a really nice short-nap black velvet. I like that.

There's one instrument missing.

The hinge seems to be broken. I could do a repair.

It's had a hard life. Dad would have got it in the fifties, when he went to technical college and did draughting.

This is from another set.

I don't know if I'll keep those compasses. They're much newer—one of them might even have been mine or Helen's from school.

This looks like a school one, that you put a pencil in.

And that one too, don't you think?

That's an older one.

But do you think I should keep those? I mean that's a compass too, right? The one in the case?

Yeah. It's got a lead in it.

So—don't keep those?

I'll keep that one. I'll add that to my tools.

You don't want the older one? It's just a bit rusty on the spike.

No. This one's easier to work with.

What about this one?

No. It's from another set, and it's incomplete.

That's nothing special—just a little pencil sharpener.

I could do with a pencil sharpener.

I've got a couple that I've found, so don't keep that one, because it's all corroded. I remember Dad using this. It's got verdigris now.

What's verdigris?

It's when the metal starts going green and rough, like that.

I might try and clean it, because I do remember him using it.

You need some more leads.

No, Dad's still got lead in his pencil. Even though he's been dead since 1995.

Inappropriate. You could take that off and soak it in something—maybe CRC—but I think you pull off that and you throw all the lead down inside. I haven't got my glasses on, so I'm not sure. But keep it.

That ruler I think was mine from school, so chuck that. These are older. What are they called? Set squares. See, that's got L CHIDGEY scratched into it. Keep that?

Keep the green ones and get shot of that one.

Is that the getting-rid-of pile?

I would say so.

Okay. We'll keep these two.

These curves—I had them in tech drawing at school. I think they're called parabolic curves.

And they're for drawing arches?

Well, curves on paper, when instead of drawing straight lines you need to draw a curve.

Yes, duh, clearly they're not for drawing straight lines.

It's standard 1980s tech drawing equipment from school.

Get rid of that as well?

Yeah.

So keeping . . . is this the keeping pile? The box is stuffed—we'll get rid of that. I do feel sad, throwing out Dad's possessions, but we just can't keep everything, and I need the room. Three-sided rulers—I remember him using these. Shall I keep that one?

No. I'd say not.

That one we can probably get rid of, do you think? I don't know. These look exactly the same. Shall we keep the rulers?

If you want to. It's up to you. I don't know what to say.

This one's got a notch out of it. So when you're measuring it wouldn't be exact.

And when you draw a line it's going to be jagged.

I guess we'll keep those. Do you think?

If you want.

I don't know. There's a big album that says Dad's Photos on the front, or Les's Photos. I opened it and I wished I hadn't because it's all dead animals. All hunting shots. I don't know what to do with that. I guess we keep it. It was a big part of his life . . . but I don't ever want to look at it. I'll see if I can resurrect the pencil. See if I can use it. So those we're getting rid of—but I don't want to throw them away myself. You have to. Is there somewhere we can put this?

What do you mean, somewhere we can put this?

To store it.

I don't have anywhere. A box in the cupboard?

## 18

Shall we watch the Jamie Oliver doco on sugar?

God no.

## 19

Did something come in the mail? What was in the boxes?

Mum's metronome. It was my grandmother's, and it used to sit on top of the writing desk which I've now got in our spare room.

But why did you post it home?

I didn't want it to get crushed in the suitcase or crushed in the boxes that are coming up on the pallet. And they were already packed anyway—it was a last-minute thing. I went down to the post office and boxed it within a box, and sent it off.

You could have brought it in your carry-on luggage.

With the baby? All I had when I came on the plane was the baby's bag with nappies and milk and food. It would have got banged around.

I thought you were allowed to bring a bag for the baby.

I did on the way down—I had a bag for the bubba, and another bag, but it was incredibly difficult going through five hours of travel carrying both of those and her. And trying to protect this while dealing with her—no.

You could have turned it on and kept her entertained. Made the time pass. Tick, tock, tick, tock. Or is it tick, tick, tick, tick?

The eternal flight with the bub on my lap . . . it wouldn't have passed the time any quicker for me. I just would have been worrying about her smashing it to bits. She would have got hold of it and smashed it.

You make her sound so destructive.

This sat on the writing desk in the hall at my grandparents', and I do remember one time—it would have been before Didda died, because Nana moved into Peacehaven after that—I remember opening up the bottom. I remember being fascinated by the insides of it and wanting to put something inside for posterity, near the mechanism.

Like Billy the budgie?

My initials. I wrote my initials up in the corner. It's pyramid-shaped, so it has this mysterious Masonic look to it. I guess it's oak.

No, it's not oak. I don't know what it is, but it's not oak. It might be teak. Or walnut.

I think it looks more like walnut. Like my sixth-plate daguerreotype camera.

Yes, I think it's walnut. And I think the feet are ebony.

They just twist off, because the glue has dried out.

You don't want to lose them. Is it missing a foot?

No, it should have three. Though it is odd. I wonder why they didn't do four.

To save on ebony? And this would be ebony too, I think, this panel—or ebonised wood.

It could just be black lacquered. Oh you're right, it does have a grain in it. It might be ebony. Certainly no paint's come off. So this goes with Nana's piano stool, which is also on the way up. It's on the very top of the pallet, and the pallet's not to be stacked on. And it goes with her . . . ah . . . musical score books? I don't know what you call them.

Sheet music.

Sheet music. Including one little ditty she wrote in the back about boys going down George Street in Dunedin. And a triangular cribbage board is coming too, which has a big Masonic compass on it.

Why does it have that on it?

I don't know. It goes with the Masonic garb that we've got from Didda.

Is that what they used to do at their meetings? Play board games? Tiddlywinks?

It's got a cavity inside, behind this black panel—the back half of the pyramid is empty. It always fascinated me: what would be inside? What's been inside there all those years? And when you tip it back and forth you can hear something rattling.

Mysterious.

It's actually bits of glue, I think. I like the little hook and eye.

What's that thing called?

The counterweight. And that's the pendulum. It sits in there at the top, so you pull it out—it bends a little. You slide the counterweight up the pendulum to make it go slower, and slide it down to speed it up. The other weight is hidden inside. And the notches correspond to the measures on the ebony panel, so you just line them up.

Presto, allegro, andante, adagio, larghetto . . .

I've never read that.

Are they beats per minute, the numbers?

I don't know.

If I put it on sixty . . . is that about a second? One one thousand, two one thousand, three one thousand—

Yes. A second.

I was just getting started.

It probably needs winding up.

Why was it on the writing desk and not on the piano?

Hmm. Good question. The piano was in the spare room at Nana and Didda's.

So she didn't use the metronome when she played?

I guess she had it from when she learned. And the piano was in the spare room. I never actually heard Nana play. It seems very odd to think of that now, because she used to play in dance halls and so on and was apparently quite good. It goes along with never really asking Nana and Didda about their childhood—never even thinking to ask the question. I loved them to bits and they were very important people in my life, but I just never had that perspective until they were gone. Now I'd ask them millions of questions about different family members and where they lived and what they did. But as a child you just assume that their life began when you did.

What does the plaque on the front say?

France, Angleterre, Amérique, Hollande, Paris. And Belgium.

Belgium, or Belgique?

Belgique. I always assumed this was from Paris because it said Paris at the bottom. See the plaque is placed slightly off-centre? The more you look at it, the more you see it.

Also because the grain swoops off to the side. It fools the eye. It is French, though. Métronome Maëlzel. And it's got a serial number on the bottom too. Why do you need to wind it up?

Because it's not a perpetual motion machine. It's physics. You can't just go forever. So it has a mechanism—there's the other weight, hidden down there. That's the lead weight, at the base of the pendulum. It rocks back and forth. I think it applies pressure on . . . oh, I don't know how it works.

It's clockwork.

But it's not like a clock mechanism, because it's got so much free movement in it. It pushes that way, and then it pushes that way, and how quickly it does it relates to the weight.

It's a lovely thing to have.

So long as I get the biscuit barrel as well, I'll be happy. And Alice is going to learn to play the piano with this.

What if she doesn't want to learn to play the piano?

Then we have a nice family antique that looks vaguely Masonic.

Here's one that sounds exactly like yours, on this forum. Early metronomes were spring-wound, like watches, and didn't keep exact time because the springs lost tension. Look. These people are trying to figure out how old their metronomes are . . . but no one really answers the question.

And the pictures don't work any more.

Lost. Need Directions. Go Home.

## 20

Went for a B12 injection at the doctor's this morning, and the one day I didn't take my phone was the one day I sat next to two old ladies having a conversation about jewellery in the waiting room. Didn't have a paper and pen, either. Am now trying to piece it together from memory, à la Capote.

I'm actually not a gold person, I'm a silver person. But my three daughters are gold. Something something. I wear my jewellery every day. The first thing I think when I wake up in the morning is what earrings shall I wear today? I've got garnets, sapphires, something, something . . . all sorts. I put them on for myself, not for anyone else. And people accept me in my jewellery. Something something something. He wanted me to give him my sapphire ring. I said what are you going to do with that? He said sell it and buy a house. Something. I said I'm not giving it to you just to sell. I'm going to leave it to someone. I have someone in mind who would look after it.

Come through. You're heading right down the end. You know you're seeing me today?

Has Ngaire had her baby?

Babies. Twins, ten weeks early. It's been very busy here. I'm doing the work of two people. What sort of work do you do?

I teach creative writing at the university and also up at MIT in Auckland.

What's your background, to be doing that? Do they pay you for it?

I'm a novelist.

Oh. What do you write about?

### 21

Confirm that you are a human.

I am a human. Let me watch the video.

### 22

You are way too nice. Seriously—four o'clock on the last day of term, and he doesn't know how to access the course page?

Neither do a lot of them. There's a whole bunch who haven't handed their work in at all. Or just haven't ever come.

It's so infuriating.

I know. But what can you do?

Shoot them all.

Yeah. I was quite surprised that the ones who came today handed their work in.

So was I, with my lot. Obviously I put the fear of God into them. I was waiting for the malfunctioning printers, or the no credit left on my copy card, or my car's broken down, or the dead nanas—there's always quite a few dead grandmothers brought out at this time of year. But there weren't any.

Mm.

Where did I see your photo the other day? Your new author photo—the one of you lying down.

I look like I've had plastic surgery.

Hey you know that box in the staffroom, where you can buy books and things? They've got an adult colouring book. I don't understand that at all.

Neither do I. I went and bought one, though, when I was doing the writing workshops in prisons. I thought it might calm some of them down. But the one I thought it might calm down, it didn't calm down at all—she was just *scribbling*, with a manic look on her face.

Was she colouring outside the lines?

*Way* outside the lines. But there were some of them who liked it. If I was in prison I'd probably like it too.

We went to the wānanga in Hamilton for three years—not that you can tell now, but we learned Māori for three years—and part of their whole philosophy was colouring in. We were given coloured pencils at the start of the term, and there were scenes in our homework books that we had to colour in. We sat there feeling like twats, doing our colouring in, but the idea is that it changes the brainwaves to alpha waves, and makes you more receptive to learning.

Out of the left brain and into the right. That kind of business.

Yeah. I don't think it helped my acquisition of Māori. But we were almost the only Pākehā in the class, so we were religiously doing our homework.

You just don't learn a language like that.

No, you don't.

I've been to enough Samoan night classses to know that sort of thing doesn't work. You'd have to go off and do a whole adult colouring immersion class.

Perhaps we could apply for funding for that. To help our pedagogical practice.

It just feels like a waste of time. Why would I waste my very limited free time colouring in, when there are so many other things that I could be doing? Like actually writing something. Which is obviously never going to happen.

Or even reading something.

Or even reading something. Fuck.

It's the macramé of the twenty-first century. And it also sounds vaguely X-rated, doesn't it—adult colouring. Like you're colouring in genitals.

That'd be more fun. I might do it.

You probably really can get them. I stumbled onto this website—a right-wing Christian blog—about how adult colouring books are portals to the devil because they use mandalas. They put people into a trance state whereby they're much more receptive to the Evil One. Maybe that's why everyone's doing it.

Maybe.

### 23

Jamie Oliver? No?

### 24

Thank you. You have been successfully removed from this subscriber list. You will no longer hear from us.

Did you unsubscribe by accident? Click here to re-subscribe.

### 25

I said it feels very weird being out in crowds of people. We don't belong here. I look around and I can't see anyone I'd want to talk to.

And I said that's because you're judging by appearances.

I said I'm surrounded by unattractive people wearing grubby bandages and ill-fitting clothes, with greasy hair and dirty children and skin conditions, sipping on their buckets of Coke and puffing on their fags, and displaying their trashy cherry tattoos on the backs of their knees, and just generally insulting my aesthetic sensibilities every way they can.

And I said we must be part of mainstream society if we're doing our big appliance purchases at the mall on a public holiday.

You said regular society the first time. We must be part of regular society.

I am chaos theory. I can't do the same thing twice. It's part of my dyslexia—I think of the same thing and I swap it all around and get confused so I say something different.

Like yes dear of course those jeans are slimming. All right, we're standing here. Potential customers. Here we are. Shall we just ask?

Yeah.

Hi—can we get some advice on a carpet shampooer?

Absolutely.

We've got five cats, and we don't know much about them.

Absolutely. Absolutely. Sure. Sure. That's what we're here to help for. Obviously you can see quite a few different models. The blue one. The green one. The difference between different models is how effective they are in terms of cleaning and removing the stains. Which basically means how many times you have to go over the carpet to remove a stain, and ultimately what there is also to consider is the suction power, which means how much water it's going to draw back from the carpet as well. Have you ever shampooed the carpets at all?

No.

No. Only with a Rug Doctor.

How did you find that?

It was all right. It was quite heavy, wasn't it? But you're not doing it every week.

No. That's the biggest thing that you've got to consider when you look at a shampooing machine—it's going to save you a lot of time and money. Because when you have your own machine in comparison to trying to hire one, you have the freedom to use it as you want, when you want, at a time suitable for you. Which means you don't have to do the whole house in one go. You don't have to move the entire furniture of the house. Basically what a Rug Doctor is, according to me, it's basically a bigger version of this machine. When I say bigger, I don't know if you've noticed, but on the Rug Doctor the brushes are basically flat. They don't spin—so they don't scrub the carpet. What's good about the Rug Doctor is being commercial it's got big water tanks and it's got a good suction power, which means it draws the water out pretty good. But when it comes to actual cleaning, it's the difference in the brushes that can make a lot of difference in the cleaning.

So that one has flat brushes?

Yes. That's got flat brushes, whereas all the other models have actually got spinning brushes. What that does is it actually spins and scrubs the carpet, helping you take out the stain quicker. Have you got any stains that you're trying to action, as such?

Just her.

That's normal, you can't do much about that, I've got a two-year-old in my house so I know exactly what you're talking about.

It's not really stains, it's more—

General cleaning?

Yes, general cleaning.

I'll just quickly serve this person, if you don't mind. I'll just quickly process this.

I'm trying to remember—I think that one got okay reviews online. I don't think we should buy it today, though. We should just find out about it—don't you reckon?—and then go and look at reviews online, and—

Right! As part of our experience to customers, we show customers the difference in different cleaners. Because of the brushes and the type of cleaning action they've got. How about I quickly go through that with you? Vegemite. That would be your worst enemy, I would say, so I'll use that as an example.

I'd go for red wine, but I guess you wouldn't keep a bottle of that here.

Ha, ha. No, if we had that, you'd probably find all the staff members drunk when you come in, and we'd probably lose our jobs. Ha, ha. I'll just do it there if you don't mind.

That's what Alice would do. Smear the Vegemite into the carpet.

That's why we say this is your worst-case scenario. So this is if things get really out of control and you have the worst situation of your dreams, then how are you going to tackle that, basically. So we categorise them into three levels, basically, on the way the brushes work. We personally call this level one because it's only got that flat brush, so it doesn't really do much in terms of cleaning the stain. So what it means for you the customer is you'll have to go over the stain several times. I'll turn it on and . . . [inaudible]. I've done five strokes so far. The stain is obviously quite badly visible, and in terms of suction, that's the amount of water that I've picked up. Now this one is level two. If I turn this one over, it's got two rollers. So not one roller, but two rollers. So it's basically scrubbing twice on the same stain. So let's turn it . . . [inaudible]. So that's one less stroke in comparison to that, and the stain is quite visibly almost gone. And then if you look at the difference in the water collection as well, this one's picked up a lot more water. Basically what that means to you, in accordance with what's going to happen at home, is less times you have to go over, less moisture that's going into the carpet, and less time to dry. And then if you jump to level three—this is the level three, as we call it—this has got two rollers as well, but the difference is if I show you between the two, if you look under there, it's got less brushes on the roller.

Oh yes.

So with this one, each roller has got two rows of brushes, and with this one, each roller has got six rows of brushes. So it's spinning basically three times more than that, hence scrubbing the stain three times more as well. And it has also got a built-in heater. So what that does is it heats up the water for you, and it's actually got an air vent from where it's blowing hot air as well. Helping you dry the carpet even quicker. The other thing you have here is this knob.

Yes.

With which you're able to control how much chemical you want to use. So you've got light clean, normal clean, heavy traffic. Because let's face it, bedroom is not going to have the same amount of foot traffic and dirt as living room.

Yes.

Because you spend more time in the living room. So high-traffic areas, you want to increase the chemical ratio; low-traffic areas you want to decrease the chemical ratio.

When you say the chemical ratio, what's the chemical?

All of them use carpet shampooing machine-cleaning chemicals. It's not your ordinary chemical. They are specific for shampooing machines.

It's not just water, then.

No. Just water would definitely not do the job. It's like your clothes. You wash your clothes after wearing them one, maximum two times if you're wearing them the full day. Carpet in the end is fabric as well. All the oils that we lose from the skin, the dead skin cells and everything—vacuuming is taking up the dry part, yes, but all the oils and creams and stuff that we put on our body that eventually goes on the carpet—that needs to be taken up as well.

And so do you use the liquid—the chemical—according to the brand that you buy? They're not really interchangeable?

Yes. To some extent yes. So I'll put this on normal clean. [inaudible] One . . . two. I've only done two strokes, and that's quite an effective result. More effective than what that is. With shampooing machines, you can either work harder or you can work smarter. Harder is you're trying to save time by going over too quick, but eventually you'll be going over more times. Slightly slower, you allow the brush to actually do the job, which is scrub the stain out. Now if you see that there is a particular stain which is not coming off, you've gone over it a couple of times, what you're also able to do with this is you've got the feature of clean shot. With that [inaudible] the chemical directly onto that stain. And because it's got a stronger chemical ratio, it's going to action and break down the stain much more quicker for you.

Mmhmm.

And then what you do is you let it soak for about thirty seconds, and go over it with a water rinse. So with this machine, what you gain is you've got two separate containers. You've got one container which is with chemical and water, and another container which is just with chemical. And from there it mixes accordingly, and the biggest thing is it's got a water rinse, which means once you've shampooed a room, you go over the same room again with just water.

Oh yes.

To remove any leftover chemicals.

Oh right.

The same as a washing cycle, but in your carpet. Your first cycle's always a soap cycle where the soap goes in, and once the washing is done then the rinse cycle takes place where it's only clean water going in to remove excess soap.

Yes.

So how did that water suction feel in comparison?

A bit drier, yeah.

[inaudible] That's where I finished. So if I come back again it will pick up that as well. So out of the three levels, which one would you want to consider?

Well it does come down to price. What are the prices?

Which one should I start with? Whereabouts do you want to—that's the only level one that we've got. The white one there is what we call a one point five, because it has got a spinning brush, but it's not as effective as having the double. Because it's only got a single roller. And the suction power on that is not the same as on that. Then you've got that green one there, and this blue one here. These two machines are practically the same— the difference is this blue one here also comes with upholstery tools as an option that you can attach for one-off cleaning in between. There'll always be the situation where you've shampooed the carpet on Sunday and then come Tuesday or Wednesday the child has done some sort of accident or you've managed to spill coffee, so instead of trying to clean up with the whole machine in that scenario, you've got the upholstery tool to attach and action one-off stains. Or if you've got fabric couches, fabric car seats—is your couches leather or fabric?

They're leather.

Okay. And car seats?

No, they're fabric.

So having the upholstery tools allows you to clean car seats, couches, anything to do with fabric, whether that be pillows or mattresses—

And which model has that?

This model comes with that, with the double rollers, and it's on special for four ninety-nine at the moment.

Speaking of stains, someone's got a dirty nappy.

And then if you start going up, you've got this one, which is above that one. All the models that I'll tell you about now, they've all got the upholstery tools. What you gain in that is that not only it's got the roller with the six brushes, it's also got scrubbing brushes—so in the front it's got a roller, and on the back it's got scrubbing brushes that scrub as well. Two separate big tanks, so it has a good capacity. This one here is seven nine nine, then we jump up to this one which is nine nine nine—it's basically a bigger version of that—and then you have this one here, which is twelve nine nine to buy outright. It's got all the features, and the upholstery tools are actually attached to the machine.

Mamamamamamamamama!

Okay. Could we just get a note of the prices and the models?

Ah . . . yep. How would you like me to give it to you? Like on a card or something? They are on our website, if you want to jump on our website.

It'd be good to know which—

I can write them down if you want. So which models would you be interested in?

Um . . . probably from this one up. Do you think, Alan?

Yeah.

We do have the option where you can get a higher-level machine if you want, which will do the job more effectively and save you time, and pay it off interest free. We've got direct debit options, we've got automatic payment options, and there is no interest. Sorry you didn't have much time, otherwise I would have shown you what else other machines can do, but her nappy needs to be changed, which is definitely more important. I've got a two-year-old at home, I know everything about that.

Thanks for your help. We'll have a think.

What do you think?

I don't know. It felt a bit like the Las Vegas timeshare hard sell.

He wasn't that bad.

I mean the last one was obviously the Rolls Royce of carpet shampooers, but I don't know that we want to spend $1300.

I don't think so.

I want to look online at reviews. I have read good things about the Wertheim. The Vegemite spread on the carpet was a good trick. Did you think that he was going a little bit more slowly over the Vegemite stains with the more expensive models?

No. No, I thought about that, but I was watching him. No, I think the sleight of hand was he did five strokes on the first one, four on the next one and then two on the next one. To compare them you should do the same number of strokes on all three. It's like a staircase argument—they push you up a staircase and drop you off the top.

I was trying to read exactly what chemicals are in the cleaning solution, but I couldn't see it anywhere on the bottle. What if it's 1080? Or Agent Orange?

I don't know where we parked the car. I can't remember.

There. Right there. Straight ahead of us. Is that it?

No. That's a completely different car.

Well somewhere along here.

No, it's down there.

So the same spot, just a different bay. So I did actually remember.

It's not the same spot, it's completely different, and a different-coloured car.

Not really.

It's got five doors.

We were seeing it from the nose. It was foreshortened.

It has big headlights. And it's grey. Ours has normal headlights and it's black.

## 26

Tense is a complete pain. Even I can't be consistent about that, and I'm just writing about my own research. I keep telling myself to stick a note above my desk saying either PRESENT or PAST.

## 27

I think that tooth looks whiter than my other ones.
Which one?
The one that looks a lot whiter. Can you tell?
Not really.
It had a brown spot on it, so it looked like I had food stuck in my teeth all the time.
Did he bleach it?
No, he put a cover over it.
That's what he wanted to put on my teeth. That's the one thing he can do. How much was it?
A hundred and ninety dollars. It wouldn't have been that much at the old dentist. I feel stupid. And ripped off.
When it says first appointment free, you've got to think you get what you pay for. If you don't pay anything—
Yes, it's my fault. I'm a big failure.
The whole place looked like an abandoned aquarium. A swimming-pool supplies place.
There was an empty fish tank in the reception area. And the shelves on the wall with those little Chinese bells were all wonky.
No one was in the waiting room, and the receptionist was also the dental assistant . . . very dodgy. Like they'd moved in overnight. There was this woman in that room off behind the receptionist's desk, yabbering away the whole time you were having your appointment. She was screaming away at someone. I was terrified that I was going to get her—that she was going to be my dentist. You see health clinics in the Third World like

that—concrete floor, sparsely painted room, all one colour. I expected to find a UN person behind the desk wanting to give me a bag of flour.

The first thing that happened when he sat down was he knocked the entire tray of instruments off.

I heard that in the waiting room.

It wasn't a good sign. And on the form, where it said do you have any allergies, I put latex, which I always do. I'm not sure if I have a true latex allergy, but in the past I've felt a bit itchy from it, and Mum's allergic to it, so I thought better safe than sorry.

And he shoved a latex glove in your mouth?

Yeah, when he started, I thought that tastes like rubber—I'm pretty sure those are latex gloves. And then after he'd dropped all the instruments, he came back with non-latex gloves on. He said oh, you have latex allergy?

He didn't take long to check my teeth. He just had a quick look around and made a few notes.

He gave mine a very quick check too. Only X-rayed that one tooth, and didn't do a clean.

No he didn't do a clean for me either, or X-rays. He could see that I was going to start saying no to things.

The chair felt like it was leaning off to the right. Did you think that?

I tried to put my head back on the head rest, but it was totally out of place. He goes oh, okay, and starts adjusting it, and it fell off. Three times. He couldn't seem to get it to lock, and in the end, when he did get it in a tenable position—not very comfortable, but workable—it kept rocking back. And he was just like oh yeah, whatever, I don't know how it works.

I didn't even have an injection. At least I won't look like I've got some kind of palsy for the rest of the day.

He had the little picky thing, and he said there's a receded gum here, and it makes the tooth very sensitive. And he prodded the sensitive area while I was looking with the mirror, and I said ow, and he just kept on doing it. He probably worked for Pol Pot in a previous career.

There was this one moment, when he'd got the new tray of instruments, and he was sitting there staring at them like he couldn't decide which one to use. He couldn't remember which one did what.

That's probably why the receptionist helps out.

Oh and I had to sign this consent form, and it said Consent to Extraction at the top. I was skimming through it wondering what I was signing. That was when I was already in the chair—I was lying down trying to sign it.

Extraction?

Yeah. He said no, it's not extraction.

But it *says* extraction. A general waiver, if he fucks up?

Mm. A lot of the time I was just lying there nodding. And after they took the X-ray of that one tooth, the computer froze, so they couldn't look at it. We'll have to find a good dentist in Hamilton. I don't know how you do that. Ask on the Trade Me message board, maybe. I should have done that first. Or ask John and Margherita who they go to.

We are not going back there ever.

Yeah. Fuck.

Disaster.

What a waste of money. And time. I'm a failure. I'm such a fucking failure.

Let's never venture out again.

## 28

Every now and then I have a perve at him. He is actually very good-looking, eh? Just a bit too nervy for me.

Yes he's quite ethereally beautiful, in a skinny white boy sort of way. I often imagine him speaking Elvish to Liv Tyler.

## 29

Thank you for your time, but we are looking for people with a different profile. Submit.

## 30

Time to expose the baby to some Art. She thinks it's a game. Fiona Pardington's photographs are attuned to death. I've got the wrong glasses. Oh, dead things. I don't want to see the dead things. Death permeates this entire exhibition, larger than life. It would be amazing to have one of these on the wall, wouldn't it. Well, not that one; I don't like that one. One without dead things. I'm following you. You keep walking away. The post-mortem cast of an infant child, done by the father. The opium jar. The woman entangled in the seaweed. The Marquis de Sade's skull. Surrender to the power and potency of photography. Are you running away from me? The cast of a man with severe tertiary syphilis: let that be a warning to you. In the 1980s, Fiona Pardington was seen as a feminist. That's an odd thing to write—as if she's left it behind. She uses the phrase 'a beautiful hesitation' to describe photography's power to arrest time. You're going too fast. Did you see the one of the guy holding the rooster? Nice cock. She really does master light. Take a photo of her next to that. It's going to be too dark. She's got demon-baby eyes. Next to that, then. Alice. Alice. Alice. Alice. Where's Mummy? Where's Mummy? Have you taken it?

## [ MAY ]

### 1

If you can't see my mirrors, I can't see you.

### 2

Longtemps, je me suis couché de bonne heure. Parfois, à peine ma bougie éteinte, mes yeux se fermaient si vite que je n'avais pas le temps de me dire: «Je m'endors.» Et, une demi-heure après, la pensée qu'il était temps de chercher le sommeil m'éveillait;

### 3

Catherine. Hi. Head right down the end—I'm all ready for you.

How's the workload? They haven't found someone to replace Ngaire yet?

No. No. It's pretty intense actually Catherine to be perfectly honest with you. And obviously it's flu vaccine season and stuff. It's a big juggling act at the moment. But it certainly—just take a seat for a minute while I talk to you about your smear—it certainly makes the day go extremely fast, I can tell you. Which I guess is a good thing, especially when you've got a life outside of work, which I certainly do, which is awesome. Okay, because I don't know your history, I can have a look through, are we doing three-yearly or yearly smears, Catherine?

As far as I know, it's three-yearly.

Okay. Cool. So have you had any abnormal smears in the past?

A long time ago I did have one, and then it was fine again when it was retested.

Fabulous. Okay.

So does that just mean . . . what does that mean?

What do you mean?

If there's an abnormal one, and then—

So if there's an abnormal one they do it every year. They keep an eye on you, Catherine. But if you've had three consecutive . . . or even four . . . three or four consecutive ones and they're all fine they say you can advocate to go back to three-yearly. But if you've got a family history, if you've had a mum that's had cancer, you know, all that kind of stuff, then I always say oh look, just do it. But three-yearly is perfectly fine. Okay, so we'll just put three-yearly smears here, Catherine. Right. Now. The results will be about a week or so. Would you like me to phone you, text you, or send you a letter?

A letter would be good, thanks.

A letter. I'll make a note of that.

Although that's really slow these days, isn't it. Three deliveries a week.

Do you want me to text you? I mean basically if I was concerned I'd phone you regardless, but then again don't just think oh my gosh there's something wrong if you get a phone call. But I can send you a letter, Catherine. Whatever you want.

Just a text would be the easiest.

I'll make a note. Now. Periods? Getting your periods still?

No, that seems to have . . . taken a hike.

Stopped? So is it a menopausal-type thing?

I think so, because I've been having hot flushes as well.

And any contraception?

No. We did years of IVF, so that's not really an issue.

No contraception. So when would your last period have been?

Probably in January—but they'd been erratic for about a year.

Okay. Yeah. Okay. Yep. Okay. Right. And are you coping with those menopausal symptoms okay, Catherine?

It's not too bad.

No. Cool.

I'm on progesterone cream, which has helped hugely.

Awesome. Okay. Cool. All right. Have you got family, have you got children?

Ah—via surrogacy. We've got one daughter.

Okay. All right. That's cool. So I'll just put here nil pregnancies. How old's your daughter?

Eleven months.

Okay. Will you have others?

No. We're both forty-six, and it was such a mountain to climb, to—

A journey. Yeah.

To find our surrogate, and—

Did you know somebody? Or how did that work?

No. No, we met Leila through the forum that we were on for about four years. First when we were doing IVF, and then donor-egg IVF, and then when we were looking for a surrogate.

Okay. Any other gynae issues that are paramount, Catherine? Was the reason that you couldn't have children with IVF something to do with your partner or husband, or you?

It was me, but it was never really clear what it was.

Okay.

Probably something autoimmune. I have—

Yep.

I have coeliac disease, and—

Okay.

It was probably just my body rejecting—

Sure.

Whatever was put back.

Totally. Any discharges, or anything that you're concerned about, Catherine?

No.

Awesome. So. What I'll get you to do is I'll shut the curtain, come up on the bed, take your trousers and undies off—I'm left-handed, so I go that way as opposed to that way, in case you're wondering—and just pop that over top of you. As I say, it's a big juggling multi-tasking act at the moment. Crazy. And of course—as you'd be aware—it's all the documentation. I obviously go back and recheck at the end of the day and just ensure that I've covered my bases, but you've got to be really vigilant with what you write and who you're dealing with. Cool. All right. So. No other issues, no other nothing, it's just basically that we're due to have our smear that you're here today, Catherine, is that right?

That's right.

Perfect. Thank you. And good on you for keeping that up to date and doing it.

I'm just wondering about the three-yearly versus—

Yeah.

One-yearly. It is on my mind that I've been absolutely blasted with very high doses of IVF hormones—

Yep. Yeah.

Do you think it would be worth going yearly, because of that?

Totally your choice, Catherine, and not always, but sometimes—not always—you have a little bit of a warning in the fact that you'll find that when and if you're sexually active, sometimes—say if there was an issue there—not always—you'll have a bit of bleeding in between, you'll have some pain, you'll have a little bit of discharge, all that kind of stuff. Entirely up to you, Catherine, honestly. There's no indication, really. Yes, I mean, in the back of your mind there is—it's like one of those what-if type things. But if it releases you and you think yep, okay, I'm covering that, especially because I've got a daughter, well and good, but I wouldn't be overly concerned about it. Especially if you've got no family history, you know, your mum and your sisters have all been healthy—so unless you got to the stage where you haven't been having periods, and then all of a sudden, each time you had a sexual encounter—have you got a male or female partner?

Male.

Male? Never assume. I wasn't. So if you have a sexual intercourse encounter and it's like oh God that's really sore, or whatever. Sometimes if something is not quite right up there, that can be an indication. But there's so many factors, Catherine. And at the end of the day, you don't want to be a scaremonger. We can be thinking about all sorts of things that could happen. You know that. But you're certainly within your rights, Catherine, if you want to do that, and pay for that, then that's fine.

How much is it?

I'm not sure. Because we've got some funding, so I'm not sure whether yours is funded or not. I'll double-check to see whether yours is funded. Where'd you get that gorgeous ring from, Catherine?

It's my wedding ring. We bought it from an antique shop online, from the States.

Did you? Gorgeous.

It's 1930s.

Is it? Do you have a history on it or anything?

No. I don't know anything about it.

All right. Bring these ankles together, legs up. Yep. Perfect. Yep. You're into it. Great. Please let me know if it's *really* uncomfortable. Obviously it's not the greatest experience, but just try and think you're somewhere else, Catherine. Put yourself in Hawaii. Okay. Bit uncomfortable as it goes in. Okay. Now. This cervix of yours is tilted to one side, or behind, or whatever. Could you clench your fists for me and put them under your hips? That just pushes it up. Cool. I know that's very uncomfortable for two secs. Are you that way or that way?

I'm not sure . . .

Are your fists that way or that way?

Oh. I thought you meant was the cervix that way or that way.

No no no no. No. Okay. So. To the naked eye it looks absolutely fine. Obviously that's why we do it, though, to double-check. Okay, I'm doing your smear now, Catherine. You might feel it in your tummy. You might think it feels funny in your tummy. That's where I always used to feel it. Okay, pop your knees together, but don't throw your legs out just yet or you'll send the tray flying and I'll have to redo it, which would be very frustrating. Okay, so hopefully that wasn't too traumatic for you, Catherine. It's another good job done and out of the way. I'm going to give you a tissue in two secs. Bear with me, Catherine.

4

I'm having major doubts about including that.

It gave me gynaecological dreams last night. I was having smear tests in my dreams. We're at that age—God knows what's caving in down there.

Do I really want people to know that I have a tilted cervix? That I'm not having periods any more? That I've got autoimmune issues? That it's my fault we're infertile?

Mm.

The one line I couldn't bring myself to put in was 'Just parting your labia now'.

You should definitely put that in! It does stuff that we tell all our students to do.

I keep thinking of you. I keep hearing you say that if you're feeling uncomfortable about going to a particular place in your writing, then that's where you need to go.

Part those labia!

Shine that light! It feels very exposing, though. I never write about those things when it's a character, let alone when it's me. And also . . . isn't it terribly self-indulgent to think that the world wants to read The Beat of the Speculum?

You have to stop calling it that. But the world wants labia, I'm telling you.

Who does she think she is? What makes her so important and interesting?

The world needs labia. I think it's brave. I think there's still feminist clout in a woman being brave enough to say . . . are we recording this?

Yes.

I'd totally forgotten about that. I'd forgotten that you'd even mentioned it. There'll be huge chunks that you can't use now. I said the world needs labia. You're getting very sly at this.

How am I going for time?

## 5

The hydrangea doesn't need any other floral elements for it to be texturally and compositionally interesting. Fortunately my husband is no longer frightened of colour. Ann's décor choices imbue the house with a feeling of calm and a high degree of sophistication; books can actually transform the look of the room if displayed attractively. Opposite: Tabitha and Isaiah at play. The bathroom reprises the deluxe element. Above left: Ann in her office with cavoodle puppy Leo. I love the indoor-outdoor concept, which means the children can go from their play spaces to the pool. Invest in one or two statement pieces that really speak prosperity to you. The large framed artwork is an original Matisse sketch. My favourite room, says Ann of the formal living space, but the décor also speaks to her husband's interests. Generally place things in sensible places. Jane's favourite place in the house is this corner.

### 6

I've got parasitic worms living inside me, and it's great.

### 7

What time is it?

Eleven twenty-eight. Why?

I don't know. Why would I be asking what the time is?

I don't know, why?

Because I'm in the kitchen.

Yes.

And there's no clock.

No, there's no clock. It was very loud. I couldn't concentrate. I couldn't read. It's down in the bedroom with the cat—with Mintiemoo. Who didn't seem too impressed either.

It was a present from Aunty Gladys.

No wonder it's so loud.

### 8

Say happy Mother's Day, Nana.

Happy Mother's Day, Nana.

Not you, the baby.

You want to touch my glasses, don't you? You always want to touch my glasses. Nana hasn't put all her rings on for you to play with. I forgot. She's looking for them and I haven't got them all on. No. I sold them. There's none on that finger today. I had to sell them to buy the bread. But those ones are always there. Grandad put that one there, sixty years ago. Yes, he did. It cost him two weeks' pay. She's so beautiful. Can I take her home?

Yep.

Catherine sent me to the supermarket to get Parmesan and I got everything else and I didn't get the Parmesan. So you've got regular cheese.

I like regular cheese better.

Today's your lucky day.

Good, it's not Parmesan!

I've made the inevitable risotto, I'm afraid.

Well you know I just love it and we never have it at Sunset Court.

It's hard thinking of something that both you and Alan can eat. It's difficult finding something that's vegetarian and gluten-free for Alan, and not spicy for your very unadventurous palate.

Hello. Hello. Are you coming to say hello to Nana? Hello. Hello darling. Nana's got her dinner. No, you're too little to have that yet. Oh dear. This looks nice. I always love your meals. I mean our meals are lovely, but they've got to be basic, cooking for a hundred or something. I never find anything wrong with them. There's one lady who always complains. The potatoes aren't cooked, the gravy's too thin or thick. Every day at one of the meals she finds something wrong. Les, who's just gone from our table, but he used to be there—we used to have a competition about what was going to be wrong today. We used to make Gwen laugh. The guy that's there now I don't think would make her laugh. She's very quiet. I don't know whether she didn't have a good marriage . . . I don't mean she's grumpy. But she's very quiet, and she just seems like somebody that's been sad.

Who's the new guy at your table?

Don't know. Don't even know his name. I don't know whether he's dumb or not. Haven't found out yet. I don't know what he says half the time.

It's slim pickings with the men there. You better find out his name, before someone else swoops in and nabs him.

Looking around the place, I'm going to stay as I am, I've decided. I don't think you need to worry, Catherine. You're not going to have a stepfather. I can think of nothing worse than getting married again. I don't want to compete with Myrna. She's had three husbands. And I think there might have been a few somebodies in between. I don't know whether they dumped her or she dumped them. One of them got killed.

Not by her . . . ?

It might have been and she's not letting on.

How did he die?

Car accident.

Now you've got newsprint all over your hands.

I didn't think of that.

Grubby grubby grub.

She must be getting tired. I know I am.

What did you get for Mother's Day?

Flowers. And a home-made card. And a semi-lion.

A what?

A lion. Lion. A semi-*lie*-in.

Oh! I thought you said a lion. I was thinking animal.

Right. I got the front half. I'm getting the back half for Christmas.

I'm ready for her nap now.

Does she eat well? Oh, look, cleaning the table for Mummy.

She likes cleaning. We have high hopes for her.

She's far too intelligent for a normal one-year-old. She's about an eighteen-month-old.

If she could change her own nappy that'd be good. You can't have that. No you can't. It's very old.

Don't break Mummy's necklace. Where'd you get it?

On eBay.

It's lovely. Do you know how old it is?

Nineteen-twenties. No, you can't have it. I know, but you'll break it.

You don't give her much salt.

No, she hasn't had any salt.

People used to give children lots of salt when you were growing up. But we didn't, other than what it was cooked in. Your father was terrible. Their whole family. I remember the first night I went to dinner there. Grandad had the salt—Grandad had everything first—and then Les, and then he gave it to me, and I didn't have any. I think they thought I was a bit odd . . . I was already a Catholic. And then the second time Les's cousin came to dinner and she got talking about Catholics and she was going on and on, and Grandad was saying gosh it's been a hot day today, trying to shut her up. She had it all wrong. She knew all sorts of things, about the priests going over to the convent and what have you. It was only the second time they'd met me, and nothing would shut her up. And obviously somebody told her afterwards that I was a Catholic because about two weeks after it was Reta's twenty-first, or somebody's party, and I sat beside her and she hopped up and ran away and sat somewhere else. So I thought, I'm going to go and sit beside her. So I did. But I was still a Catholic.

Let's make this quick.

Who needs to sleep? Are you talking to me and I'm not looking? Do you know where all those stones come from, Catherine?

Well, Grandad.

I'm just trying to remember the place he used to get them, and I can't.

Birdlings Flat?

Yes. She's going to be pretty, isn't she. She's got a lovely face. She's very bright for her age. She'll be at school at three. How's your wrist, Alan?

It hurts every time I pick her up.

You should get tongs or something.

I never envisaged it being this exhausting. Day after day

after day after day. There's never any let-up.

It'll get a lot worse until she gets to school.

Some mornings I'll hear her call out Dadadada at six thirty, and I'll look at the monitor and she's standing up in bed staring at the camera.

I hope she's not like her mother. If Catherine was reading and got to page nineteen and said cat instead of hat, we had to go back to the beginning. Not the top of the page—right back to the beginning.

At the moment she gets bored very quickly and keeps on turning the pages, so she probably takes after me.

Or she rips them out.

She's an intelligent little girl for her age. She's going to be clever, I can see that already. She's far too observant. Not that that's a fault. I've never seen a child like it.

Here we are. I made a Mother's Day brownie.

Isn't it beautiful. What is it?

A brownie.

A brownie. Isn't it lovely. How did you make a heart-shaped cake?

With a heart-shaped tin.

I didn't know you could buy heart-shaped tins.

Do you want a tea or coffee with it?

A coffee would be lovely. We have nice coffee, but with a hundred cups to make it's not quite the same.

Give Mum an inside bit. She doesn't like the ends.

The clay. No.

So she's got minimal edge.

I was going to give her that bit there.

No clay at all, Catherine, look!

Do you want some cream?

Ah . . . just a wee tiny bit. It looks so nice. I don't want to spoil it with a lot of cream. Mmmm. Did you make it?

Yes.

Chocolate cake is my favourite cake. It was your father's too.

I might be making this for Alice's birthday, but if we're going to have thirty people here it's not really big enough. Unless you cut tiny little bits like that. Four, five . . . nine, ten . . . sixteen . . .

What are you going to have for her? An afternoon tea?

Something requiring minimal effort.

You don't have to ask me, if you're just having young people. But I'd love to come.

Another piece of brownie, Mum?

I might be naughty and have another one. Or am I only allowed one? It's so nice. We have cake, but it's bought cake. Did you make it? Chocolate cake's my favourite.

No, don't eat the arrangement. No. Jiffy's chewing on a leaf. He's a problem cat.

More problem than the baby.

At least the baby's going to grow up.

It's hard to believe she's one.

Well, eleven months.

Mm. Is that the chocolate cake recipe that I used to make?

No, this is a brownie. A gluten-free one.

Is it gluten-free? It doesn't alter the taste, does it? I wouldn't have known it was gluten-free. It's very nice. It just tastes the same as my chocolate cake.

You're sitting in brownie crumbs. You're worse than Alice. We need to get you one of those silicone bibs.

I think I need one.

There are people with bibs in your dining room.

Yes.

It's all a bit depressing.

Yes, but they don't sit with us.

I don't imagine the dinner conversation would be up to much.

Gwen's not going to speak to me if I have to go to that table.

She's lovely, Gwen. We don't have much in common—she's quite a different person—but we have a nice time at the dining table. She's got family but she doesn't seem to see them much. She's always asking me how Alice is. She doesn't have good health, and she's not as old as me. I'm one of the oldest there. There's one lady in her nineties. I think I'm about the third oldest. They were counting up the other day.

That woman who lived next door to you when you were in the townhouse—she was in her nineties, wasn't she?

Yes, but she died.

What do you want to do for your birthday?

We don't have to do anything. Take me to a movie. That'd be lovely.

I wonder what day of the week it is. I think it's an Auckland day.

It doesn't matter. We can make-believe another day.

Hang on—no, it's not an Auckland day this term.

You can make my birthday on whatever day suits you.

Do you want to do something with your friends?

No. No, we have a morning tea on our birthdays. I've been to two this week.

I feel eighty-five.

Do you? I suppose I did when I had children. When I look around, I'm very lucky. They've all got walkers and wheelchairs and can't hear.

It's a bit of a problem if you're trying to go down the corridor and someone with a walker who can't hear is in front of you.

And can't steer straight either. Yes, it's quite dangerous sometimes when you're going down to the dining room. You're liable to get run over. But of course it was a sensible place for me to go to, so I don't have to shift again. And I'm quite happy there.

The new rest-home coordinator seems to want to get people joining in with the activities.

It doesn't really apply to me, because I do heaps of things. Some people get up in the morning and they have their morning tea sitting in their chair in their room, and their lunch, because they don't want to go down to the dining room. They don't get out of their chair and go and have a little walk. I'm trying not to get like that for as long as possible.

She seems to want you to go to the—what is it? The Triple A classes?

A twelve-step programme?

Not AA. Triple A. Exercise for oldies. She's still allowed a sherry.

They all just sit there and stick out a leg, and then they stick out an arm. I don't know why she even suggested it. All the nurses think it's hilarious. They couldn't see me going there. She's fairly new—I think she's trying to do all the right things—but I'm certainly not going to it. I do what I like. I'm sort of in the wrong place, but the other place isn't quite enough. There's nothing in between.

You mean a serviced apartment? No, you need a little bit more help than that provides.

Yes. Yes. There's nothing in between. The nurses are very good—everyone's in bed by eight o'clock at night.

You don't have to be.

The nurses have to get them all into bed. Put their nighties on. Most of them don't go out of their room. They sit there. They read the paper—I don't know how they make it last all day.

They probably can't remember what they read five minutes ago.

That's probably right. But you see, Dad was very alert.

Your dad?

Yes. He was riding a bike at ninety-nine.

Ah . . . was he?

How old was he when he died?

Just a few weeks off a hundred. We were all waiting for the Queen's letter.

He didn't have a bicycle accident, did he?

Eh? Oh he probably did—that's why I never saw him again.

He wasn't quite sure how old he was. He didn't know, did he?

No, he had no idea.

Remember when we got his birth certificate after he died, and he was a couple of years older or younger than he thought he was? I can't remember which.

Older. And his birthday was nothing like the thirteenth of June. He couldn't read or write, and I think when he came out to New Zealand and they asked him his age, he got it wrong.

They probably couldn't understand him, with the Irish accent. I mean it's difficult enough understanding the Dublin cousins.

And cousin Pat, if he's anything to go by. The only thing I could understand was when he was handing me whisky.

Dad never lost his accent at all. For about the first ten years, Les never knew what Dad was saying, and I'd give him a poke and say yes, and Les would say yes.

He wasn't speaking Gaelic, though, he was speaking English, wasn't he?

He spoke Gaelic until he was twenty, so I think he was mixing Gaelic and English.

Did you learn any Gaelic?

No. A few words, but I can't remember them now. One reason was I went to a convent school, and any Irish who went to a convent school weren't allowed to speak Gaelic. So I wasn't allowed to speak Gaelic. Not that I wanted to. I don't think Dad could have taught me Gaelic because he wouldn't know what it meant in English. If you know what I mean. When he said it in English he wouldn't know what it meant in Gaelic.

That's very confusing.

He only had a simple education, and he was the second eldest in a big family. He didn't go to high school. He could sign his name, but Mum always wrote the cheques out—he couldn't write a letter or anything like that. He was a lovely man. Mum was a bit of a terror, but Dad was lovely. Except nobody used to know what he was saying. The girls at work loved it when he rang me up and asked could he speak to Pat McGough. The girl who answered would whisper it's Pat's father, and then the next one would come on and say who did you want to speak to? Dad never realised. Uncle Owen, his brother, he didn't have much education either. And then there was one sister who came out—Annie.

What happened to her?

Well, she got married, and then died. Nothing happened to her.

She wasn't Mary's mother though, was she?

No. No. Mary's mother was . . . ah . . . Aunty Annie.

So she was Annie.

Yes, she was Aunty Annie.

But a different Annie.

Yes.

So how are you and Mary cousins?

Her father was my mother's brother.

Oh, your mum's side. And is she the one who was bitten by a spider, or something mysterious?

Yes, and died almost immediately. They never quite found out what happened, but it must have been something in the wood. It was winter time, and the firewood was behind the cowshed. She went out there, lifted the wood and was carrying some in, and just fell down. She just dropped dead. And they found this bite on her hand, but they could never work out what it was.

It might have been something innocuous to most people, but she had an allergy.

Or a katipo. It could have been a katipo. Is that when Mary came to live with you?

Yes. This is a lovely cup of tea.

Except it's coffee.

Oh. I thought it was gin actually. I don't know why I said tea. Probably because we always get tea at home. Have you displaced a bone or something?

I have very poor posture—I always have. It's been a lifelong problem.

What?

Very poor posture.

Oh, posture.

It's part of being tall, and not feeling confident about being tall. It gets on top of me sometimes.

I can remember at school there was one boy, and his name was Noel Legg, and he was tall. And he was always made to sit in the back row.

That's the thing. You end up feeling you're being made an example of.

I remember he'd go and sit in a seat, and Sister Virgine would say you're too big to sit there, go and sit in the back row. I never thought about it at the time, but after I grew up I thought he must have felt awful.

Linda's very good about posting family photos on Facebook. We have a cousins page. Is that the Bowdens? She wasn't sure if it was Des Bowden.

He was nearly your father. I was engaged to him.

I didn't know you were engaged to him.

Well nobody knew. But I was.

How long were you engaged to him?

Mum didn't know. We were talking about getting married, and then one day I decided I didn't want to. And I rang him up. He was terribly upset about it.

What did you say to him?

I said I don't want to go out with you any more, I suppose. I don't know what I said. Thank goodness I didn't marry him. He got old and grumpy at about thirty. Not at all like your father. They were great friends—I just swapped from him to Les. One night we were at the Halswell Hall at a dance, and Les was there. And Des brought him over. And then Les came and asked me for a dance a bit later, and I had a dance with him, and then on the Saturday night I went to the Coronation Hall dance, and Les was there. And he took me home. And I rang Des the next week and dumped him. The girl he started going out with after me used to say I don't know why you got rid of Des, he's lovely. I said you can have him then.

But she didn't end up marrying him either.

No. Dad kept calling Les Des. Dad used to say how are you today, Des my laddie? Les would have been the last sort of person I would have married. I didn't like short men. I was going to marry a wealthy farmer, and a Catholic of course. My friends used to laugh, because their husbands would come home from work in those days with their pay in a little brown envelope. The men used to open it and count out six pound five or something, and that was for the little woman for the groceries. And then the rest went in their pocket, and they looked after the accounts. Les used to bring his envelope home and I used to open it and give him five pound or whatever it was for pocket money. He never had a clue in the world how much we had in the bank. I remember going to get a mortgage—it must have been to buy the section, before we were married, and I was paying for it. Les had no money, because he was an apprentice carpenter. And the man in the bank said but what about your husband? And I said I'm not married. I said I'm getting married, and my fiancé's going to build a house on this section that I'm buying. And he said shouldn't he be signing it? And I said no, because I'm paying for it. I was getting furious by then. He said but he's going to be your husband. He didn't understand me. I said I'll bring him in. So I rang up Les, and he came in, and he sat there, and he didn't say anything because there was nothing for him to say. I signed everything, and he lost two hours of pay. And then I paid Les to build the house, and I gave him half for a wedding present.

Is that them, then? The Bowdens?

Yes. It doesn't look anything like the handsome guy I used to go with, but I think it probably is.

But you don't know the other couple?

Well I know the faces but I can't think who they are. I know her face quite well and I just can't place it. I sort of know his face too. It's a long long time since I've seen those people. Who are they?


Longtemps, je me suis couché de bonne heure. Parfois, à peine ma bougie éteinte, mes yeux se fermaient

9

What is worm therapy?

Is it safe?

Do I have to go to Mexico?

I have heard bad things about medical treatments in Mexico.

Can you ship organisms to me?

How will I know if I am successfully infected?

Can I infect anybody else while I am hosting hookworms or whipworms?

Will I get worse before I get better?

How long do the worms last?

Can hookworms and whipworms reproduce in my body?

What if I change my mind?

Can I accidentally kill my worms?

What happens if I accidentally kill my worms?

Are hookworms and whipworms easy to eliminate?

What is the difference between a cure and remission?

10

You are posting as None. (reveal your identity)

11

There's a New Zealand woman who's doing the worm therapy, for autoimmune issues. In her case I think it's Lyme disease.

I knew someone who had that.

The theory is that they secrete substances that dampen down the human immune response, so that the host won't recognise them as an invader and kill them. They stop the immune system going into overdrive. Wait, maybe it's not Lyme disease . . . maybe it's something else. What's she got . . . ah . . . she's a human resources manager from Palmerston North.

Where do they come from?

People's poo.

Right.

You can self-harvest. People do.

I can't see you doing that.

No. No. You buy a vial of worms, and stick them on a bandage on your upper arm. And they burrow through the skin and into the blood vessels, and then they travel through the heart and lungs and up the windpipe to the throat, where they're swallowed back down into the gut. And they latch on and start living off your blood.

Why don't you just swallow them in the first place?

Because that would be gross.

Right.

So should I order up a vial of hookworms from Mexico? It's several hundred dollars a pop.

To pay someone else to go through poo.

To sift through poo, yes.

If they're so small, how do you find them?

Because the adult ones are a centimetre long and the width of a human hair.

Right. So you just fish through until you see some.
Basically.
Give them a good rinse in the colander.
The colon-der. I don't know. I feel like I have enough parasites in my life.
Why are you looking at me and the baby?

## 12

Shall we have a story? This one? This one? Come and sit up here. Let's have this one. In the light of the moon a little egg lay on a leaf. That's the moon. And that's the little egg. And that's the leaf. We're not finished. One Sunday . . . In the light of the moon a little egg lay on a leaf. One Sunday morning the warm sun came up and . . . In the light of the moon a little egg lay on a leaf. Bubba. Have a look at this one? Try again? Put that one away for later. One Sunday morning the warm sun came up and—pop!—out of the egg came a tiny and very hungry caterpillar. No no no. No no no no no. Oh God. He started to look for some food. Are we finished? Are we finished? Come on. Come and sit over here. With the pukapuka. Let's read the pukapuka. He started to look for some food. On Monday he ate through one apple. But he was still hungry. On Tuesday he ate through two pears, but he was still hungry. On Wednesday he ate through three plums . . . In the light of the moon a little egg lay on a leaf. There's the little egg. There's the leaf. There's the moon. Yes, that's the little egg. And that's the moon. One Sunday morning the warm sun came up and—pop!—out of the egg . . . Are we done? Okay. You can't have the phone. You can have that. No. No.

## 13

What street is this?
Rangiātea Road.
And those two houses down there?

Also Rangiātea.

How do you say it?

Rangiātea.

I'm doing a survey and it's so confusing, because there aren't any signs.

There's a sign just back there, where Thomas Street veers off to the left. It changes its name to Rangiātea halfway down.

It's lovely out here, isn't it, with it being so rural. But how long do you think it will stay like this?

I don't know.

It'll all be subdivided.

Well, there's only one house going in behind there.

So all this is Rangi—how do you say it?

Rangiātea. Yes.

Oh well, enjoy your peaceful spot while it lasts.

## 14

Tell us what you're doing for Privacy Week.

## 15

I'm finding all these errors and inconsistencies. They don't wear dirndls in Leipzig. Lilies don't flower in autumn. The German army was no longer in Africa in 1944. I have things happen before they happened. It's making me very nervous.

## 16

Experts say the real danger is likely to be much closer at hand, on the average household deck. People get away with doing things they shouldn't do in the residential suburbs. Who's telling the verifiable and specific story? We will workshop this at the staff meeting. Have a think. Have a checklist. It's good to be prepared to say something—otherwise I will shoulder-tap.

## 17

Book of unused acceptance speeches. I would contact celebrities and invite them to contribute.

## 18

We don't think in words, we think in pictures. Your blue sky is not mine. You say beach and I'm thinking Mount Maunganui and you're thinking the black sand at Taranaki.

## 19

Incident ahead. Take extra care.

Creative New Zealand acknowledges the time and effort you have dedicated to your application and appreciates that you will be disappointed with this result.

## 20

Mind-training lessons from monks and psychopaths could help us care without crumbling.

## 21

Did you know it's International Fish Migration Day?
Don't fish migrate every day?
Well, yes. They don't all have to do it on the one day.
So why do we need an International Fish Migration Day?
To raise awareness about migrating fish.

## 22

Longfellow translated it, but I think I can do better. I need a one-syllable word: doubly with your one-syllable refreshment. Fresh refreshment. Fresh revitalisation. Light refreshment? Then it sounds like God's giving him a sandwich. Some finger food.

## 23

I wrote it and I rewrote it and I kept thinking what the fuck are you doing, this is a really stupid thing to get up and talk about. Because I was talking about my brain.

What was Jeanette Winterson like? Tell me she wasn't a bitch.

She was nice. Very no-nonsense. Tiny. I was in this full-on going-to-the-Oscars dress, and she was in jeans and an old shirt. She said to me afterwards I really liked what you said. I scuttled off and bought a copy of her book and asked her to sign it. She said oh yes, I want to write something nice.

What did she write?

I can't remember. After the gala there was a line stretching out forever and ever of people wanting books signed, but she was really concerned about getting to her partner who was apparently at some bar. Which is the point where I could have said I'll come with you and help you find her. But I didn't. I got someone else to do it. I just didn't think.

That could have been your big moment. You could have got drunk with them.

Anyway I was in really high heels. And she was somewhere in the CBD at a bar. But that could have been quite good, right? Taking her to find Susie Orbach.


I was looking at one translation, and he's misunderstood the German verb totally. The poet is talking about how as a child she discovered her love of poetry and used to take refuge in the land of the poets—the imagination. And he's understood this particular verb to be enraptured, and he translates it as enraptured by the tearful throng of sisters there. But the verb doesn't mean enraptured, it means transported away in the sense of taken away from something negative. So the poet's talking about being transported away from the noisy—not tearful—throng of sisters in real life. He's got it completely round the wrong way. And that's the translation I used. So now I'm looking with suspicion at his other three that I also used. I've had to start translating them myself.

I'd say something to you in German, but I know nothing.

And all through the text I've spliced in—often subliminally—quotes from German songs or poems or speeches of Hitler or speeches of Goebbels, and I've used English translations for those. Now I'm having to back-track, and check if I need to get copyright permission for any of it.

Oh God.

It's taking forever.

What a nightmare.

And the Hitler quotes—some of it's disputed material. Hitler's Table Talk was published in 1951 and it was supposedly verbatim—what the Führer said at afternoon tea and at dinner and at morning tea and so on. There were two secretaries who were charged with noting everything down in shorthand, but how accurate was that? And what was changed or added during the editing? And then when it was translated there were questions over reliability, and copyright issues. And I'm still finding my own mistakes. There's a scene where a mother and daughter are lying on the daughter's bed and they're looking up at the ceiling where the daughter has hung pieces of shrapnel from threads. And it's evening, and it's in November, in Berlin, and I say that the train passes outside the window and the sun catches on its paintwork and flashes into the bedroom. And that could not possibly happen in November in the evening.

Because there would be no sun.

There'd be no sun, and also they'd have the light on, and it's blackout conditions, and they'd have the shutters closed.

What else could make it sparkle?

I've figured out a work-around, but the issue is more that I've only just realised the mistake.

I think there are always going to be things like that.

But I must find zem all! I must eradicate zem!


Do you know how to make the phone stop flashing? What happens if I push the flashing envelope? There's a note I wrote myself at the start of last year: message star to delete, and then stop flashing, question mark. I have no idea what that means.

Where's the message button though?

Um. Do you just press star to delete it when you're in the message? Hang on. I'll see if this works. I dial 8765, which is not my extension, and I press 1 for yes and 2 for no.

Why do you dial not your extension?

I'm not sure.

Would you *like* to access your *set*-up options?

2.

Would you *like* to do anything *else*?

2.

If you'd *like* to try an *extension* you may do so *now*.

2.

*Thank* you and *goodbye*.

Shit. She's quite passive-aggressive, isn't she. I think 8765 is just the general number to get through from any phone to your messages.

Ah.

There are *no* new messages. Would you like to *leave* any messages?

2.

There are *no* old messages to *review*.

But there are! It's flashing—there's the flashing envelope! Sue said she knew someone whose phone was flashing for over a year.

Would you *like* to access your *set*-up options?

2.

Would you *like* to do anything *else*?

2.

There are *no* new messages.

Fuck.

Would you like to *leave* any messages?

2.

There are *no* old messages to *review*. Would you *like* to access your *set*-up options?

2.

Would you *like* to change your *greeting*?

2.

Would you *like* to change your *group*?

2.

Would you *like* to change your *transfer* or *delivery* options?

2.

Would you *like* to change your *personal* options?

2.

*Set*-up options *complete*. Would you like to *review* them?

2.

Would you *like* to do anything *else*?

2.

There are *no* new messages. Would you like to *leave* any messages?

Fffffuck. 2.

There are *no* old messages to *review*. Would you *like* to access your *set*-up options?

2.

Would you *like* to do anything *else*?

2.

If you'd *like* to try an *extension*, you may do so *now*. *Thank* you and *goodbye*.

Piss. Okay. I'll just cover it up with a bit of paper.


I'm using you, basically. Just pretend this isn't here.

I thought there was a rule about phones in class.

There is, but only for you, not for me. What did you think about the challenges of writing historical fiction?

Trying to get like a balance between the truth and a good story. And like not offending people. Misrepresenting things.

Dialogue especially. Like how did they speak?

How authentic am I? Am I a nineteenth-century novelist? Or am I a twenty-first-century novelist trying to sound like a nineteenth-century novelist? You can tie yourself up in knots.

Some things aren't really like historical, they're just like of their time.

The facts have to be accurate enough for us to *know* it happened, but there's got to be enough fiction to believe it *could* have happened.

If you're writing a character based on a real-life figure, you have to be sensitive. Like you can't have a character who means a lot to a culture and like turn that character into an arsehole. People will be offended. I'm going to use a video game as an example.

How dead does the person have to be before they're fair game? Two hundred years? Is that all right?

But in New Zealand you're not going back that far—all the people involved will probably have descendants.

The lines are blurry.

The lines are very blurry.

I struggled with the book, and it was because of what you said. The characters came off really cold to me. It all made sense in the last five pages when he says no one knew my name. Right, so you've made this guy up.

I thought that was quite accurate, because history would be littered with people like that dude, who've seen all these big things played out, and like their story is completely invalidated because there was no historian or journalist there to hear it.

I think that's where we're going. We're looking at those minor people now—we're getting into that next level of the storytelling of our own history. We're starting to be a bit more bold about different versions and understanding there's not just one version.

We talked about how there are certain events in history that you can't really alter. Like if you're writing a story about the death of Christ, he has to be crucified, or if you're writing about the execution of JFK, he's got to die by sniper.

History's always altered and suppressed.

You can't ever really know what Hitler said over a cup of tea.

We used this word verisimilitude but we crossed it out.

### 24

Do you feel like you're going backwards, or just not forwards?

I keep stumbling onto neo-Nazi websites. I'm reading away thinking great, this is the chunk that I haven't been able to find—and then I realise it's a white supremacist site.

It doesn't feel as bad as it has, and it doesn't feel as bad as I thought it would. It's the centre of a spider's web of tension.

Dad had a German pistol—a Luger. I think the story was that a friend's father had taken it from a dead German soldier as a war trophy, but the friend's wife didn't want it in the house. The friend gave it to Dad, but Mum didn't want it in the house either, so it was hidden up in the roof space, above the manhole. I didn't know. It was hanging over our heads, this German pistol, all through my childhood.

You're not nearly as bad as you think. Do you mind if I put my hand across your collarbone?

### 25

PLEASE CONSIDER MOTORISTS CROSS IN GROUPS

## 26

We talked to people who might look at moving to the likes of Ngāruawāhia. What, if anything, is there for them? It ain't the future—it's next week, it's next month, it's next year. That's the sound of the sun as it pulses in and out like a beating heart. Does the sea make us more vulnerable?

## 27

I said to her, do you think it's okay for me to put people's images on the slides? And she said yes, in this context—but when he said he was a direct descendant I was thinking is it still okay? Am I being way too white?

We tend to assign these characters to myth, and don't think of them as having a bloodline that goes on, and that living representatives might be sitting right across from us in the class.

I asked him, do you know how the family line goes? And he recited it—not the names, but the relationships—and it is a direct line to Te Rauparaha.

That kind of genealogy is so unthinkable to us. We're hopelessly lost after a couple of generations. Our threads just snap. It's strange that we don't keep a closer track of where we come from. I guess when we go under hypnosis we're all related to Mary Queen of Scots. Never Bruce the ditch-digger.

Never the night-soil man. I could see a family resemblance, though, and other people in the class could too—maybe you just see what you're looking for. He said he has a temper and his family always ascribe that to Te Rauparaha. He nearly ran me off the road a couple of months ago. By accident.

Why are we driving to Ngāruawāhia?
To have your birthday dinner at our place.
Oh that's right. I knew that, didn't I. Your mother's quite stupid.

*

196

The new manager's overdoing it a bit. She thinks we're all old and silly and don't know how to hold a cup. I suppose it's a big responsibility. She came and sat in my room the other day and asked me where the names fitted.

What do you mean?

She had a list of the names, but she didn't know which was everybody.

The people who live there, you mean?

Yes.

The inmates.

It's probably a list of troublemakers. Were you on it?

Yes. I was on it.

You're the ringleader. That's why she was sitting in your room.

You always did look like an IRA terrorist in your passport photos. Didn't you? She had a particular knack—a set to her mouth. Very grim and Irish.

I have a bomb strapped to my body.

When I was staying with Trish and Derek, that's when the mad cow disease was. Trish wrapped mine up in a plastic bag and we sealed it all.

Shoes, you mean?

What did I say?

A mad cow. You had a mad cow in your bag.

Yes. And it didn't fit very well—its legs stuck out.

You didn't have any steak over there, did you, Mum? That might explain a lot.

That's probably it.

The real danger is the antibiotic apocalypse.

People come in from overseas. They reckon that's where a lot of things come from.

Mum was told off when she was in Gwen's room. What were you standing on?

Gwen wanted something off her shelves and it was about

THE BEAT OF THE PENDULUM

six inches high. One of the nurses came in and said get off, you might fall. And they've started the silliest thing. After I don't know how many days, everyone moves and sits at another table.

It sounds like the Mad Hatter's tea party.

I think it is the Mad Hatter's tea party. And you're not allowed to choose who you sit with, and you can't sit with the same person twice.

Some of them would be so confused they wouldn't know who was who anyway.

That's exactly what happened. There was a lady and a man—I don't know their names—and the other two people at the table started to talk to them and they didn't know what they were saying. I think they're waiting to go upstairs where the mental people are.

## 28

Unsettled and unstable sums it up, with the works on offer: winds, rain, lightning, snow, and a few glimpses of sunshine. A cold unstable sou'west flow has plans to set up camp and hang about for the next few days. Right now, it's six o'clock.

It could be Huntly or Ngāruawāhia, so just what is the state of houses in those small towns? Why dozens aren't fit to live in. Feeling the burn of a different type, firefighters raise a stack of cash. Going at it with half the rugby team: it might sound dodgy, but that sort of conversation could help keep your teen safe. The photographs making Johnny Depp's divorce drama even worse, and it became famous as the way to save a person from choking, so why did the man behind it use it for the first time this week? Seventy-four thousand people were killed when a second atomic bomb hit Nagasaki three days later. It was a cluck a minute: we take you inside a special event that really is something to brood over. I had a bit of a tight hammy but I managed to get my head round it. The story just keeps getting better.

## 29

I feel manipulated, but I can't stop watching.

## 30

What is in Ngāruawāhia? It's no fault of the people who live there, but the town is rotting. It's preferable to hold on for Mercer than to stop to pee in Ngāruawāhia.

## 31

What a beautiful song. Even though it was written in the pre-National Socialist era, it perfectly embodies the spirit of National Socialism.

Help us out, would you, Vengeance? Where might one find reference to

# [ JUNE ]

### 1

Unsubstantiated statements. Unexplained evidence. Implied conclusions. You're better off looking like yourself. The world will give you something to cry about.

### 2

I'd love to just write on it: this is a turkey. Don't bother.

### 3

On this one it looks like she's waxed a little too far in the middle of the arch and taken away too much. There's a notch missing.

Just draw it in, or brush it over a bit. It'll be fine.

Draw it in. *Draw* it in.

That's what people do. People draw eyebrows in all the time.

The reason I have my eyebrows shaped and tinted is so that I don't have to put eyebrow pencil on and look like I've been busy with the crayons. I need to tweeze.

You're going to have a whole Bert and Ernie situation if you try to level it out. Because then you'll have to do the other side, and then the other side, and before long you'll have half a cookie and no milk.

4

Not that she's your blood relation, but you used to get a runny nose too when you were cutting teeth.

5

Where are the rest of the prizes? The bubble things.

Sorry?

You know, the prizes we bought. The neon chalk, the bubble things, the bangles, the tattoo pens.

I don't know. No idea.

Well it's a bit of a disaster if we don't have them. I need to rig the games. I think we should do Pin the Tail on the Donkey first, because that's the hardest one to rig. Though Pass the Parcel's quite hard too, isn't it. We need to decide who's getting what prize. Shit. How do we do this?

I don't know. We just have prizes. They play the games.

No no no. It doesn't work like that. Every child has to get a prize.

We dole out what's left at the end.

No.

Then I don't know.

Why am I counting only five prizes? I was sure I got six, and we need six.

Use the box of crayons.

No, that's a shit prize. I thought I got something at The Warehouse. Crap. Oh—the teddy-bear puppet kit. Okay. I just cleared there to wrap presents. Don't put that where I just cleared.

Well, I need to put the food here, so I can feed the baby.

Well, I'm working too. And I need wrap the prizes and also put the birthday cake somewhere it won't get sat on or wet. There's no fucking bench space in this house. Or none that I'm allowed to use.

I just need to put the food here for the baby.

The cake won't fit in the container. I don't know how but it's bigger than last time even though I used exactly the same baking tin. The heart-shaped one. I got it in here last time, when I made it for Mum. It'll just have to not be in a container till this afternoon, because it's not going to fucking fit. I need to sort out who's winning what. Where are the fucking prizes? Fuck. I just broke the packet the bangles are in. Right. Poppy's having the teddy fucking puppet. I don't even know Staci's daughters' names. They're made-up ones.

Staci 1 and Staci 2.

Right, Poppy's having the teddy puppet. Freya's having bangles, and Staci 1 can have bangles too. That leaves Korbyn, Quiniah and Staci 2. So Korbyn can have the bubbles. Tattoo pens can be Staci 2, and neon chalk can be Quiniah. Who do we want to win Pass the Parcel?

Probably Freya. It'd be an easy one for her to win.

Mm. The thing is, if someone else accidentally wins—

You mean legitimately.

If someone else wins, then we need to do a quick reshuffle of the prizes. The bangles are Freya and Staci 1, so I reckon we try and go with one of them for Pass the Parcel.

Okay.

And then whoever doesn't win it will get the other . . . wait, does that work? Shit, I don't know. We've only got three games and we've got six prizes for six kids, so for Pin the Tail on the Donkey we could have the closest, but also the funniest?

What?

The funniest placement of the tail?

Oh right.

And for statues, we can have last one standing, but then also best mover . . . and one more thing.

Quietest?

Or we could have another Pin the Tail on the Donkey prize. Dizziest. Because you spin them round. And I'm going to put

202

chocolate in between each layer in Pass the Parcel. Although I was looking online for ideas for party games and lots of parenting forums I went to said don't do Pass the Parcel. In ominous tones. But no one really explained why. I think it's because there are tears and tantrums when just one kid wins, after everyone's had the chance of holding the prize. I don't know. Too late now. How many layers do you think I should do?

Layers?

Have you never played Pass the Parcel? You play the music, the kids sit in a circle and Pass the Parcel round, and when the music stops the person who's holding the parcel unwraps one layer. And then the music starts again.

Um . . . two, three?

No.

I don't know. I've never played it. I don't understand it.

I don't understand how you've never played Pass the Parcel. I'm thinking twelve. I'll do twelve. Hi! Yes! You nearly did some walking! Shit. Staci's not coming. And Fiona's not coming either. Mahina jumped on the hot stovetop and they've got a paws emergency. Mahina's a dog, right?

I think it's a bird.

Birds don't have paws. They've got a paws emergency. Shit. So now they get two prizes each. They're probably going to leave with more than they bring. We should charge them. Cover expenses. Would it be rude to put out a koha basket? Anyway, on the second-to-last layer you put recognisable paper so you know that the next one is the prize. So when you see this paper—the green and gold squares—the next layer is the prize.

So if someone undoes that, they get the prize?

If someone undoes this, there's still one more layer, in which is the prize. Is that confusing? The baby's playing with a plastic bag. She's putting it over her head. Four layers in and I'm losing enthusiasm. Maybe I could wrap some of Mum's medication in the layers, instead of chocolate. By the way, unless it's urgent, don't encourage other people—especially children—to use my toilet. Fuck. The mini quiches. I burnt the cunting mini quiches. Do you think they're all right? They look like shit, don't they.

They look fine.

No, they look—no. I know what fine fucking means.

They look great.

They look like crap. They're all fucking burnt. Fuck. That's more than paprika can fix.

Can I try one?

You can try the worst one. That one.

Mmm. Really good.

Fuck. The recipe said 190 fan bake for twenty-five minutes. I thought that sounded quite long, for mini quiches, so I did them 190 fan bake for twenty minutes and they're fucking burnt. Fuck. Did next door ever say if they were coming?

No, but when I dropped off the invitation Willie was asleep in the chair and I just gave it to Korbyn.

They have seen it, right?

This is what I'm thinking. Maybe since they haven't RSVPed, they haven't seen it.

Do you want to go next door and make sure? Say we're just wondering about attendance because we've got prizes for the games. Otherwise we'll have to go out on the streets of Ngāruawāhia and round up some urchins to swell the numbers.

Okay.

I'd just like people to get here, and then they can go.

6

It's quite hard to pick up the threads if you haven't been watching. It's a lot of strange political decisions with some death and some dicks.

7

As a sex worker, it's very difficult to make ends meet.

204

## 8

This article is about the far future as postulated by science. For the far future in fiction, see Far future in science fiction and popular culture. For the far future in religion, see Far future in religion. For other uses, see Timeline of the future.

## 9

As I walked along the street today with Detlev, I was transformed by the thought that there might be bones beneath my feet, bones where they dig up Blindgänger, except they don't evacuate anyone for the bones.

## 10

I shouldn't have had that conversation.
Stop talking.
I have almost no voice.
You need to stop talking.

## 11

Don't sell the bearskin before you have caught the bear.
Don't sell the bearskin before you have killed the bear.
Don't sell the bear's fur before you hunt it.
Don't sell the bearskin before the bear is dead.
Don't sell the fur before shooting the bear.
Don't sell the fur until the bear has been shot.
Don't sell the skin of the bear from the forest.
Don't sell the skin till you have caught the fox.

## 12

The Vengabus really is coming.
What is?
The Vengabus. Vengaboys. They're playing Hamilton in October.
Oh dear.

Grab your friends and bring back the memories for what's going to be the party of the year as the Euro kings and queens of dance-pop the Vengaboys bring their crazy outfits and non-stop fun to New Zealand. I was thinking I should go, just to see if that would—

Make it worse.

Get it out of my head.

It's right up there with the Wriggles.

The Wiggles.

Yeah.

Toot toot, chugga chugga, big red car. Oh God, now that's in my head.

You need to find an off switch. I think my suggestion of not talking deserves exploration.

But it's *in my head*.

But you keep on letting it out by talking about it.

This is tragic: to ensure the party is jumping all night with hit after hit, the first lady of dance, the oh-so-sophisticated Brit Sonique, will perform her Top 50 hit 'Sky'. That's all that Hamilton deserves, really, isn't it.

Yeah.

We don't get Nick Cave or the Cure, we get the Vengaboys and their Vengabus. And Sonique.

Maybe for Hamilton to become more interesting and contemporary we need an urban terrorist attack. You could kidnap them and set them alight.

And how would that help my earworm?

It'd give you other things to think about.

From a prison cell. With the Vengabus in my head.

### 13

Anyone can ask a question of God, and the most popular will be answered. I wonder how many people expect the world to reward virtue? It's about God weeping alongside everybody.

206

Being happy in the bad times sorts the men from the boys. It's not a matter of defending God; it's not God who is a master puppeteer in the sky, pulling the strings, saying you're going to die today and you're not. That's a humorous response. This is the only way the world can work: by allowing chance and tragedy and happenstance. Good of you to join us on a big topic, summarised nicely.

## 14

I'M A PUPPET

## 15

If you want to build your bomb shelter on a small budget, then consider doing it yourself. By building your own bomb shelter not only do you save money but you get the opportunity to design and build your very own bomb shelter.

## 16

RAGE SALE
0 METRES

## 17

We are a community of racial realists and idealists. We are White Nationalists who

## 18

It's cold in here. I might have to close the window.
I just opened it a minute ago.
Say hi Nana.
Yes, I've got my rings on. Yes. How are you all?
Frazzled.
You're not frazzling Mummy and Daddy, are you? I've got to do something with that top Helen sent me. It's rather huge.
Is there a size on it? It's a fourteen. You're a twelve at most.

And I think it's a big fourteen.

It looks quite wide.

I don't know what to do with it. I don't know how she thought I was that big.

It's a shame, because it's quite nice.

Would it fit you?

No, it'd be too big on me.

I thought it would be.

I don't know why she thought it'd fit me.

Give it a good chew. Chew it, with your teeth. She's keeping her eye on it. Making sure you don't grab it.

No, Nana won't eat it. She's a good eater, isn't she? What should I do with the top, do you think?

I don't know.

I might pin it in and see what it looks like. Here's Daddy. Here's Daddy with a cup of tea.

It's coffee.

Helen sent this top to Mum for her birthday and it's enormous.

It is a bit large.

It's a UK size fourteen, which I think is more like a New Zealand size sixteen.

Maybe it's meant to be a poncho.

No.

Gosh she's growing quickly.

You can get down when you've finished your fruit.

You're a good little eater, aren't you? It looks nice. Nana might eat it. You can have two because they're little. You can have two. Hurry up, Nana! She makes me laugh. You'll be going to school at three. Oh, Nana dropped a bit.

She'll still eat it.

She's a good eater, isn't she. And it's lovely food, too. Something sensible. Thanks for the cup of tea, Alan. That's Aunty Lena in the photo—no it's not, it's Aunty Helen. I don't know why I said Lena.

Aunty Helen, bubba. You'll get to meet her at Christmas.

She's met her before, hasn't she?

When would she have met Helen? You've only met Aunty Helen on Skype, haven't you.

Pardon?

She's only met Aunty Helen on Skype.

You'll get spoilt.

I did wash this jumper for you, but do you realise there's a couple of holes in it?

I think now you say it, I did know.

There's one right in front there.

Oh yes. I really can't do anything about it, can I?

Not really. I hand-washed it but I didn't iron it because I thought I'd see if you wanted it first.

It would look silly if I mended it, wouldn't it.

It's right on the front.

I'm wondering if it's from the washing here.

Do they put it through the machine?

Well I don't know what they do.

I'll take it home again, shall I? And this is a present I got for Christmas that I'm not going to use. Shower gel—I don't know if you use shower gel . . . ?

Yes, I do. I like shower gel.

There's three different ones in there. Happy Christmas.

Oh thank you.

Shall I have a sort through your wardrobe? Shall I start with the shoes? Do you want to move your chair round so you can just sit there?

I'm all of a sudden starting to realise I'm in my eighties.

Alice, what are you doing?

They don't vacuum too well under the chair.

Hot! Hot hot hot hot hot.

You still wear those, don't you.

I wear those a lot. They're very comfortable.

Don't touch. Don't touch. Hot. Hot hot hot.

I wear those in the summertime. I always put my summer ones up top, but I haven't this year. I'll have my tea, whoever made it—thank you.

Coffee.

Oh, is it coffee?

These haven't been worn for a while—they're dusty.

I used to wear them walking, but I don't now.

Do you still want them?

I don't know. I haven't worn them for ages. They're quite heavy. I don't know that they're all that comfortable. Just take them.

What about those?

I don't know. I loved them, but I never really go to those sorts of places . . . I better leave them there.

One slipper. Do you wear those? I don't know where the other one is.

Yes I do, in the winter.

Empty shoebox. Jewellery This Way Up.

That's from when I moved in here.

Do you want it for anything? It's taking up a lot of space.

I don't think so.

Ah! There's your address book that you've been looking for.

I wonder why I put it in there?

And some cards from Helen.

I was going to keep them, but . . . is that a bit silly?

We can put them somewhere more sensible than the bottom of the wardrobe.

Yes.

Christmas card from Ann Thompson. I don't think you need that, do you?

No. I don't know why I kept those Christmas cards. Oh, that's a letter from the Sunday Star-Times. They wrote and thanked me for getting it. I don't know why.

I think these trousers are past their best. They're all stained.

I remember now, it wouldn't come out. I remember. I forget what it was.

Alice. Alice, come away from the rocking chair.

I won't move.

She's got her eye on something.

She likes chaos.

Do you still wear those green shoes?

I don't know whether I do. I used to. I think I did wear them in the summertime. I won't need to ever buy any more shoes. I don't know whether I'm going to wear my party shoes again, but keep them in case.

They haven't been worn for a while.

Do you think . . . oh, stick them away in the back. One of the men might take me to a dance one night.

You never know.

I do know, because I look round the table at teatime. They're all okay, the shoes, aren't they?

Yes, they're all good.

I don't think I'll ever have to buy any more.

Now, your coat—you still wear that, don't you.

Not very often.

This jacket?

I haven't worn it for a long long time.

You wore it to our wedding.

Yes.

It is nice. I wear it in the summertime. Don't throw it out.

That as well? That?

I don't think I should throw them out, because if I did go to some evening thing . . .

Mm.

You never know. I'd have to go and buy something else. Oh, I like that. I wear that. It goes with anything. I wear the grey one if it's really cold, but I often wear the sleeveless one in spring or autumn.

What's she tearing?

Everything.

It doesn't matter.

Do you wear that?

Yes, I wear that a lot. I think I wear most of my clothes. That was Helen's, but she gave it to me.

I don't think she's going to be a good Christian. She just tore up the Catholic mass service times.

I can't go now, can I?

You might turn up at the wrong time and the wrong place.

Blazer?

What colour is it?

Alice, don't rip that!

Black.

I wear that.

Gentle. Gentle. Gentle. Gentle. Gentle. Gentle.

That's got a hole in the sleeve.

It happened here. It came back from the laundry and I forgot about it. And I liked that blouse. You can't complain, though—they're really very good.

I'll get rid of it, shall I?

Yes. I'd forgotten about it.

That needs a good wash. You've got coffee all over it.

I love that navy one. I can't remember where I got it. It's comfortable to wear, and no matter what you put it with it seems to go.

Do you still wear that?

Oh yes. If anyone invites me out to a party. I mean I don't really, because I never go anywhere, but there might be the odd time.

It's very stained down the front. I don't know if that would come out—look, it's all greasy.

I've obviously dropped something on it.

Do you want me to have a go?

Have a go. If it doesn't come out, it doesn't. I wore it for years . . . but I don't go to many places where I can wear those sorts of things now. I'd look a bit silly going down to lunch in it, wouldn't I.

What about that blazer?

Well yes, I like it. I don't have many occasions to wear it, though.

Quite a few plastic bags you seem to have been hoarding.

I don't know why I kept them.

Shall I just get rid of them?

Yes, I don't know what I was keeping them for. I must have had some scheme. I think it was back when I had a car.

Catherine, can you give me Hairy Maclary?

Here he is! Here's Hairy Maclary!

You did the Sunday Star-Times, didn't you?

What do you mean?

I got a letter. Thank you for subscribing to it.

Ah . . .

Did you do it or did I do it?

No . . .

I must have done it.

I didn't think you subscribed to the Sunday Star-Times.

Well this is probably an old letter.

Ninth of March . . . let's see? You have elected to subscribe to the Sunday Star-Times . . . no, I didn't know that.

No, well I don't think I have now. Because I don't get it.

I'll check.

You knew I had a visit from . . . now I can't say what her name is . . . the other day? She used to come round and shower Les when he was sick. I can't say her name.

Was she a nurse?

Yes. But then she came to see me afterwards.

I don't know who that is.

Her husband left her a couple of years ago. He was having an affair with the office girl. She brought me those flowers. I can't say her name. Isn't that ridiculous.

Was she a friend of ours?

Yes. Well, I got to know her when she used to come to Les when he was sick.

I don't know who that would be.

Isn't it silly. I can't remember her name. I'll ring you at two a.m. if I remember it.

What else can you destroy?

I see you've got a new person next door.

Yes.

That woman who was wailing—

She's gone upstairs.

What's this little paper heart?

Oh, that was . . . what's the posh Anglican school? The girls all came round here and gave us a present. I've forgotten what mine gave me now. That was the card. I don't want it.

She's in Form 13RB, category Female Diabetic.

That was me. The female diabetic. They brought us biscuits or chocolates or something. They do that every year.

Bubba, you're really not helping. This scarf? It's nice.

It's lovely. I love it. But I don't ever really go out at night now. But I'll keep it just in case.

I need something to stand on.

I've got a footstool.

I suppose I could stand on that.

I stand on it—well, I don't now, because we're not allowed to, but I used to.

Do you use this bag?

I used to when I went shopping, but I don't go shopping now.

I don't think I've ever seen that bag.

I've had it for years.

Do you want to keep it?

Well I never go shopping, so I don't really need it. Or should I leave it up there in case?

I think it's just taking up space.

I don't go shopping now.

I'll send it to a better place. The sherry I assume you want . . . ?

Yes, that's the one Alan gave me, or you, or whoever it was, for my birthday.

Alice, do you want a drink?

Oh, she's growing so quickly. Nana wants you to stay a little girl.

Catholic mass . . . I don't think you need this. It's February March April May. If you've missed it, there's no chance to save your soul now. Power box—do you need that?

I don't think I do here.

It's just taking up space.

I used to use it in the townhouse because there weren't many plugs there.

Shoulder strap for a bag . . . I think this is for the bag we've got at home. I'll put it with it.

Yes. I'm never going to be going out with bags now.

What about these drawer dividers?

Are they really any use? I don't think I need them. I don't have so much stuff any more.

I might take her for a wee walk to keep her entertained.

She's beautiful. I'm so lucky to see her so often.

She says Nana, Nana, quite a bit.

It's either that or banana. We're not sure.

I just love her. Thank you for coming and being so kind to me—I do appreciate it. Of course you might be charging me by the hour and I'll get a bill tomorrow.

Shall I put these lighter cardigans up the top?

Yes. That's what I do every year, but I haven't got around to it this year. I've got old in the last few weeks. Not that I don't get older all the time. But I feel older. I said that to one of the nurses and she said how old are you? Which of course is quite true. I said thirty-six, and she said I was wrong. You know Gwen, my friend here?

Yes.

She's not well. She's been in bed for a few days and she came down to lunch today and oh, she looked so white and pale.

Are they keeping an eye on her?

Oh yes. I must admit, they're very good here if you're not well. Somebody comes in and sees me twice every night. One about half past nine, and then I never hear the other one, but it's about four o'clock in the morning. That's good, isn't it.

That's not your vase, is it? Or is it?

Yes, it was Les's mother's.

I don't think it's that old. This is the one that was Dad's mother's.

Oh yes, that one's just for flowers.

It doesn't need to be up there, does it?

Put it in the wardrobe. I don't have that many flowers. But if I get some . . .

Walking? Walking?

Do some walking. Show Nana how you do your walking.

Can you walk?

Alice, come on. Walking. Walking. Walking.

Good girl!

Good girl!

Do you know where the doorknob is from that cabinet?

Yes.

Alan can screw it back on.

I can do that. You just put it on and put the screw on the back. I don't know why I didn't do it—there was a reason. Are these for me? What are they?

Shower gel.

You'll take the money from my account?

They're just a present I got that I'm not going to use. So they're for you.

Oh, thank you, yes, I like shower gel.

### 19

Okay, I'm recording. What did you say?

Being spontaneous is so much easier the second time around.

### 20

I've got my author photo shoot on Wednesday and I'm dreading it. I'm fucking dreading it.

What are you dreading?

The whole thing. Fiona Pardington's doing it, and her mate Tanya Carlson is coming as well, and she's going to dress me. It's really nice of both of them, but I don't know how to say perhaps I won't like any of the clothes you put me in, and I'd feel more comfortable in something of my own. How do I say that? I don't want my arms showing and I don't want my legs showing. Which doesn't leave many options.

What about the rest of you? You could just cover up your arms and legs and show everything else.

You definitely don't want to see the bits in between. And I go so wooden in front of the camera—I don't know how to sit, or what to do with my face.

A good photographer will direct you, though.

She mainly photographs dead things.

I'm sure she'll know how to direct you. Ask her what look she has in mind.

It was meant to be a couple of weeks ago but Tanya couldn't come, so my eyebrows are slowly getting paler, because I had them tinted and shaped specially for the shoot. I just want it to be over. What happens if I look at the photos and I hate all of them? I can't say to Fiona, oh, actually, I'll just get Alan to take a snap on his iPhone, because these are shit. Ugh. I feel sick. I feel sick about the whole book. It feels like so much is riding on it. My whole career.

I would say it's probably not.

I feel sick when I think about reviews, and I keep composing negative reviews in my head. And I know it's stupid and illogical, but I keep thinking, well, Tracey and Tusiata have both had really good reviews, so that means those good reviews have gone now, and I won't get the good ones. I'll get the remaining bad ones. Because there's a quota.

There are enough to go around.

The knives will be out, because I've been silent for so long. People will just be waiting for me to fall flat on my face.

All those stories just exist in our own heads. The reviewers won't be coming towards you with a knife out because of the things that you have in your head. But I know. I know. I've written bad reviews in my own head. Whatever will happen will happen, and then it will pass.

No it won't.


Do we need to have this conversation? Do we need to make it a legal right? I've had a wee think about this. It's not too difficult to kill somebody. We can sit with the distress or the suffering. Most pain can be relieved to a large extent, but there's breakthrough pain. Once you take that cloak away, it exposes this for what it actually is. And of course it's a can of worms. I'm too much trouble, just get rid of me. Is there a slippery slope? Allowing people to opt out because of future pain? A life that disappoints them? How we apply that is a totally different ballgame. It opens death's door for people who'll feel pressured to walk through. I think there is a way forward, not a way out. I don't think it's a slippery slope, I think it is a door. I think you're walking off a cliff. That's the thin end of the wedge; that's the horror of horrors. Killing you is an option, it's part of the caring process. The lady at the end said I'm getting older and I'm tired of life, so is this going to be available for me? You erode things. Let's listen below what they're saying, deeper than just the words. I'm not sure what is coded; what's not in the open.

Look at the moon. Expect delays.

### 21

It's very dark very early. It was dark this morning. It seems later than it is.

### 22

I want to see what the exposure is. I think we should seat you. Just relax. Tanya's going to tell you what to do. Now these images are going to be quite dark, but don't worry about it because it doesn't make any difference. Your hands look good. Drop your shoulders and stick your neck out. It is very dark. I kept forgetting that the light's going to fall off really quickly— but it doesn't matter. I'm just going to try to get the image. I'm going to leave quite a lot of space around you. I don't want to get too close because it means that we lose a lot of light. If you look down, and then look up at me. If we get your body like this . . . we need a swan neck. You need to look down, don't look at the camera, just relax your face. Relax your jaw. Your chin's looking great. Try to smile with your eyes. Think of something nice, like your baby. Now the other thing I'd like you to do is look out here. With your face. Move your face around a little. Like that. And then make your hands quite formal. Just get in a nice body-shape. Close your eyes. And open. Close your eyes and relax your face. And then look at me. You do look very . . . at the moment you look very beautiful but you look very sad. A little bit of a smile's good. Tanya, you have to make her laugh. Come on! We're losing light. Should we do the face to the side slightly? Or even more that way. And eyes back to me. You look frightened. Like a rabbit. A frightened rabbit. Chin up a bit. And relax your jaw. Try to smile with your eyes. Can you look up? And chin forward, remember, and drop your shoulders. It looks a bit dramatic, but . . . I think because of the, ah, way that you are, you look quite good when it's a formal pose. If you turn your shoulder more towards me, like that. And then neck up, remember. Drop your shoulders, and neck forward. Sexy. Close your eyes. I'll take a closed-eye one; I love closed-eye pictures. Not that anybody's going to want one. That'll be for me. And now I need you to open your eyes. More of a profile, even. And then looking round. Just move her a bit. Put her head back. The light dropped away really quickly, didn't it. Lucky I'm not a commercial photographer. I'm trying to focus on your shoulder in different places so your face is a little softer. We'll see if that works. I'm interested to know if that's going to work. You look beautiful. So Renaissance. Put that hair back. Close your eyes and have a little rest while I'm fiddling with the camera. Open your eyes. Close your eyes and then open your eyes. Look down that way, and then up at me. Some small smiles would be nice, or smiley eyes. That's nice. That's good. Warm. I don't know how you put your trust in me, Catherine. I think we're running out of light. It's not so bright now. I'm freaking out. Just relax. Actually it was good when you were looking at Tanya and just a little bit smiley. A little bit. Not incredulous. How about the hair right down the front, just for me. I reckon you should go for something like that. Relax your mouth. Blublublublublub. You can smile now. Keep looking that way. Sexy countess. Stay there. Hold a chicken or hold a cat. Get the cat. Mintie or Jiffy or whoever. I mean seriously, do you want to hold your cat? I'm going to do some that are just head and shoulders, and then there'll be a few with hands. If you sit back a bit—move the stool back. I need a bit of space. Do you want to recompose her? I think a bold look is a good idea. You need to look just above my head. Close your eyes and open them. Relax your face. I'd hate to have your death stare. You'd have a good death stare, wouldn't you? I reckon. Who should I ask about that? Alan? He should do a daguerreotype of you. You've got pretty teeth. You've got those little pearly teeth that you see in paintings of women in Victorian times, with their little smiles. Drop your shoulder. Okay, same hair, but body sideways a bit more, and a swan neck. Misty. And change your hands around, so I can see your jewellery. Just shamelessly show off your rings. Okay, can we do one that's slightly different? Much more dramatic. Do you want another dress? We'll have to be very quick. It's pretty dark. We're on the tail end of what I can work with . . . that's probably as good as it gets, but it doesn't matter, it's going to look good. Saucy. Oh look at that smile! Now I get it. Now she's all relaxed. That's gorgeous. Save the best till last, that's how it works. Okay, close your eyes. Open your mouth. No, open your eyes. Make a wee bit of a shape in there. Turn a little bit more, and then look back over. Look down. At Alan's crotch. These are great. I've nailed that. I think I've got enough. And then if I don't I'll come back another day and do some more. It might be worth it to come and take some more. Even just for fun.

### 23

Tanya Carlson saw my floral toilet-seat cover.

### 24

I agree with you about people doing that I don't know what is wrong with these people that want to be evil and mean in person and in the internet I am commenting on the post you wrote about someone going behind your back it is sad I agree all cats and animal deserve a good loving and kind home with people that will love them like they were their own babies thank you very much I Penny said this

## 25

They all look fairly standard. I think I would tick the middle boxes for most of the decisions. I think it is important that Mum is treated and kept comfortable but NOT over-investigated. I think we have to be realistic about her quality of life and taking extreme measures to prolong it (colonoscopy, chemo, etc). On the other hand, I think she should still have antibiotics for chest infections, etc. It was a bit disturbing to read that they have limited equipment for resuscitation. Most places should have a defibrillator—if not for the residents then for staff and visitors!!! A witnessed cardiac arrest still has a good chance of survival if CPR is started immediately, which is why most supermarkets, shopping centres, etc have them. Hope this helps!!!

## 26

I'm going to FaceTime you back, because this echo is driving me crazy. FaceTime me, actually—you FaceTime me.

I'll try.

Hello?

Hello.

I've still got the echo.

Is that any better? It might be because I'm playing it through this . . . I'll just turn it off. Is that any better?

Yes.

It's because I was playing you through the speaker.

Okay, so if my heart has stopped beating or I have stopped breathing (please tick only one answer), please do CPR, or please DO NOT DO CPR?

What do you think?

I don't know. I would say do.

No. The problem is, CPR's not that successful, and the chance of them finding her in time . . . she'll probably be brain dead.

Ah. Okay.

What do you think, Fred? CPR on Mum?

Not right now, obviously.

He says not really.

Not really. That's helpful.

He's sitting on the fence. She's allowed to have an opinion, he says. Maybe you should discuss it with her.

I know. I know. I haven't broached that yet. It's not a conversation you want to have.

Well I would say no, but it's up to you really.

No, it's up to both of us.

She is eighty-five. If they do CPR they'll break her ribs. And I don't think she'd want to be resuscitated to a vegetative state.

But it would be different if they had a defibrillator?

Not really.

Do you think I should raise that with them?

I was talking to Fred, and he thinks somewhere as big as that should have a defibrillator. Not necessarily for people with Alzheimer's and things, but they're going to have children visiting them, and they'll be in their forties and fifties, and if they have a sudden cardiac arrest they'll need a defibrillator.

They don't actually say they don't have one, on the forms. They say this facility carries only basic resuscitation equipment. Definitive treatment will depend on how quickly the ambulance arrives and how soon someone can be transferred to hospital.

It doesn't sound like they do.

I'll find out.

It is a difficult thing to think about, but she has to die some time, and of something, because everyone does. Fred's dad had this sudden cardiac event and dropped dead. He had a very good life, up until that moment.

### 27

A blue-black bird on the hard shoulder, its dead wing rising as I pass.

28

The colour may differ slightly from reality.

29

How do I best go about finding how to meditate. I don't want religious meditation such as Buddhist or Hindu (I am Christian and do not appreciate the methods of Buddhists and Hindus), just how to meditate and shut off the racing mind. I'd like to do this at night because my mind wanders over all kinds of things at night LOL. I went to various healing rooms, I felt absolutely NOTHING. I do listen to relaxation hymns on YouTube. Any water sound makes me anxious because I almost drowned as a child. I have been told by ALOT of different people and read ALOT of things that say meditation, yoga, acupuncture and so on are NOT of GOD. :( I just don't know what to say or do about this situation.

Diving into new age practices is not healthy for a born again Christian.

I have never heard of a healing room.

Various forms of meditation have been used in orthodox Christian traditions for centuries, such as the monastic traditions of the Middle Ages in Europe. I doubt those practices originated from Buddhism.

I really don't know but there were ALOT of pagan practices in the church even during those times.

Meditation is not for everyone. Sometimes people feel uneasy instead of calm because a quiet mind will allow unpleasant feelings to come up.

Yoga!!

From what I understand in yoga there is chanting to other gods.

Yes, yoga would be like Buddhist or Hindu. I have listened to yoga instructors that became Christians talk about how dangerous it is spiritually. Laurette will help you understand my point. She taught several forms of yoga and got deep into it before God saved her and brought her out of it. Christian meditation is about filling our minds with God's word as opposed to other religions that teach you to empty your mind.

I found some Christian yoga DVDs on Amazon—simple breathing and stretching exercises done to soothing worship music.

Praisemoves is a great alternative for Christians. I can stretch and do all that yoga offers with Praisemoves.

i love jesus with my whole body soul heart and mind, and you might be surprised to know he lived and meditated in india for some time

Can you post the scripture in the Bible that talks of Jesus going to India and meditating?

no I don't think it's in the main bible

Please quote the scripture. My husband is familiar with the uncanonized scriptures. I too have many Bibles but never have I heard that before.

not sure if i can, just google jesus lived in india

I did. No scripture.

oh ok well is that a problem

Yes it is if you can't back it up with scripture.

oh ok well doesn't worry me, namaste!

I would appreciate it if you could please spell my name correctly. I can tell you it's not in the Bible. I have read the whole Bible through several times and it was never said.

We are here to heal.

I have trouble thinking of absolutely nothing.

## 30

Today's session is a little bit chalk-and-talk, without the chalk. We won't get to the detail, but you can go through it yourself. Futures: we're familiar with futures. There are some that are free, there are some that are not. Tell me to slow down.

I should use a relevant example in here. We've got a kind of blanket, which is futures. Bang, we'll bring it straight in. We're being smarter about the way that we assess our students, without creating artificial assessment opportunities, so this is focusing on the delivery challenge. There are hands-on structured timetabled events, so the students are actually doing the thing that they're learning. The flipped classroom model: how do we implement that? What does it mean in our learning area? Everyone has been given a sandbox; it's where you can play. It's your space. Before I carry on: how are we travelling? Good? I'll just rattle through this; a lot of it is guided by analytics and data. Give it a title, say what it is, share it with your students, push it. Bang. You can just basically click the button, it pops up and says record, you talk to the camera and then it posts straight into your course. You can be walking down the street and record whatever you want to say and then bang, post it. If you want to dive deeper there are your students down here, and that brings you into your learner analytics where you've got specific information about individual students. You can see how often they've actually been into the course and actually done stuff. This blue line represents you, and email discussion opportunities and chat functionality that you've had throughout the course with the students. If you want to be someone who just consumes but doesn't share, that's up to you.

Catherine, I couldn't do Moving Fiction 1 because I had to work on Fridays and there was no way that I could, but I've got Fridays off now and I can do Moving Fiction 2, but I don't have the prerequisite of Moving Fiction 1 and I'm really upset because I have to do playwriting and the last play I saw was Hound of the Baskervilles and that might have been a movie.

# [ JULY ]

## 1

She was asking him about animal sounds and said what about a duck. He said quack quack boom. Daddy shoots ducks.

## 2

Were you taught affirmative consent? YES. NO.

## 3

Can I just say—I hated it.

I got to thirty percent and I honestly didn't want to carry on.

It took me two weeks to get through it.

It took me longer than that.

The whole set-up felt really exploitative, because it was so badly written.

I was interested in the actual story. There were things I found interesting.

The orphanage, and the experiments on the children.

It had the potential to be something powerful.

She really stuffed it up.

Lots of people online—I'm assuming mainly conservative Americans—were annoyed and angry that there was nowhere on the back cover that said the main character was gay. And so they felt ambushed by the gayness. They were saying she inserted something too modern into the story . . . like no one was gay in the fifties.

So many convenient things happened, though. Oh, I'm going to run away, I don't have enough money, but I meet this family on the train who need me to help them. Also the fact that they happen to find each other on the beach, and Naomi's all like I forgive you, I love you still, I can see how you planned it all out with the money.

Okay, questions. Was it selfish of Sam to leave Rachel in Leadville with their Uncle Max? Why do you think Sam keeps leaving his sister behind?

When he ran away from the orphanage after he attacked that guy for her, it was a bit weird that he made no contact.

And it was weird that he left her to be married off to the creepy uncle.

There were two families who seemed quite similar and I couldn't be bothered going back to see who was the train family.

I think they were all one family.

Oh.

If Dr and Mrs Abrams had known that Rachel was 'unnatural', do you think they would have still been kind to her?

Who were the Abrams?

The people on the train. Not the Cohens.

So who were the Cohens?

The uncle and aunt who live at the beach and make horses for the carousels?

I thought they were the Abrams. Weren't they?

What was the question?

Was Dr Solomon wrong to use Rachel in her experimental study of the X-ray tonsillectomy?

Yes. It's like using poor Africans. Next question.

There's a wasp in your hair.

Teaspoon. Teaspoon. Quick.

. . . and it's gone.

I could feel it crawling on my scalp.

That was more interesting than the book.

What do you think of the way Mrs Hong treats Sparrow and Jade?

Who are Sparrow and Jade?

What does it matter?

Is Dr Solomon to blame for Rachel's tumour, or should she be thanked for spurring Rachel's discovery of it in time for treatment?

Rachel probably would have found it anyway. Do we think it's cancer, by the way? I don't actually care.

Would Rachel have been justified in giving Dr Solomon an overdose of morphine in revenge?

Again, the convenience. I don't know why I'm saving this leftover morphine, I can't figure it out . . . oh, I know, so I can give her an overdose.

Tell me—because I haven't finished it—does Rachel find out what her father did?

That's the stupid thing. No one sits her down and says you've got it all wrong.

We're losing the sun.

What shall we do next?

Everywhere you look on the internet, everyone's talking about The Girls.

I'm sick of reading about stunning first novels by stunning debut novelists. They can all piss off. What about some bitter disillusioned mid-career novelists?

There's the Louise Erdrich.

Mmm. I just worry about how much actual hunting there might be in it. I don't deal well with hunting scenes. I don't mind people getting killed, but any kind of animal torture—

It's not a deer that dies, it's a kid.

I went to a romance writers' workshop—don't judge me—and there were these three New Zealand authors who had

Mills and Boon contracts, and they all said you never hurt the animals. If you hurt an animal in your book, your book will be rejected by Mills and Boon. You cannot hurt the animals.

## 4

Alice! Have you been doing some drawing? What a clever girl.

Who knows if it's really hers. They probably gather them all up at the end of the day and stick random names on them.

## 5

The baby has fallen off the change table. The mandarins are pecked open, rotting on the ground. The cat has eaten a hole in the box I bought for the velvet coat I didn't want to sell to the difficult woman who doesn't deserve it. In the satin-lined pocket I found a ticket stub from a cinema in Berlin. I must have gone there with the boy I used to love, but I can't remember. I can't remember the cinema and I can't remember the film, just the cold of his single-glazed flat in Wedding, and spreading the coat across the bed.

## 6

It is useful to think of story shape as an inverted check mark, rising from left to right and ending in a short downswing.

## 7

My rule of thumb when I'm deleting photos is to ask myself if you died, would I regret getting rid of this blurred picture of you? That's forty-six defective Alans gone. I'm trying to delete a few every day, otherwise I'll never get through all of you.

## 8

Oops! The page you were looking for doesn't exist.

It looks very grey.

It is very grey. It's been grey for days and days.

Show me the baby. Hello! Hello Alice!

I don't know how long she'll tolerate sitting here. She's never really been a lap baby.

Is she wearing her cat onesie?

She is wearing her cat onesie. It's very cosy, thank you. We think her first word might be cat. She points at them and says caa. Caaa. Caaaa. Don't you, bub? And we think she's said booooh for book.

I went to London last weekend. We were staying near the London Eye and we walked round the Houses of Parliament and Westminster Abbey. And then the next day I went to the National Portrait Gallery and the National Gallery and then back to Trafalgar Square and then off to Kensington. And we got some last-minute tickets for Covent Garden and saw The Woman in Black. The theatre was almost vertical. Really small, but vertical.

Mm. There's nothing like that here. We went to K-Mart this afternoon.

I had this lesbian couple sitting behind me, which was fine, except one of them took her shoes off and put her feet on the back of the seat next to me.

I would have said something.

But they were so nice and friendly—I couldn't. Tomorrow morning Harry and I are off on a road trip. We're going to look at Leicester University and we're staying in a disabled room at the Premier Inn. It's the only one they had left. We think it might be more spacious. I really enjoy going to London, but it's quite nice to get back home as well. Because it's *so* busy. There's *so* much happening, all the time.

Mm.

Eddie won a silver bowl. The Saint Andrew's classics prize.

I didn't know they did classics at his age.

Yes. And his friend, more excitingly, won the silver plate for history, which was won in 1988 by Chris Martin.

Oh.

The singer from Coldplay.

Right.

Because he went to their school.

Wow.

I have a photo of it. I'll take you up to see puss cat, Alice.

There's Jubby! Look! Look! Hi Jubjub! Who's that? That's Jubjub. That's Jubjub. You'll have to stop moving—the picture's breaking up.

Caa.

Did you hear that? She said caa. Look at Jubjub! He's not doing much.

But see how his eyes match our duvet?

Caa. Caa.

Cat. Cat. We must enunciate.

Hello Alice! Hello Alice!

Wave. Hi Jubjub!

Caa.

Wave!

Caa.

I do find myself getting confused between the baby and the cats, and so does Alan. If we want to wipe her nose we'll go to grab the scruff of her neck, or we'll start stroking her, or we'll call the cats bubba or the bubba Mintiemoo.

Caa. Caa.

It's nearly time for Lily to have her annual dental check at the vet's, which means they'll say she needs to go under general anaesthetic and have a descale, which is about $450.

Oh my God. Do you think they're lying?

Probably.

It's like car mechanics. You never really know. Do you want

to say hello to Eddie the classics scholar? Eddie, come and say hello to Aunty Cath and Alice. Eddie. Eddie. What? Oh.

## 10

I wonder who coined the word steampunk?
Some cunt.

## 11

In particular, the team says, the most popular are stories involving two sequential man-in-hole arcs and a Cinderella arc followed by a tragedy.

## 12

I must say I'm disappointed with the tiny magnolias they've planted by the front gate. I thought they were going to put a whole hedge in and we wouldn't have to look at them any more. You'd think they'd plant something quick-growing, so that they had some privacy, and more importantly we had some privacy. I felt sad when I first woke up, and I didn't know why. It's Dad's anniversary. I knew it was coming, but I forgot until Facebook showed me my memory.

## 13

This page intentionally left blank.

## 14

Are you still on lockdown?
Oh yes. The staff are being very careful, which is good. I think I might have a touch of it ... I just don't feel well. The man in the room next to me is awful. He's coughing and spitting and making noise. It's quite disgusting. I couldn't get to sleep last night and about ten thirty the nurse came in with a cup of tea and said she'd give him one with something in it to knock him out. We often have a joke.

## 15

I lived in a village like that, and it was very pretty and picturesque, but nothing could ever be new. No house was built later than the seventeenth century—you had the sense that it was unchanging. You couldn't make a discovery or find something interesting because it was all so trodden on. Every inch of land had been used for centuries, over and over, and there was nothing new in it. You think of the west coast of the South Island—it's wild. You only have to stop your car, walk ten feet into the bush, and you're somewhere completely wild, and not many people have been there and everything is new. Living in Laycock, I found it oppressive. When Fox Talbot was there he felt trapped by his location—he said the landscape was exceedingly dull, so he went off travelling around Europe to try to take interesting images. I had Christmas in Paris with this family and there was this one guy who said oh, New Zealand, you have no history, I went to your national museum and they had stuff from Lord of the Rings there, which is just film fantasy. And I said to him that's the beauty of it—it can be whatever it wants to be—it can invent itself. The weight of history can obliterate any creative endeavour.

I can't breathe out of either nostril.

## 16

Website featuring disgusting microwaves. People submit photos of disgusting microwaves and I add hilarious captions. Encourage submission of photos of cats on/in the microwaves. Accompanying book.

## 17

Is music the language of the angles?

## 18

There's rain at the windows and blood in the bed.

## 19

There was a pounding sound—regular, rhythmic—somewhere in the distance. I was thinking: is it from the house-build across the road? Are they excavating? Or has one of the cats trapped a foot somewhere and is desperately trying to escape? Is the clock ticking more loudly than usual? I went down the hallway looking for it, looking for it, and the sound followed me, and I realised it's my own heartbeat I can hear, because of the tear in my eardrum.

## 20

You poor thing—I can't believe you've been suffering like that while I've been away.

Why is it that the writer has to keep to the deadlines, but nobody else does? I've just had to accept that there will be inconsistencies. Not all indirect speech is in italics. When it's in real time it isn't, but when it's more of a memory, more dreamlike, then it is. So I'm being consistent within my inconsistencies. There were a couple of really bizarre things—like a random poet's name inserted in the middle of a sentence for no reason. I just want it to be over. I want it to be over so I can put my head in the sand and not read reviews.

Has me getting some decent ones helped?

No, because all the good ones are gone now.

Like there's only so many good reviews to go round. And I stole them.

Yep. And no matter how good the book is, the publishing scene is shit at the moment, and not many people are making money, and there are pieces left right and centre about how even seasoned writers are having to tighten their belts and take on teaching jobs and it's not what it used to be and it won't ever be what it used to be again.

There were a lot of writers hungry for agents, hungry for connections at the conference. There were a lot of people working the room. And all the prizes are disappearing. It's a death knell.

I'm glad you're looking at doing the autobiographical novel, though.

I will fictionalise it, radically, but the fact remains that its roots will be in real experience. I can't even look away from that street name. I can't imagine calling that street anything else. I've got the ending that I'm working towards, which is a big difference for me. I know where I'm going; I've just got to get there. I'm not sure about the structure. I think it'll be multiple points of view, and quite fragmented, and it'll play with what's a short story and what's a long one. I'm going to get up every morning and have a go. But not this week. I keep telling myself I've just come back from China.

Coming home always seems worse than going away.

It is much worse. They say that it is. I don't know why. I've been to bed and I have slept so long. Just fallen into a deep, groggy, overwhelming sleep, and then when you wake up you don't feel like you've come out of it. We got back Monday evening but my brain hasn't arrived. There's this dragging sensation and this time delay. My brain particles are still drifting somewhere out behind the back of my skull.

I used to get vertigo. I'd feel like the ground was suddenly and without warning slanting away from me.

To be honest, I feel like I've had morphine. When you have morphine, your chest slows down, like you've had a weight lowered onto your lungs. I've come home more desperate than ever to get things back in balance and start getting some writing going. But Beijing was amazing. Everything was there. All the sights.

Mm.

It was such a shame you couldn't come.

Mm.

In Shanghai, at the conference, we had these buffet banquets and it was traditional Chinese food, and if you got there at the wrong time all that was left were these big tubs of—honestly, I don't know what meat it was. Sometimes you'd go ooh, that looks like chicken and bean sprouts, and then back at the table you'd go no, that's not chicken, that is suet slash offal. Once I got myself a plate of what I thought were mushrooms and cabbage, but got back to the table and no, it's some kind of frilly stomach lining. You tell yourself you're not going to be that westerner, but by the end of it you're just craving something familiar.

### 21

Have you lost a bit of weight? Is there anything going on? Your bowels? How are they working? Haven't changed in any way? Any blood or mucus in your stool? Have you tried challenging yourself with other foods? What happens when you do? Any urinary symptoms? Passing urine okay, no problems there? Any gynaecological symptoms? What period of time have you noticed this weight loss? What are your energy levels like? Any palpitations? Any lung issues? What sort of symptoms are you having today? Were you in any pain? You didn't use cotton buds or anything? Any fever? Do you want to lie down on the bed? You're not having diarrhoea? Are you okay with antibiotics? You're a bit sore on the external canal, aren't you, when I pull on your ear? Do you know how to do a Valsalva manoeuvre? What do you essentially eat these days? I better write that down.

### 22

To be honest this is all very upsetting.

### 23

Thanks to my wasting muscles, I can now zip up my sexy red boots.

## 24

Someone's been squawking in the car. Haven't you?

Have you been squawking? I don't believe it. Come over to Nana?

What's that pile down there? The antimacassars off your chair—are they to be washed?

Yes. I was going to get them washed.

Do you want me to wash them?

Yes. Please. If you send things like that here, they lose them forever. They've lost my bedspread at the moment. You know, my . . . what do you call it? It's not a bedspread . . .

Your quilt.

Quilt. Yes.

How did they lose that? It's quite big.

I don't know. They took it after I had the bug the other day. They said we'll wash it for you, and they washed my blanket and everything, but I didn't get the top thing back. Are you getting curls? Come on. Come to Nana. Oh. Oh dear. It's all right. Is Nana that frightening? Look, she's tired, I can see. What are you doing there?

Me?

Yes.

I'm just transferring these over to your hangers.

How have you got my blouses?

We washed them for you.

Oh, I see. Thank you. Every time I see her I'm sure she's grown. Have you growed? Have you growed? They've taken my top thing and they've never brought it back.

I've had these forms for ages that they like you to update every so often. I've been meaning to go over them with you. About your wishes in case you . . . go into a coma or whatever.

I didn't know about that.

We did them ages ago when you first moved in, and you elected to have a DNR . . .

Oh yes, when I first moved in.

Which is Do Not Resuscitate.

Yes. Yes.

So they just want me to update them and make sure you're still . . .

Yes. No. I don't want to be resuscitated, thank you.

In order to help guide us to provide healthcare that meets your needs, particularly at times when you are unwell and less able to communicate, please answer the questions at the end of this form. It is impossible to cover all scenarios and foresee all eventualities.

Anything you say may be used against you in a court of law.

If someone has advanced dementia and develops symptoms of a cancer, the process of investigating this can be upsetting to them, and once the diagnosis is confirmed it is often decided not to treat, so the process of investigation has caused upset for no gain. So I think they're basically saying . . .

Yes.

You know, to think about how far . . .

Yes. Yes.

How far you go in investigating serious illness.

Yes.

Fluids. When someone is unconscious and close to the end of their life, palliative care experts have advised us that not giving fluids does not cause distress or discomfort.

Oh.

CPR. This is the most difficult area to advise and decide on for many people.

She's really titchy. We need to get going.

Okay, we'll just quickly do this. What do you think, bubba? CPR or not? This facility carries basic resuscitation equipment . . . treatment will depend on how quickly the ambulance arrives . . . blah blah blah . . . those with existing heart or lung

THE BEAT OF THE PENDULUM

or kidney problems or cancer or dementia have a poor chance of survival should they need CPR.

Oh.

I talked to Helen about it, and she said probably the middle option for all of them.

Yes. Which is the sensible one?

I'd probably go with the middle one.

Yes. That's the best one. It's the sensible one. If I was sixty I might tick the other one. You've got a nasty cold, haven't you?

It's dragged on and on. At this point I'm ready to tick the box saying please just keep me comfortable. Have you got a pen?

We need to get going. She's had enough.

Okay, I'll fill them out at home.

What's the year?

## 25

Please answer the questions as though you are the resident.

If I become more unwell (please tick only one answer in each section), please treat problems to help my quality of life but not prolong my life if it is close to the end. Please only do blood tests and X-rays when absolutely necessary. Please use antibiotics but not if I am close to dying—let me go peacefully. Please do not use extra fluids to prolong my life if I am close to dying— let me go peacefully. If I am so sick that you think I need to go to hospital (please tick only one answer in each section), please send me to hospital for fractures and things that will help my quality of life. If my heart has stopped beating or I have stopped breathing (please tick only one answer), please DO NOT DO CPR. When I am dying the following are important to me (please tick as many answers as you like), keep me comfortable. Take out tubes and lines that are not adding to my comfort. Let my family and friends be with me. Stop medications that do not add to my comfort. Attend to my spiritual needs. Other: _____

## 26

We were giving each other sideways glances, you know, because we'd hear this big roaring, the wind, just the wind and rain, thunder and lightning. And you could hear the sea and it sounded like it was just going to come in through the front door. We're going to get washed away. We need protection from the sea.

## 27

What does it mean if you have no moons?

## 28

Maybe I am doing it wrong, but this item is pretty much useless. I have no complaint with the seller however as they were prompt in delivery and packaging was good.

Slightly upset that the pen did not come with ink. Felt slightly misled.

Haven't used it yet to comment.

Item NOT as described. Pen you sent has no tiger on it, instead has a rose! A bit disappointed but will keep it.

My case has already broken glue come away

Went to use my bubble machine today and it doesn't work

Quick trade but lid was broken so not too great. Good though, thanks

Adapter is great! Although it does overheat after 20 minutes? Never the less great buy

It is ok with the price but very bad packing makes so many damage

Hi there would like to know when I would receive my tattoo gun?

## 29

One day we'll look back on this and laugh.

### 30

I used to go out with a meteorologist. Sometimes, in the middle of the night, I'd turn on the radio and listen to him reading the shipping forecast, predicting the future. Dad thought he was a bit wet.

### 31

First of all tell me what you plan in your mind; what you want to be. May I see your breasts, please? It's a major decision to make in just a few minutes—deciding on something that will be with you for life. I make a cut there, and a small cut—two small cuts—around your previous scar. Take care of yourself. We can start to look at the wounds. I think we get a good result in your case and I hope you have a sweet dream. But it'll be over before you know it.

When I woke up this morning I was like, oh, that's a different feeling. Obviously him being the doctor, he knows best. If you can pay to be happy, then why not. I want the confidence that I see in these other women and I believe that surgery will help me. I'll be a happier person and a more confident person. Fingers crossed that's it; fingers crossed I'm happy after this. He instantly makes you feel at ease. He does the markings all over, but then he gets the laser out and does laser beam measurements. Before I knew it they were wheeling me in. I couldn't see through the bandages. I'm confident in his hands. This moment is mine; I'm going to own this moment. I can continue on with my normal life now. It took a while to be able to move my arms. There was a lot of pain. I'm nervous. There's the fountain out the front, and the lady takes you to the chairs that are set up like a wedding with the big bows on the back.

She's feeling safe in his hands; she is incredibly happy. Surgery of any kind carries a risk. She wants this to complete an incredible journey that began in a women's refuge seven years ago. It gets better every day, honestly; only time will tell. We're just a bit nervous that they're going to decide while she's under. There are always risks involved; any complications at this stage could be disastrous. This will allow him access to her chest structures. I don't know any more. She's in pain. They came with a wheelchair. Suddenly it all became very real, especially lying down on the bed, and you see the massive lights. Those lights are intimidating. He determines where the nipple will sit.

# [ AUGUST ]

### 1

People aren't made for speed. Slow down.

### 2

Her attention span is . . .
Like Daddy's.
What?
I thought we could go to the library afterwards and get her some different books. But—the snot. The faecal matter.

Let me have a look at those ears. Your dad's going to hold you tight. It's not good to be too comfortable at the doctor's—it means you come and see me too often. Are we chatting?
Warbling.
Vocalising, though, are we?
She says Mum, Dad, Ma, Da . . .
Caa for cat.

At least she's not freaked out by Dhanesh. When I was little Dr Harichandra had to come to the house one night because Mum and Dad thought I was at death's door. I'd never seen an Indian person before, and I screamed and screamed and screamed, and would not let him in the room—he had to consult from the hall. Where's Children? Perhaps we won't get books that can be torn.

Yeah, I think get board books.

We'll get board books, bubba. What do we like the look of? Ten Little Monsters? Scarface Claw? What's that on it? Eww.

How can you do that? How can you open a book and immediately find—

Faecal matter.

We used to go to the Invercargill Public Library when we went into town. It had this display on a table—a model of an ideal home. It was an octagonal-shaped house with a central courtyard, which the roof sloped down towards. It was avant-garde. In each of the little rooms there was sixties doll furniture. And Southland Museum had dioramas that are still there and haven't changed. It's like looking back on your childhood.

You don't want the Lord's Prayer?

No.

I want to wash my hands.

### 3

What do we mean when we talk about voice in writing?

I . . . I wrote . . . I wrote down how . . .

Shh!

Shh!

I . . .

Take it away.

I wrote down how particularly in fiction voice can be getting into someone's mind and knowing more about them and what they think and how they act.

It could be an instinct coming from your heart.

The ability to connect. So . . . yeah. People will often have similar experiences with voices that they relate to. So a voice can do that.

Mine was the good and the bad. Like you can't just make a voice. Like you can't like just make them all good. Because that's not who that voice is. You have to take the good with the bad.

I thought voice can be a beautiful voice.

And your voice can be a vessel, too. Like speaking for those who can't. And being a messenger.

And I also thought voice can connect to the history. Some of the things that happened in history still come back.

Voice is often biased or subjective because of past experience. Voice isn't just this all-knowing thing. It's got a definite perspective.

And often we as readers need to ask ourselves do I trust this voice?

I was wondering whether as a writer you have to adopt or adapt a single voice. Why are you not able to be ten characters in your story?

Tone.

We just wrote random words.

Monologue.

Consistency.

We ran out of crayons.

We had things that didn't directly have to do with actual voice. Like emotion. Influence. Perception.

Internal monologues and stuff.

4

We have to catch life in the form of syllables.

5

I'll sharpen my pencil and delete regrets.

6

Is there an opinion on kinesiology? I went to see one and asked different questions and apparently my body said no to everything except for moving to Portugal.

7

I'm worried now that we haven't been teaching her colours when we go to the supermarket. We're not pointing out vegetables. I felt a bit judged. What did she say? It's all about being mindful. So we need to teach her to be mindful of vegetables?

No, I think it's about us being mindful of opportunities to teach her. Bubba, where's your numbers book?

What if she grows up not knowing what red is? It'll be all our fault. She'll run red lights.

Purple red green. Green yellow blue. Green. Green yellow blue. Yellow. Where's yellow? You point to yellow. No, that's 5. That's 6. Where's yellow? Oh my God, she doesn't know what yellow is.

We must demonstrate with a banana.

8

You always have expectations. She's been shooting from a very young age. In actual fact they've got a trap outside their backyard, on their local farm in Timaru. Had a bit of bad luck with her mum a few years ago—she passed away. It's something of a family affair—she's got three brothers. Young Sam, he's in a wheelchair which is unfortunate, and he also shoots. Which proves that shooting is for everyone: young ones, paraplegics, old people. And ladies. The ladies are just as competitive as anybody else, and we do compete against each other openly. Shooting gets a bum rap. Everything bad round the world is all related to shooting and we have a lot of trouble getting media coverage on shooting. This is just absolutely fantastic.

I remember years ago when another one of our shooters did very well for New Zealand, and you walk down the streets, and everybody that knows my wife and I are involved in shooting says oh the girl with the funny voice and the funny hat, oh didn't she do well. The name eludes me at the moment. But this is going to be the same.

## 9

These are magic. We have two cats—one ginger and one Persian. The Persian doesn't shed at all, oddly enough, but the ginger one sheds everywhere. All over my fiancé's work trousers—he's just over there. He's very affectionate and comes up and rubs against your leg. I just wet it with warm water.

## 10

This article must adhere to the biographies of living persons policy, even if it is not a biography, because it contains material about living persons. Patience is low for problematic editing *even in a possible good cause.* Editing the article yourself is not recommended. In some cases the 'Streisand effect' can mean that your involvement might draw a spotlight to the article or its past edits. Instead of being suppressed, the information receives extensive publicity and media extensions such as videos and spoof songs.

## 11

Publishers are always very worried about dates. They want the latest thing.

Which I am not. I am not the latest thing. It makes me want to hide under the duvet.

We've shifted a generation. We went to sleep one night and woke up in the next generation.

I think we should reinvent ourselves. Come out as bisexual. It will help both of our careers.

If you and I came out as bisexual no one would get excited. We're old. We're in the generation where no one wants you to be bisexual. They're just revolted either way. They don't care what you're eating, they're just revolted either way.

I don't know how to talk about the book beyond the basics. I have permanent brain fog. I'm sure there was so much I needed to say to you when I finally saw you, but it's all just fluttering away.

Are these things that have literally been shrapnel in your mind? It's not the beginning of the end.

I feel way less articulate than I did when my last book came out.

You always say brilliant things.

No I don't.

You do.

It makes me feel sick. I've said everything in the book, so just fuck off and read it.

Probably don't say that. Probably edit that bit.

## 12

Did I hear something? That Harry got a scholarship or something?

He got a prize.

That might be what it was.

It was a silver cup . . . no, it was Eddie. Eddie got the silver cup for classics at school.

That's right, that's what it was. My nails are disgusting—I must have forgotten to cut them.

Don't they have a manicure person who comes to Sunset Court? You should book in with them.

I normally just do them myself. I must have forgotten— they're disgusting. There's an article in . . . oh, the paper or something. I've kept it. A girl who used to go to Sacred Heart. They lived over in . . . I can't remember the name. I've cut it out.

She's in parliament or standing for parliament or something.

Let's have a look at the patch on your head that he did a while ago. It's much better, isn't it.

And what's he doing today?

He's taking off that little bit above your lip.

Oh I see. I suppose they're the same thing. One of those silly old lady things. They're called old age. I had a nice note from . . . now I can't say. She's a niece, through Les. Just a hello how are you note, but it was nice. I hear from Peter quite regularly. He makes sure I'm being good. Did I tell you about somebody who called in and saw me the other day? I can't remember her name. I haven't seen her for years.

Where does she live?

Wellington. She used to come and see Les from church. I can't remember her name.

You mean when he was sick?

Yes. She used to bring him communion. She was lovely. And her husband ran away with his office girl. She was driving past and thought I think that's where Pat Chidgey lives, so she came to the office and they said yes and brought her down. I wasn't quite sure who she was but she knew who I was. We had a lovely time. She said she was driving past and she saw the name and thought I reckon that's where Pat Chidgey lives. So it was lovely, we had a great time. Her husband used to be late home for dinner every night. I went out one afternoon and she was coming up the street and I could see she was crying. I ran to her. He wasn't doing overtime—well, he *was* doing overtime. Every week when he brought his wages home he'd give her the housekeeping, and he used to give her more because he said I've been doing all this overtime. What am I here for?

You're having the little skin cancer there removed. It's just the same as the other ones you've had removed, which are very very slow-growing, but he said it's better to take it off.

Yes. And the other one cleared up.

Yes.

I love that jacket of yours. Not many people could wear it. Is Alice saying lots of words?

She's saying caaaa for cat and booooh for book and bohhh for bottle.

Maureen Quirke's just had a big operation on . . . I'm not quite sure. Somebody told me it was her hip and somebody told me it was her back. It was probably her knee. She's been staying at her daughter's.

All your bits seem to have lasted quite well, don't they?

Yes. I really keep very well, when I see other people with walking sticks and wheelchairs. Dad was very fit, you see. I think Mum would have been, but she had to lie on the sofa and have cups of tea. Oh she was a funny lady—well, I think I wasn't wanted. I think that was it. But that wasn't my fault, was it. Dad was lovely. You often remind me of my father. Not to look at, but your sense of humour is sometimes clever. Dad was like that too. He was very uneducated, and he used to ring me at work sometimes, and the girls in the office just loved his accent. He'd say can I speak to Pat McGough, and about four of them would go to the phone and Dad never had a clue. Who did you want to speak to? I want to speak to Pat McGough. And they were all falling about laughing.

They're always running late here.

Patricia. Would you like to come through? So just confirming that we're going to do this one on the upper lip here? This one here?

Ask her.

Yes.

If you can just move up the bed a little, Patricia. We'll take your glasses off now.

Are you warm enough?

Yes, I'm quite warm, thank you.

No trouble with your blood pressure or anything? Sorry

about the bright light. All I'm going to do at the minute is just draw on your lip.

No pacemaker?

No.

I'll get you to come up here, Catherine. Have I operated on this area before?

No.

So this is probably the skin cancer here, but she also has this red area here and this white area here. That could also be cancer. I didn't plan to cut all this out today. I anticipated that it was just this bit. Um. I'll look at it with my dermatoscope. The difference between just cutting this bit out and that bit out's quite significant in terms of complexity. I'll just have a wee look here. It's going to smell a little bit, this swab. It's got alcohol, but not the kind you can drink.

I won't take a sip.

You can see this red area now. So that makes an easy job difficult. I'm having one of those days. It's hard for me to say. I know that this is cancer here. This is definitely all skin cancer. That's easy. The difficult patch is this—is it skin cancer as well? And is the bit in between also skin cancer? If we were to cut all this away I would need to do quite a big operation and take all of this tissue here, and then take the leading edge and advance it all that way, and then close it. Fortunately she's got a lot of lax tissue so we can. We could actually get that all removed today, but she'd have a relatively long scar. Whereas if it was just this it would be a shorter scar, not quite as wide. Sometimes when we're not sure we actually just take a biopsy here, a biopsy here and a biopsy here, and maybe a biopsy here, and just get them all tested. And then that'll tell us if I need to take all this skin out as well. Having said that, all this skin looks abnormal to me. The important thing is the history. If it's been there for a long time it probably is involved skin. It's hard to tell. I'd planned to do just this today—that was what

I had in my mind—but with these other areas . . . Patricia, do you remember if your lip's changed? I guess you won't, will she, with her memory loss.

Have I what?

Have you noticed that this area above your lip's been changing?

Slightly. Not massive. But it has changed a little bit. I'm worrying about my beauty.

I understand. I suspect that probably is involved. Would you like me to biopsy it and then get her back at a later date to confirm that, or . . . ?

If she was your mum, what would you do today?

It's kind of how cautious you are going through the gates. It's kind of like opening and closing the gate and then getting to the other side rather than running straight through and getting to the same point. We may get to the same point if we biopsy. It's probably more the inconvenience for you, bringing her back, and having to have two procedures. If these come back positive then she'll need the whole upper lip removed.

Oh.

You will still have a lip, Mum.

You'll still have a lip—we'd replace it for you.

Oh, I see. Make sure it's a smiling one.

Yes, a smiling one. And if these come back negative that's good—we could probably take this part out and treat that part with cream.

How long have I had that for?

Quite a long time.

I think you've got to look back and think what would you regret not doing? And if we did a big operation for her and this leading edge came back as skin that we could treat by other means then we'd probably feel like we'd done a bigger operation than we needed. This is slow-growing, this one, so if we biopsy these two areas then I feel confident in what I'm treating. It just means we'll have to rebook her in a month's time. If it was my mum that's probably what I'd do.

Don't go ruining my beauty.

Okay. Let's do that.

I'm not often uncertain but I'm a little bit uncertain about this. Even if it gives me confidence that this is cancer, I need to then judge from the edge of that right up to the top of the lip and be a little bit more aggressive around the corner of the nose and stuff like that as well. So it will change the operation that we do.

What about my beauty? That's what I'm worried about.

Your beauty is in the eye of the beholder and you're doing very well at the moment. So what we're actually doing Catherine is mapping this area. I'll just draw on here. I'll have that as a reference for next time.

I've always had fine skin. All my life.

It's the Irish.

It probably is. I can't change that and be German or something, can I?

Okay. All right. I'll just pop a few little injections in there. It will sting a little bit.

It won't leave a big scar on my face?

No, it won't. That made your eyes water a bit, Patricia, did it?

I think you poured some water in them.

Are you all right, Mum? Are you all right?

My lip feels a bit funny. Too much talking. How's my beauty?

You look lovely. Especially with the pen.

We need to make sure the biopsies get into the right pots.

And that they *get* into a pot! Just putting a couple of stitches in now.

I hope you're making it pretty. You should be matching them to my clothes.

Do you live near Patricia, Catherine?

About half an hour's drive away.

Based in the Hamilton area, though?

Mum's in Sunset Court Retirement Village and we're in Ngāruawāhia.

It's been really popular, Sunset Court, hasn't it. Have you found it okay? Good food?

It's grown and grown. Mum started off in one of the stand-alone townhouses, and you were there for about nine . . . ten years?

You're part of the furniture.

And then a couple of years ago she moved over into the main complex, which is the rest-home part, but there's also the hospital. And a dementia unit as well. Where they lock you up, don't they, Mum.

Mm. Yes. No, they're lovely. Lovely meals. Lovely room.

Nice and warm?

Oh yes. And if I feel the cold I've got another heater. They don't care. Am I getting up now? I was going to have a little rest! Cup of tea, please!

Are you all right? Just sit there for a minute.

Just take it a bit slow.

Do you want your glasses?

I was admiring these.

I collect art deco jewellery—that one's twenties and that one's thirties. They're my wedding and engagement rings.

They are stunning.

And I was looking at your jacket and thinking—

She always has everything unusual. She had a skirt made for her when she was about five, and she would only wear it inside out.

Is it possible to know beforehand if it's going to be the more extensive procedure next time? So I can prepare Mum?

Don't go ruining my beauty.

You're looking gorgeous. Would you like to have a look in the mirror?

No thanks.

There's one here.

No.

You've just got to get it the right way round, because you don't want to look at the other side.

I certainly can't go down to lunch.


So he didn't end up taking off that little area today, because he just wanted to take some biopsies of the area around it and make sure he's getting the right, um, amount.

Oh. That's sensible, isn't it.

He's taking the conservative approach.

Yes.

Because he said those little skin cancers, although it is skin cancer, they're very very slow-growing. And that's what Helen said too.

Oh yes. It is cancer, is it?

A little skin cancer. They're very common in people your age and they're very slow-growing . . .

I see.

So you don't have anything to worry about, but he just wants to make sure that he gets the right . . . bits . . .

Yes.

So you don't end up having to have two procedures. So you'll come back in a month. He's put in a couple of little stitches where he took the biopsies, and the nurse at Sunset Court can take those out in a week, to save us coming back here.

That's sensible, isn't it. You paid, didn't you?

Yes.

Well, I paid.

Yes. Come on. This is taking forever.

It must be stuck on red. When I talk it's all funny. What's that building over there?

The grey one?

Yes.

Don't know.

I seem to remember going there once. It was somebody, for something, and it was years ago. I don't know whether it was Helen. And every time I see the building I try to remember what I went there for.

It looks like it might be a business now—it might have been something else then.

I don't know. I can just remember the building. I don't know what I went there for. It might be the police station.

I think it's a restaurant. Maybe. I don't know.

I love this area. The river.

Hamilton doesn't really make enough of the river.

No. No it doesn't. Not like Christchurch does.

I'm glad I didn't stay in Christchurch though.

Yes, I'm glad I moved. I always used to think I'd go back, but once you've been away a long time you sort of forget.

Plus it's freezing.

We had two years in Invercargill, so think about that.

Where did you live there?

Two Lowe Street. Carter Holt rented it. And I boarded a boy—he was a carpenter—and I got the money. I think I got twelve dollars or pounds or whatever it was a week—it was quite good money. Because when you're cooking three potatoes it doesn't take much to put another one in. He was a bit slow. He wasn't mental or anything, he was just a dull sort of a boy. But he was a really good worker. I did very well out of boarding him. How do you like our water feature? They keep things nice, don't they. What are they doing there?

Digging something up. Or burying a body.

I noticed a guy from over that side hasn't been around. That's probably what it is.

They seem to be doing a lot of digging.

I didn't have anything with me, did I?

257

No. I'll go and find the nurse and tell her about your stitches needing to come out in a week. Look—Memory Lane at three p.m.

Right. Yeah. Okay. Yes. Yeah. Yes. Okay. Can—yep. Yes, it can. Yeah, definitely. I'll be here tomorrow, but not Sunday. Okay. Yeah. Oh right. Okay. Yes. Yep. That sounds good. Yep. So I'll—yeah, I think, I think that sounds reasonable. So I'll let the doctor know that, and—yep. Yep, that's fine. Yeah. So the doctor will see him again on Tuesday, and see how things are going then. No. Yeah. Yeah. Okay. Well we'll be able to contact the doctor over the weekend if we need to. Yeah. Okay. He has—he has got some medication charted that we can give him if he needs it. If he does get agitated. So we'll keep an eye on that. Yes. Yeah. Yes. Yeah. Okay. Yep. That's fine. Okay. Thank you, Julie. Bye.

Hello.

Hi!

I've just had Mum—Pat Chidgey—at the dermatologist. She's got some stitches that'll need taking out in a week and he asked if the nurse here could do that. Rather than having to cart her back there.

Yeah. Yeah. It's not worth it. Sutures out, seven days.

Is it you who gives me this, or Helen?

Helen.

It's good. I really enjoy it. I'm not a magazine person, but it's quite good. It has reasonable articles. I don't like the Woman's Weekly. I don't mean this Woman's Weekly. The other one. Is it you or Helen?

Helen. We give you the Listener.

I love the Listener. Not only is it handy for the television, it's got nice articles. And I'm not so good reading books now. You tend to forget what page forty-eight was when you get to page ninety-seven. What's this I'm sitting on?

New Zealand Fashion Week. Shall we just recycle that?

Is today Friday?

Yes. You've got some old newspapers and magazines under here that need to be recycled too.

I think I was keeping them for something and I think it was something I was going to show you. So just leave them there and I'll have a look one day. I can't remember what it was. Are You Being Watched? Sir Colin Meads Faces A Battle.

You've got a bit of a pile here.

I think they're all things I'm going to show you. There was something about a girl that went to Sacred Heart. She lived out in . . . somewhere. And she's now in parliament.

I don't know who that would be.

When I find it I'll show you.

Your pearls are in my pocket. Do you want them on, or in your jewellery box?

I'll put them on. You were trying to steal them. They're very old. I wish I knew how old they were.

I think Dad bought them for you.

That's right. I think for my twentieth birthday. That was the first birthday we had together. And everyone was advising me not to go out with *that* boy. Because a) he wasn't a Catholic, and b) they lived in *Sydenham* and were *working class*.

You did it all wrong.

I did. He was horrible, wasn't he. Aren't people funny? Quite a few told me that. You're not going out with Les Chidgey from *Sydenham* . . . ? If you saw all the dopey boys that lived around where I did! Mrs Hight lived down the road and had a son called Arthur, and Arthur was the biggest idiot you've ever known. Talk about a farm boy. And my mother and Mrs Hight kept on making me go out with him. And one night they made a big arrangement that I'd go in on the bus with Arthur and we'd go to the movies. So we had to go down to the main

road and get on the bus. And when we came out of the picture
theatre I ran away and got another bus.

Poor Arthur.

Poor Arthur.

Did he find someone eventually?

Yes, he did find somebody—quite a suitable match. Poor
Mrs Hight and my mother were so upset. You nearly had Arthur
for a father. You wouldn't have been as pretty with Arthur for
a father. Oh dear. He was wealthy, that was the only thing.
Where's my bedspread, do you know?

They took it away to wash it and they can't locate it. There was
one more place they were going to look, and if they can't find
it there, they'll replace it. We'll be able to buy a replacement.

I hope they can't find it. You're dealing with that, are you?

## 13

I'm going to keep breathing for a while I think.

## 14

Do we know if it was cancer? The whole family's laughing
but me.

## 15

I dreamt of a boy I mistook for another. We followed the
rocky shore to the white lighthouse and his eyes darkened in
the sun. He took me home; from behind a curtain his girlfriend
said well, you're here now. She had his children, and I, the
barren one, talked to him of literature and music.

## 16

Bringing the family together at meal times could never be
fun. Stand alone. Don't underestimate the mirror; a mirror can
fill an empty space. The hanging concept is now making its way
into all living areas. Looking into the property from the road,

one would never guess . . . but be careful. The reflection fools the eye. You don't want a repetition of an undesirable sight. Mirrors are windows you can move around, but a mirror can be a wall. You can create a portal that from a distance looks like you can walk through it. Achieve an invisible finish; make the furniture recede. The hidden storage will look like nothing. I once placed a large, full-length mirror on the wall at the end of a short hallway in an old miner's cottage. I needed something to make a statement, which resulted in giant bromeliads. Just having a mirror with nothing around it is not effective. It would shout 'I am a mirror'. Where you place the family will dictate how successful the illusion is.

### 17

I have thoughts about all of these.
Look at your cheekbones.
It's called makeup.
It doesn't look like makeup though.
In this one I look cadaverous and sad.
It's sadder, but it's beautiful. I actually love it.
With the hands.
Yes, with the hands.
A friend said I'm gesturing at my crotch.
No, I love the composition.
I look like Morticia. I look like the mother of the prom queen. I look like I write vampire erotica. I look like I'm off to an over-forties nightclub in Ibiza.

### 18

Life, like video games, isn't about having fun.

### 19

Big drama here with Mum . . . she's been v distressed about her new neighbour, who's been coughing all night, and keeping her awake. She's had a v bad run with that room . . . this is the third neighbour in a row to be problematic. Sunset Court staff admit it's an issue and they've heard the current guy. It's our theory that they keep that room for the most unwell inmates as it's right next to the nurses' station. Alan and I had a meeting with Denise (manager) and she said we could shift Mum to a different room—one that has an external wall on one side and the bathroom on the other. There are a couple of this type about to 'become available' (best not to think about why). We thought Mum probably wouldn't want to move and would find that quite upsetting, but there's really no other option. We told Denise we'd float the idea with her . . . but Denise got in first (inexplicably) and talked to Mum about it herself! Mum now in tears and v bolshie, ringing several times a day, saying they haven't TOLD her anything, they just EXPECT her to MOVE . . . etc. We're trying to implement damage control . . . but in the end we still think the best thing would be for her to move. Though we've told her she doesn't have to. What do you think????

20

I think it would be best for Mum to move away from the death room. Maybe they could show her both rooms that are becoming available and she could choose. It may make her feel as if she is back in control. Not ideal for her to move really . . . I think she'll get quite disorientated. We are in DC. VERY hot but lots to see and do. Off to New York on Sunday. Xxx

21

I feel we should be watching the Edmund Hillary drama tonight.
What's that?
It's about Edmund Hillary. And it's a drama.
Fuck that.

Witness the incredible story . . . iconic Kiwi . . . landmark series . . .

No.

Mm. I don't really like mountains.

## 22

This activity will result in some people receiving event notification reports which have been fabricated. Please note that during this time you will not need to respond to any of the incident reports you receive unless you are notified in person that an actual incident has occurred.

## 23

It's got pretty insane here . . . Mum's convinced that Denise is scheming to get her out of her room so her aunt and or cousin can have it, and wants to shunt Mum 'upstairs' to where the mad people are. She rang Peter and told him Alan and I had been to see Denise in secret and she saw us all sneaking up to the place where they put the mad people because that's where we're planning to put her . . .

Shall we go to the library, bubba? Go to the library?
More filthy books. And not in a good way.

## 24

We can't put chlorinated water into a sausage; it's going to taste like a swimming pool.

There are voices under the rubble.

## 25

John Campbell was ejaculating all over the radio about the Olympic athletes arriving home. Writers never get that kind of airplay. Writers Land In New Zealand After Record-Breaking

Effort. Hundreds were there to welcome them, many of them schoolchildren. It was a morning for children simply to see their literary heroes. If you look beyond me, the story in a way is all of these kids who are so utterly inspired by the writers, and look at the eyes on those children. Look at their wonder. And their excitement. And their sense of possibility. What's your name?

Jordan.

And what's your name?

Angelina.

Angelina and Jordan, do you have a favourite writer? Who's your favourite? Who's the writer that's most special to you?

Catherine Chidgey.

Catherine! She's cool, isn't she, Catherine! Why is that? Why does everyone love Catherine so much?

She's a big inspiration to many of us.

What inspires you about Catherine?

To be honest, everything. Everything she does.

Catherine, I've spoken to a lot of kids this morning who are excited about seeing you. And I've been watching you sign autographs with that magnificent smile, and I wonder if you know how much you mean to these children. It's pretty special, isn't it?

It's humbling. When I was their age I had a lot of inspiration to be a writer.

It's a powerful message. That *they* can be writers. They look at you, and they understand they can do it. If they try hard enough. If they work hard enough. If they believe strongly enough.

I think that's so cool about what we do. Whether you win a book award or not, it's what you stand for, what we stand for. Sometimes there are dark times when you know you've got to keep going hard, but when you stand on the podium and you hear the national anthem . . .

This is magic, isn't it, because all of those thousands of hours that you've spent alone on the book—and this tells you how much it matters, right?

It's fantastic. Just so many people saying that book was inspirational, it was such a great book. We're working by ourselves a lot of the time, but when you see a response like this, you think this is why I do it.

How many autographs did you sign, do you think?

At least five hundred, I reckon. I've got no control left in my hand.

RSI! OSH! You've got a workplace injury!

They just keep filing in. I've never experienced anything like this before.

And that's the point, isn't it. All the writing you do—all the thousands of hours on the book—and this is the public acknowledgement of what it means. A morning to remember for children who may or may not go on to be writers, but won't forget the day they met them.

Hey, I get to make shit up for a living. I seriously think I've got the best job in the world. If my results can inspire kids to start writing—it's pretty special. It makes me want to work harder, to write better. To take my book to a whole nother level.

## 26

There was a truckie sitting out there for ages—this guy with a beanie on—he had the big prefabricated concrete walls on the back of the truck and he must have been sitting there waiting—

They've been doing that since early this morning.

Yes, but—

A whole procession of them. That place is going to be *massive*.

Yes, but what I'm saying is he was sitting there waiting. He must have been waiting for the call to say we're ready for the next two walls, bring them down. And I kept looking over and thinking is that actually a guy, or has he just hung his jacket on the window? And then I went right over to the kitchen window and was peering out, but without my glasses on, and I thought I don't think that's a guy, so I went and got my glasses and came back and had another good stare and then he moved and I realised that he must think I'm staring out at him. But I didn't like that he was just sitting there for about an hour, staring in at me. I had the feeling I was being watched the whole time.

They were doing that this morning. They were parked up for ages.

But why does he have to stare in our window at me sitting at my computer?

He probably glanced over and saw you staring at him.

The cat just made a phonecall with her arse.

## 27

These are extremely uncomfortable seats.

Aren't they.

Your face is looking healed after the biopsies.

I know, it's wonderful.

You do heal very quickly. What's the date today? I think it's Friday that you're . . . what *is* the date . . . no, it's Friday week—

I thought it was.

That we're going back to—

Mm. Yes.

—to get however much he's decided to remove removed.

I hope he doesn't ruin my beauty.

You really can't tell where he's taken off the other ones.

He's very good.

It's a big pool. I was thinking it was going to be a little kiddies' pool. I guess they do hydrotherapy in here.

It's always beautiful. The water's shining and clean.

There's never been a Code Brown, then.

A what?

Never mind.

You knew I had a bit of an upset at Sunset Court, did you? It's all fixed up though.

Oh that's good.

It's lovely.

That's good.

I'm staying where I am, and I've had a lovely apology from Denise.

Oh that's good.

It was her fault. All the staff knew it was her fault, but they couldn't say. She wanted her aunty to have my room. That's all it was—such a simple thing.

Mm.

But it's all fixed up now. She came in yesterday with a lovely couple of cakes and a cup of tea, and she sat down, and had a cake and a cup of tea, and she said she was sorry and everything, and I said it's all forgotten, I don't know anything about it. So it's all gone.

Oh that's good.

Yes. Well there's no use going on and on and on about it. She did admit that she'd made a mistake, so I said well I made a mistake too, even though I didn't, so we both made a mistake and it's all better. So that's good.

Mm.

I can understand her wanting her grandmother to have the room. But it's all over now.

Hello bubba! Are you ready to go swimming?

I'm surprised you couldn't hear the screaming from out here.

Were you screaming? Were you screaming? I think Daddy's making it up. He's a good dad, isn't he. In your day, fathers didn't do things like that. Les could change nappies, but nobody ever knew. He wouldn't change nappies if we had anybody staying.

Only three in the class today.

What's today?

Saturday.

It didn't used to be on a Saturday, did it?

No, it was a Thursday.

Why is it a Saturday?

Because they have the classes in twelve-week blocks, and then they change to the next one.

She's so beautiful. I just absolutely love her.

Leila's decided she wants to help another couple have a baby.

Oh!

But she's decided that she's too old to use her eggs, so it'll be a gestational surrogacy, where they go through an IVF clinic—

Yes.

And it would be the couple's own—

Yes.

Genetic material put into Leila.

Yes.

She's got a couple in Christchurch she wants to help.

What an amazing lady she is.

She joked when she had Alice—because Alice was so enormous—ten pounds twelve. She said if she ever did another surrogacy it would be gestational, and she'd be on the lookout for a small Asian couple. Don't drink the pool water, bubba!

No, that's not good. No.

Now what was I going to ask you . . . I want to buy something and I was going to ask you to take me.

New quilt?

Yes.

We're going to do that today.

Oh, she's so lovely. I'm not being silly, but she's very intelligent for her age. I presume you know.

Nothing to compare it to, really.

When I see other grandchildren . . . but then you were always very quick. Well, you're not the mother, are you—not the birth mother—but I think they learn off what you do.

Mm.

He's a lovely dad. Not that you're not a lovely mum. But it's not very often that men do that. She's so pretty, isn't she? Who do you think she's like?

Leila.

Yes . . .

Don't lick it. Don't lick the flutterboard.

Don't look. We were all scared of swimming at her age. And we had a river running through our farm. Where's Alan going?

To get bubba changed. Which might be a lengthy process.

He just loves that baby. She is beautiful. Look at all the other funny babies.

There was a man at the start wandering round with a nappy not attached to a child.

A nappy without a child?

Mm.

It's cousin Pam's birthday today—I saw on Facebook. She's sixty-one. Only two years younger than Dad when he died. That's strange to think.

What would Les have been? Eighty-three?

He would've been eighty-four. Eighty-five in November.

Oh yes. And I'm eighty-five now.

Yes, you're eighty-five.

No, forty-two!

That makes me negative four. I'm not really sure how that works.

Magic.

Look, the trees are coming into blossom already.

For goodness' sake.

Attention everyone? Everyone with lime-green wristbands? Please line up for the eleven o'clock hydroslide? That's the eleven o'clock hydroslide?

I'm sorry if I've been a bit difficult about all these things.

That's all right.

They're all fixed up.

That's good.

A few of us were talking the other day, and we were saying we don't miss having a kitchen and a fridge and all of that. I did when I first moved in, but I don't any more. I'm very happy where I am. I can't remember a house now.

## 28

Image may contain: 1 person, people smiling. I am not a robot.

## 29

What Marcia Brady looks like now is JAW-DROPPING.
What Rebel Wilson looks like now is JAW-DROPPING.
What Marina Sirtis looks like now is JAW-DROPPING.
What Kirstie Alley looks like now is JAW-DROPPING.
What Precious looks like now is JAW-DROPPING.
What Deanna Troi looks like now is JAW-DROPPING.
What Phoebe Cates looks like now is JAW-DROPPING.
What Nicole Kidman looks like now is JAW-DROPPING.
What Nadia Comăneci looks like now is JAW-DROPPING.

## 30

What's jaw-dropping is that developmental genes are turned on after death, Professor Noble said.

## 31

Someone is typing a comment . . .

# [ SEPTEMBER ]

## 1

Jiffy has his own Trade Me account, and he sold a deep fryer for seventy-five dollars. The listing said pick-up only, and you must pay by bank deposit within three days—because otherwise people bring cash, and they go, oh, it's smaller than it looked in the photos, and then they don't pay, and you're left with a crappy deep fryer. The three days came and went, and the guy just kept emailing: Hi Jiffy, where can I go to collect equipment? Hi Jiffy, can u give me an address to pick up equipment? Hi Jiffy, maybe tomorrow at 4:30pm I'll be there. Hi Jiffy, can I go to pick up equipment now? I kept emailing back saying you need to pay by bank deposit and then we can make a time for you to come round. And I signed off as Catherine, and he just kept on replying: Hi Jiffy, can I go to pick up equipment now? Hi Jiffy, can I go now? I don't know that he realised he was addressing a deaf cat. In the end I thought okay, maybe he's not understanding, so I said yeah, come round. So he gets out sixty-five dollars in notes, and then he has ten dollars in coins in his shirt pocket. And he hands over the sixty-five dollars and says is okay, is okay? And Alan says no, it's seventy-five dollars. And he says is okay? Okay? Clearly he'd come intending to haggle dollar by dollar by dollar. Jiffy's blacklisted him.

2

Where's Vladimir Nabokov when you need him? Perched louchely on a Berlin balcony, of course.

3

I've been keeping my distance from the baby. She was running straight for me, arms up, and I had to shut myself in my office and get out the disinfectant. I just can't do it. Cold, cold, cold, cold, cold, cold.

4

There's a bird out there in the long grass. A quail. I was chasing it away because the cats are going out soon. It's quite large, with a long tail.

Quails aren't very big.

I think it's a pheasant.

You said it was a quail.

Quail, pheasant—it's a bird. About the size of a smallish pūkeko. Over there, by the neighbours' fence.

It looks like a chicken.

You think I can't tell the difference between a wild bird and a chicken.

I think you've chased it over to the property that has gun dogs.

They don't run around, though.

Yes they do.

They don't come over this far, though.

Peta's looking out the window at me looking at the bird. Hello! Now she's turned her back to me and sat down again and pretended it never happened. Awkward. Ooh, the bird's on the move. It's moving its head like a chicken.

Would you like the binoculars?

That'll really spook the neighbours. Aah! It's looking at me! There it goes. It's running backwards! That's really weird. I think it's a female pheasant.

So now it's a pheasant. It was ludicrous when I said it was a pheasant.

It was ludicrous when you said it was a quail. Did you see it? I think there's something wrong with it. It was running backwards.

There's nothing wrong with it. It ran perfectly normally away from me. Oh. It is running backwards.

Yeah.

Maybe they do that. Maybe it's a thing they do. It's probably scratching up the dirt—it'll be using its front claws to scratch the dirt and get the worms to come up.

Can the neighbours see me? Are they looking at me with the binoculars?

No.

I mean, I don't mean are they looking at me with the binoculars—are they looking, at me with the binoculars?

No.

Why is it just hanging out behind our house?

Because that's what they do. They live in long grass. This is where it's ended up at the end of the day. Scratching for stuff.

But where's its mate? Do you think it's hurt? It doesn't look injured.

No, it ran normally away from me.

Backwards.

Not for me. It's only now you're watching that it's running backwards.

I'll just stand behind this wall.

### 5

It's Catherine Chidgey speaking. My mother Pat Chidgey has an appointment with Daniel Frost on Friday. At her last appointment they decided to take some biopsies rather than doing the surgery that day, and they were going to let us know before Mum's appointment on Friday what the results were. I was just wondering if someone could tell us.

So who's performing the surgery, do you know?

What's that, sorry?

Who's she coming to see?

Daniel Frost.

I'll just put you through to a nurse.

Thanks.

Hello, you've reached the voicemail for Cheryl Galloway. Please leave me a detailed message and I will return your call as soon as possible. Thank you.

Hi Cheryl, it's Catherine Chidgey here. My mother Pat Chidgey is seeing Daniel Frost on Friday for surgery to remove some skin cancers on her face. At the appointment that she had with him three and a half weeks ago, he decided just to take some biopsies rather than doing the surgery then, to see if he needed to do a much more extensive procedure. Someone was going to let us know before this coming Friday whether he'd be doing the much more extensive procedure or whether it would still be quite a simple one, so that I can prepare Mum for it. If someone could let me know what the results of the biopsies were, that would be great. Thank you. Private bloody clinic and they can't even bloody do what they said they would do, which is let us have the results of the fucking biopsies so I know whether to say to Mum, yeah, they're going to have to cut away half your face on Friday, or it's just a tiny little spot like they originally thought.

Yeah. God.

Because I could tell she was pretty freaked out, at the appointment.

Yeah.

And that's why I asked, can someone let us know. So I can prepare her if it is going to be quite extensive. Fuck.

Yeah. Crikey.

Recording terminated because you were not speaking. Message sent.

Oh!

For plastic, dermatology, vascular and cosmetic enquiries, please select from the following options.

Shit! It recorded me! It recorded me! Shit! Shit! Shit shit shit shit shit!

Could you leave another one? And say look I'm sorry but I didn't realise that I was still recording?

Oh God. I think I better just leave it. Pretend it was my disturbed twin. Oh God.

It's time for our meeting.


Hi Catherine, Cheryl calling from Dan Frost's rooms. Look I really don't know *what* he will be doing with your mum on Friday. He *is* in tomorrow and I *will* check it out with him, and I *will* let you *know*. The biopsies have come back as solar keratosis, which is just layer upon layer of sun damage with no nasties in it, but it *may* still need to be addressed, because those areas don't heal up on their own and *may* be better to be removed. But look I *will* check this with him tomorrow, and I *will* call you back on your cellphone and just make sure that everyone *knows* what's going *on*. Okay! Thanks Catherine! Bye bye!

6

What am I going to say when she rings back?

Play dumb.

Not mention it?

What's the point in mentioning it? If she knows about it, it's awkward. If she doesn't know, you're just dobbing yourself in.

How can she not know? I could just tell her—

No.

I could just—

No. It's a compulsion with you, isn't it?

I could just say sorry if I sounded a bit—

No. No. No.

I could be vague. Sorry if I sounded a bit fraught yesterday, but Mum's quite anxious about the procedure and needs to know beforehand.

No. No. Just pretend you didn't hear the bit at the end of the message and it's fine.

But I did hear it.


I don't trust you any more, with your taping procedures. I get the feeling that underground surveillance is going on.

I want to dig a hole.

### 7

I'm worried about the bird.

I'll have a look for it today. But with all of those huge concrete trucks going down there . . .

Oh, don't!

I just mean it would have run away.

Backwards.

Maybe.

There's a thread about birds running backwards on thatquailplace.com, and one woman said—

It's a pheasant. Not a quail.

Yes, but the site is for individuals interested in raising quail *and other game birds*. You will find information about many game birds, including coturnix quail, bobwhite quail, pharaoh quail, button quail, *pheasant*, partridge and other game birds. One woman said her pheasants started walking weird, like they were staggering, and then they started running backwards, and then they died. And then they started having seizures.

That seems odd.

Jim from West Virginia had the same thing with his

ornamental pheasants and Barbary partridges. And so did a guy from Nova Scotia with his bobwhite. He massaged its tummy and gave it some vitamin E.

What foods are high in vitamin E?

Spirulina? Could we give it some spirulina?

## 8

Bubba just said shit.

Shit.

## 9

I don't think your door's shut.

I don't know what I'm doing.

You're going to the dermatologist. You're just having that tiny little spot taken off. I'm hoping that Cheryl won't be one of the theatre nurses—there was an unfortunate incident in which I recorded myself on their answerphone after I thought I'd hung up.

Little operations and things are quite frightening. I shouldn't be driving home.

You won't be driving. I hate to break it to you.

Oh, I wanted to. I often wonder if I could drive now. I still remember what you do.

We won't put it to the test.

No. I might run into a pole. I never miss it. When I first stopped driving I found it just awful, because I'd driven since I was fifteen. In those days you could get your licence at fifteen if your mother or father signed something. And of course we lived on a farm and Mum came in with me and said that I wouldn't be driving into town at that age but it would be handy. Because our place was funny: the house was here, but the entrance to the farm was away round on the other road. It was because Dad's uncle bought it and then later Dad bought another bit and it joined onto the farm but there weren't any gates.

It sounds a bit Irish.

It does, doesn't it.

Look at that magnolia.

Isn't it beautiful. I wouldn't have known it was a magnolia. I used to know all the names of the flowers. When you've got a garden you know the names, but I don't know them now.

We planted a magnolia outside our house. It flowered when we brought Alice home.

She's lovely. I just love her. I could keep her.

Some nights that seems like a good idea.

I don't want her at night. She's very alert for her age. I think she's going to be quite clever. Well, Alan's pretty bright, and from what I saw of her mother when I met her, she is too.

Mm.

Has she gone overseas?

No, they were planning to go back to England, but they've decided to stay on for now.

Does she keep in touch with you?

Oh yes.

It's silly keeping all these things secret. We didn't when we adopted Helen. Some people did, but it was so stupid, because somebody always tells somebody else. When Helen was seven—I can't remember the girl's name now, but she was sitting beside her at lunch one day, and she said to Helen I know something about you: that's not your mother who brings you to school. I don't think Helen quite understood. The girl went home and told her mother, and her mother rang me up and apologised.

I just have to think where I'm going here. I'm going . . . back that way.

We had a concert last night—Malvina Major sang. I thought I might go. Do you know what they were charging?

What were they charging?

Twenty-two dollars.

Oh . . .

Ridiculous. A lot didn't go, because by the time they pay $600 a week, it's expensive. Mallory's thought she was going to donate the thing—not charge us. It's all elderly people, and people in wheelchairs.

So you went, or you didn't go?

No, I didn't go—I didn't feel like paying twenty-two dollars. I think she lost a lot of people by charging that much. I could hear her from my room, in any case, and she was only going to sing about three songs. If it was say even ten dollars I might have gone, but twenty-two dollars . . . I've heard her sing lots of times, and I've got a CD of her singing, so I thought I'm not going to pay twenty-two dollars. Is Alan over his cold?

Yes, he is.

And bubby?

Yes.

And you?

I don't know. I think I am. We've had so many, back to back.

Do you think children bring it home?

Yes. They're filthy.

I remember when you and Catherine were—no, you're Catherine, aren't you.

Last time I checked.

Ah . . . you and Helen. Particularly when you were younger. You always caught the colds that were going around school. Did Helen say Harry won something? Have I got that right?

Eddie won the school classics prize. A silver tray.

Oh yes. I knew she said something, but I couldn't remember. It was a bit of a funny present to give a child.

What was?

A silver tray. For a child.

I think it's a commemorative platter that's engraved with his name, and then he gives it back at the end of the year.

Yes. Yes, I would imagine that's it. They're growing up, the boys, aren't they. Well, so's yours. Every time I see her she's grown about a foot.

She said shit yesterday.

Oh. It might have been shush.

No. It wasn't shoe, either.

You came home from school once—you were about seven—and I wish I could remember the word. We were sitting at the dinner table and it was something like bugger. We were just sitting there having our tea, and you looked at Helen, and it wasn't bugger but it was that sort of word—and you looked and Helen and said it. And Les looked at me and I tried not to laugh and he tried not to laugh, and he said oh, we don't like those sorts of words, we don't use them very much.

I don't remember that.

No, you were probably too young to remember. Is Alice saying much?

Apart from shit . . . she's saying caaaa for cat, and boooooooh for book and bohhhhhh for bottle. She's having trouble with the ends of words. She says bubba, and mama, and dada, and nana. She says shoe a lot. She'll bring me my shoes and say shoe, shoe, shoe.

I seem to have a runny nose. I don't think it's a cold—they put antiseptic round our rooms. They always do that and it makes my nose run.

Do they hose you down?

Yes, you've got to take your clothes off and they hose you down. They keep the place very clean. I've never heard of people getting poisoned.

Hi, how're you doing.

Hi.

Hello Patricia, hi.

Hello.

How are you, good to see you.

Hi again.

Hi, good to see you. Yeah, so here we are again. So the results did show that I don't need to worry about taking all that red area. It is sun-damaged skin, but it's not invasive cancer. So we'll do the original surgery. So that's good news. It's relieving. I know what I'm doing, because I've been here before.

Yes, I know exactly what you're going to do. Don't make a mistake.

No, I won't. This is Annabel and Pip, who'll be helping me. Bring your head the other way. Looking to the right. Not quite so far. Back a little. You'll see a bright light.

Do you have a pacemaker?

No, I have nothing.

Nice and still now.

There'll be an injection in your lip. A wee scratch now. You'll feel a stinging in your lip.

That was cold, I'm sorry.

This'll make you a bit numb for a few hours. You'll feel it coming into your cheek. Is that starting to feel less painful?

It's all right. It is painful.

But it's numbing off, is it? There's a bright light coming and I'm going to ask you: does this feel sharp?

No.

Does this feel sharp?

No.

Does this feel sharp?

Oh!

You will feel pushing and pulling. You shouldn't feel any pain. She's doing very well, Catherine. Lift your head now. You're up quite high, so we're going to drop you down slowly.

I won't be able to talk tonight. I don't think I'll go out of my room. I don't think I'll go down to the dining room. I'll frighten them all and they won't have any dinner. They can bring me in a sandwich. It hasn't spoiled my beauty, has it?

No.

Thank you for sending me home when I can't smile.

So next Friday for the stitches. With Cheryl.

I'm not taking you to university, am I.

No. You're taking me home.

Why have I come this way, then?

We're sightseeing. Look at that lovely house.

We'll press on. Wait, this is the way. I can go this way.

Oh yes, you can go this way, but the other way's a little bit shorter. Not much. If you hadn't mentioned it, I wouldn't have even noticed.

Mm.

I like Hamilton. I don't know that I would have chosen to live here, but I quite like it. I'm quite happy here. I've got plenty of friends, and I know where to get the bus and everything. And I'm very happy.

You wouldn't want to be along that side, right by the main road. They must be a bit peeved, those residents. It wasn't a big main road before, was it.

No. No. I see a lady from there—once a month or six weeks we have a cup of tea—I just can't think of her name—and she says she's got used to it. She doesn't hear it now.

Maybe she's deaf.

I hadn't thought of that. I better go and sign in. Out. In.

Down this way. Down the hall.

I couldn't think where I was. Aren't the poppies beautiful. It's always nice and swept and clean, isn't it. Though looking in the rooms as you go past is a bit depressing.

I don't look.

I try not looking but I can't help it. I don't know where the lady opposite me's gone. Her things are still there, but she's just disappeared.

That's nice blossom on your windowsill.

What's her name . . . she lives in Hamilton. She was Les's

nurse. I can't remember. I don't know why I can't remember her name. Her husband ran away with his office girl.

She brought the blossom, did she?

Yes. She knew I lived somewhere in Hamilton and she was driving home and she saw Rest Home, so she came in and went to the office and said you don't have somebody called Pat Chidgey do you? I can't think of her name at the moment.

All right then, I should head off.

I'm going to walk with you, to get out of the room.

## 10

You missed the penis-shaped cloud.

Did you take pictures?

No. It was moving too fast. 'Twas but a fleeting twilight vision.

## 11

I'll ring you back. I'm just getting dressed, and the man's waiting with holy communion.

## 12

I think we should vote for this candidate. She's promising reduced rates, but also no swerage spills. You don't want spilled swerage. Oh, she's standing for mayor. And she can't spell. I vote neigh.

A girl walking past a hedge, ripping off fist-high leaves.

## 13

I'm not sure what to do with it.

Most people know what to do with their poo.

I'm not sure what the etiquette is. Do I just hand it to the receptionist? I think there might be a dedicated poo box.

Is it in a shopping bag, so you can't see it?

No, it's in a plastic bag. You can see it.

Put the plastic bag in a shopping bag.

I don't have a shopping bag. Oh, it's been lying on its side . . .

You had to do it, didn't you. You had to get it out. Jesus Christ. There's something seriously wrong with you. Put it away, please.

You can't see it any more. I've wrapped the paper round it.

Just put it back in your bag.

No. You can't see it.

But I did see it, didn't I.

I didn't deliberately get it out to show you.

But you did. You did show me.

So, you don't shit?

I do shit, but I don't usually have to peruse your stool.

I didn't ask you to peruse it.

Hm.


Okay, that was bad. I asked the receptionist where to put it, and she pointed to a black box. So I went to the black box and there was a sign saying please ensure you display—

Your poo.

—date and time of collection. And I had only written the date on there. So I had to ask the receptionist for a pen, and then fish the sample out and write on it. And then I gave her back her pen. And then she said oh, the Pathlab guy's just in there, if you want to hand it to him. He's just in the Pathlab room. So I thought maybe I should. So I knocked on the door and he was in there, and I said I've got a stool sample, where should I put it? And he just looked at me and said in the black box.

### 14

I'm growing very suspicious of the presence of pets. In my talking book this morning there was a dog. Why do they have a dog, unless they're going to kill it off? And sure enough, the dog dies horribly.

## 15

I buried one of Liam's toys once—you had to give it love and feed it, and it just would not shut up.

Needy.

So needy. And it had this grizzly sound if you hadn't looked after it and it was sulking. You'd think it would recognise that human beings go to sleep. Children don't need to be woken up by the robot telling them to feed it and love it. It ended up wrapped in towels and stuffed in the hot-water cupboard.

What sort of example are we setting children, if we give them toys that need constant attention? With Alice I'm already trying not to respond to her every squeak.

I haven't been to the urologist yet, and that's a cause of anxiety.

Well obviously you have to get yourself prioritised.

I'm sorry I interrupted you. What did you say? When I'm conversing with you, I don't *seem* to be involved in the conversation—I *am*. All right?

A big relief.

It'd be a shame to do any harm.

Think about how this person lives and breathes, is connected, real or excellent—you only have fifty words, so choose them wisely.

## 16

Your door's open.

I should know that by now. I hate this corner. Cars coming from everywhere. Did I tell you my friend Gwen died?

No. When did that happen?

Yesterday. Yesterday. Yesterday.

She hadn't been herself for a while, had she.

No, she hasn't.

When's the funeral?

I think it's on Friday.

Today's Friday.

Oh.

I'll find out. Do you know her surname?

Gwen . . . yes I do, but I can't say it now. But I did have a lovely night with her, the night she died. I sat with her until the ambulance came. She was so pleased. I sat on the bed with her. I'm very glad I did that. That's better than going to the funeral, really. She's a very quiet person and she doesn't have a lot of friends. She's always had bad health. She had a pretty rough husband, too. I think she never had much money and I think he was pretty awful—just one or two things she said.

Did she die in hospital?

Yes. But I got in the ambulance with her and gave her a big cuddle. So that was nice.

When was that?

I don't know whether it was last night she died, or the night before. She was quite shy. I don't think she ever had good health. And she never had much money. Oh, look at the blossom coming out—that's always the first blossom to come out, that tree. I haven't been over the bridge for ages. I haven't been to church for ages either—well, we have church at home. That's quite an ugly church, isn't it. I don't know who designed it. I think it's horrible. And they're the silliest stairs to walk up, for older people. They're stupid. Hamilton has ugly houses. I think they're awful. I remember years ago when Hamilton was new, and it was called the ugliest city in New Zealand. It's always been ugly. Do you think you'll stay there, or would you like to move?

We're not going anywhere in a hurry.

No, I like it. I'm quite happy here. I think everybody is. It's a very easy, pleasant place. That's where I used to get my petrol.

Do you need to get anything while we're out? New stockings or anything?

No, I'm quite easy on my stockings. I don't know how people go through them so quickly. I think they probably don't cut their toenails.

Hello!

Hello. Pat Chidgey.

You're seeing the nurse today!

Yes.

That's fine! Have a seat!

I'm cross about this hole in my jersey. But I can't prove they did it. But they must have done, because I certainly didn't. I must have a look at my jerseys and see if I need another one.

We're coming up to spring . . .

I haven't put my watch on. Yes, I should probably just stick with what I've got, because it won't be that long before I can get into blouses. I'm a bit cross. They must have known they'd made a hole, but I've got no way of proving it. Do you want it?

Well, I can get rid of it for you.

No, they give them to poor people. Myrna who moans about everything can't believe I'm not going to do anything about a hole in my jersey. How can I prove that they did it? Wouldn't I be popular! She complains about everything. The potatoes aren't cooked, or the chair's only got three legs. Gwen and I used to sit there and wait to see what was wrong each day. I get on all right with her because I've known her for years, but she's very demanding. She never makes her bed or tidies her room. I mean we don't have to, but honest to goodness . . . the staff aren't stupid. I've never known anybody to find something wrong with everything. The tea's too hot, too cold, too black, too green. And the bread's stale and the meat's tough . . . The cooks there are cooking for a hundred people. They can't make cute little pies. She was a bossy, unpleasant person when I knew her thirty years ago and she hasn't changed. I have to be friendly because we live in the one place—but three husbands tells you enough, doesn't it. Are we early or are they late?

We're a bit early, but they're running late now.

Did I ever tell you about finding somebody from the rest home when I was living in the townhouse? I went for a walk one night. I'd only been living there a few weeks and I was walking away round the back, and there was this lady wandering along. You could see she didn't know where she was. And I said are you looking for somebody's house? And she said I don't know where I live. And I said you don't live round in Sunset Court, do you? And she said oh yes, that's where I live. So I took her back and took her to the office. And they still tease me sometimes, if they see me coming back from a walk. Where's the lady you found? They've never forgotten it. It was lucky really, because she could have got lost. She's died since. I'll miss Gwen.

Will they put someone else at your table?

I would think so. She was a lovely lady. I think she'd had a bad life. Bad health when she was young, and married a horrible man. I miss Dorothy too. We used to go out together, to the movies and so on. It's just nice to get out. Not that I feel . . . I'm very happy there, so you don't need to worry. Does little Alice like going to daycare?

She loves it.

It's a good start for school then. She's very friendly. Very open.

Yes, she's very sociable.

You'll have to watch her at sixteen.

Mm.

Who do you think she looks like?

Leila.

I thought that . . . but it doesn't really matter.

No.

She's very like her.

Mm.

Ultimate anti-wrinkle formulation from Nivea.

I think it might be a bit late.

Perhaps I could put two on at a time. Is Leila still here, or did she go back to England?

No, they're still here. They've decided to stay a bit longer. She's going to be surrogate for another couple, in Christchurch.

What an amazing lady. Will Alice know Leila?

Oh yes. Yes, we visit them quite regularly.

But I mean, she'll know who she *is*?

Oh yes. Yes.

That's sensible. There's never any surprises then. I think I told you about my cousin Mavis—Mum's sister's daughter. For her twenty-first birthday, they gave her her birth certificate. And they weren't her parents. You know—like Helen.

Oh my God.

Do you know what happened? We went home from the party, everyone went to bed, she packed her bag, and when they got up in the morning she'd gone. And nobody ever saw her again, for years. Lena went up to Wellington with the Catholic Women's League, and she went into a shop, and the girl serving at the counter looked at Lena and Lena looked at her. And it was Mavis. And she and Lena always kept in touch after that, but she never caught up with her family again.

Mrs Chidley? I know I said that wrong.

Chidgey. Nobody says it right.

How are you? You look good. Come on in.

Hi. I'm Catherine.

Yes. I'm Cheryl. I think I spoke to you on the phone, actually.

Ah. Yes.

About this.

Yes. Well . . . yes.

So we're just taking the stitches out today, Patricia. There are some deeper ones under there still, and when they dissolve the skin will relax back again, it will drape, it will look more natural.

I'll shut my eyes now.

*

Do you need someone?

No, no—I was just trying to find out—Mum said her friend Gwen who sits at her table died, and we wanted to—are you on hold?

Yes. Hi Phil, this is Kimberley calling from Sunset Court, how are you? I just wanted to check if you received the email for the agreement for June. Oh, did you email that back? We don't seem to have received it this side. Are you able to send that back to us again? By any chance? I haven't received anything this end, so I don't know what's happened there. The initial agreement. Oh, okay, because I haven't received it this end. I was just wondering if you're able to send it again to me. Oh, okay. What's your email address again? Okay. I'll try and get that to you today. Okay. Thanks Philip. All right. Bye. I'm afraid we don't know anything about the funeral. I'm not too sure. Was there no notice or anything in the paper . . . ?

I don't know her last name.

Gwen Lang. L-A-N-G.

Okay, I'll look it up. But she died on Saturday, did she?

Yes.

So it's probably already been.

Could have done. I'm not too sure.

I don't have anything to show you or tell you. I've got nothing else to give you. My flowers are dying.

### 17

What's the name of your Christchurch couple? I've forgotten.

Marie and Chris.

So have you met them in person?

I went to Christchurch a week after I emailed her the first time. And I went to Fertility Associates and I've had my first counselling session.

So will you fly down there for the treatment?

No, they'll come up here. They've got three embryos. They have to get their CYFS approval and police checks and everything again, even though they've already got one child.

Guess what Catherine and Alan! Guess what Catherine and Alan! Poppy's gone to get a toy phone for Alice!

Not in the eyes. Not in the eyes.

Will they transfer two, or just one?

One.

I guess you don't want to end up with twins.

It could happen. Even with one, it could happen.

Really? Even at that stage?

Yeah—someone on the site just had twins for her brother, and it was a single embryo.

Do they know what the quality of the embryos is? Like, do they look . . . gimpy?

No, I think they're all good ones. They got six from the first round, and the first two didn't defrost, and the third one was Greta.

One in three chance, then.

When I'm twenty-three will Freya be twenty?

Who am I? I am the blue dog. I am the rabbit as well.

You have to be that one.

A monster!

He's the daddy.

He's a worry bag. It's a German thing.

The monster?

Yeah. You write down your worries and give them to the monster and it eats them.

Oh yes—the Sorgenfresser.

Is that what it means?

The worry eater. Ja. Guten Tag. Ich bin der Sorgenfresser. Ha ha ha. It is very humorous. I can't be all of these people.

You can be the little sister. You can be a baby.

I think the dog is going to chase the rabbit.

No. Dogs chase cats.

Are there any cats to chase?

No. I don't have a cat.

Then it might have to chase the kiwi. Which would be very bad. But look, the kiwi can fly!

But he can't.

He's been taking lessons from the seagull.

We heard some kiwis but we didn't see any because they only come out at night time.

What did they sound like?

Kee kee kee. But they should say kiwi kiwi kiwi so we know what they are.

Like the moreporks say more pork, more pork.

Or ru ru, ru ru. Depends on what you're trying to hear.

You're not reading the last page, are you?

I hate hearing my voice.

You can be a big sister. I need some babies.

I might put the baby hedgehog in the mouth of the Sorgenfresser. Sharing! We are sharing!

Is that a little sister? Is that a little sister?

Shall we have one brother?

You can be that one. I want to be *that* one. It's my toy! I want it!

We know who we are, okay?


There's a Gwendolyn Lang who's a naturopath. There's a Gwendolyn Lang who died in 2012. There's a Gwendolyn Lang who's an associate professor at AUT.

I imagine it will have happened already. It's very likely been and gone. It's too late.


## 18

She'll be the victim and we'll be the bitches. She's got her little pets, and they do her bidding. Mark's the one who's managing the redundancies, but I think he's just doing what she wants. I heard that the only person who could have done a good job pulled out as soon as he met her. To be honest, if they said we'll do voluntary redundancies, there'd be a queue of us. I would take it, and then I'd contract myself back to different projects. She wants everyone to work like she works. I remember this motivational speech she gave about work-life balance, and her work-life balance was that she would go and watch her son play soccer and work on the sidelines. Take her laptop and a chair. That speech is infamous. It's not a healthy environment. Last year they put a whole heap of staff on performance management. You're monitored all the time. You have to report to somebody. One of my colleagues pulled out of a project— he said look, I'm under so much pressure, and I realise I'm dropping the ball. But she said okay, if you can get two papers into this journal by the end of the month, I think we can get you off performance management. Two papers! I can't fathom it. I think they'll merge us. People are frightened for their jobs. She walked around when the department had just laid a whole lot of people off. Some of the ones who had lost their jobs were still there, waiting to work out their contracts. There were some doors shut and she was very upset. The message that came back from her was that the department has to have its doors open. She probably thought she was being motivational. We all got a door wedge.

## 19

## I'M DELICATE, TREAT ME WITH CARE

## 20

What do you feel for? What do you sense?

Movement. The heartbeat, and the rhythm of breathing. Fresh blood. Is it over?

The book is at the printer, yes.

And your body?

The usual.

Is it ever going to change?

Probably not, no.

No.

I keep thinking, if I just finish this . . .

I remember you saying that about the book. As soon as it's off, everything's going to be fine.

No, that was an illusion.

Isn't it all.

## 21

Pizza toast for breakfast! Oh la la! #pizzatoast #breakfast #mycrazybreakfast #foodpics #pizza #toast #morning

## 22

I need time at the end to go back over it and make it sound like it hasn't been fed through Google Translate. There are jokes and names that don't work in English.

What's your pen name going to be?

Something Teutonic.

The name of a past self.

I've got the clock in the bottom drawer. Remind me to stick it back on the wall.

I'm getting words down. But I'm very uncertain of what it is I'm doing. I keep telling myself—why don't you just start at the beginning and go to the end, like everybody else?

I don't do that.

It doesn't seem to be working that way. Is it a smart move for somebody who's not even sure they can write anything beyond a short story?

If that's where it's taking you, that's where you need to go.

I have a feeling of this is not working, I don't know what this is, combined with an inability to stop doing it. Everything

I write now, I'm thinking you're making this worse. This is one more random scene and you don't know where it lives. I don't have time, so I just have to force myself to move ahead, anywhere. Anywhere I can. Go there. Whether that's smart or not. I don't have an aerial view of the thing.

You probably won't for a while.

I think I hit twenty-nine thousand words this morning.

Holy shit. That's a third of a novel! That's a third of a decent-sized novel!

I don't want it to be a big novel, I want it to be a short novel.

That's half a novel!

It's a mess at the moment. It's a lot of words. And I don't know if any of those words will be in the final cut. I'm very aware of how much you dropped from yours. Then I read this terrifying article the other day about David Foster Wallace writing The Pale King. And every alleyway that his genius brain took him down, and structure never cohering. I thought shit, I can't afford to do that.

Instinctively, this seems to be the way you write a novel. It's the way I write a novel.

I can't write a line—I always write a net. I know what the centre of the net is, but all the lines fan out from that and I get glints from over here or over there. You know? And they're all connected, but the connections twitch and pull on each other at different points. And I'm waiting for someone to say that I'm a total man-hater. Nobody has yet.

I've pinged a student for plagiarism. Of course I can't say that.

Delete delete delete.

The thing is, I think she can write. Although can she? Is it all plagiarised? One piece she wrote was really good, but she set it in L____, when the whole focus of the exercise was writing the voice of *home*. And I remember asking her why she was setting it in L____, and for whatever reason your senses start tingling, and google google, and up a big chunk of it pops, written by a guy who lives in L_____. I remember sitting in that workshop, talking about how moving it was, how hard-hitting it was. Now I know why it's set in fucking L_____—it's plagiarised from a guy living in L_____! I'm so angry. She's taking the piss. She's totally taking the piss. I feel like saying you have offended me. I feel personally insulted. I put such a lot into teaching that paper, coming up with exercises that are tailor-made for you. Instead of trying to find your voice, you just turn round and steal a voice from somewhere else. Of course I can't say that. I can't say any of that.

I better disappear.

## 23

Catherine, your phone's location is being tracked and recorded. Your email is being monitored. Every search you do online is saved. You may think you have nothing to hide, but this information forms a picture of your private life, which everyone has the right to keep private.

## 24

Watch your language. No naughty words. How are my nieces?

One's still accounting and one's still lawyering.

No husbands?

Erin's getting married in December.

Yes, I thought she was.

Alice has grown so much since her first birthday.

They seem to do it very quickly. They're little babies, and then they're not.

You know that cuckoo clock I bought for Alice? I bought one for Tilly as well, but I lost a piece of it. The piece that hangs down. And a few weeks later I remembered that I'd put some bigger clothes away in her wardrobe. And it was sitting in between the pile of clothes. I can't bear losing things. I have to put jigsaw puzzles together before I put them away.

I think this is your one, Mum. See if it tastes right.

No, it hasn't got sugar in it.

This is your one, then. And that's Brian's. He won't mind.

No, he won't mind. I'm his uncle. Oh, no I'm not.

No you're not.

No, I'm his aunt.

Brian, that's your coffee there.

You're a good girl. Thank you.

Careful. Careful. You're going to bang your head. You're not really watching what you're doing, are you?

I haven't quite got the gist of feeding Tilly solids, so I thought I'd ask you. I've been giving her a little bit at nights— she's sometimes interested, sometimes not. But how do I know how much to give her? Do you just feed them until they stop eating? And when do I go to two meals?

It's so hazy now.

What's she been having?

Veges. I started her on veges because I didn't want her to get a sweet tooth.

When did we go to two meals with Alice?

We started solids a week shy of six months, and then . . . I honestly can't remember. It's a blur.

I know I came down when she was only seven months and you gave her a plate with real food on it and I said what on earth!

Have you been reading the book, Donna? The book we gave you?

I did read it.

I'm sure there's something in there.

Maybe I need to give her more.

Give her more, yeah.

And then do I do breakfast or lunch?

I think we went to lunch next, didn't we?

Possibly. I'm surprised how little I can remember. I have such a bad memory. What did I do last Tuesday? I have no idea.

Someone was telling me no pumpkin at night.

I'd like to put a house like that on a section. Whole lot smaller, put a fence right round it and give the rest of the land to the farmer, and all I have to do is come home and mow a wee bit like you've got here. I'm counting on driving trucks till I'm seventy—I want to work till I'm seventy. I don't know why. I'll fall over before then. But I went to buy some cattle the other day and they were $1000. This time last year they were only seven hundred. It's not the butcher shop that's ripping you off, it's the bloody farmers. Me and my mate went out to see this woman who runs a fifty-thousand-acre farm up the north end of Colorado—might even be in Wyoming. There's beef cattle bloody everywhere over there. She said she's making a fortune out of it. And up there they only lease their land for nine months of the year. They lease it off Wyoming County or Colorado County. When the snow comes they've got to take all the cattle away, and they go to the slaughter, or the mothers are sent away and the babies go to the slaughter.

We lived on a farm and we only saw Dad at mealtimes, it was so big.

And what's the car you bought over there?

A Corvette Stingray.

Is that the white one I saw on Facebook?

Yeah. Ugliest-looking thing you've ever seen. A real hooner's car. High-powered. It's only a two-seater—that's what I'm worried about. Because I bought a Triumph Stag once and it was like driving a coffin. This one's not much bigger.

What'd you get searched for?

When I went through those camera things this guy goes get over here. He wanted me to go into this room with him and leave my bag. I said well I'm not going in there, he can do me right here. Because I had $8000 in American cash in my bag, and a whole lot of cigars as well, so I decided to make a bloody scene. So this guy bloody searched me, I can tell you, right there and then. I said hang on, why did you want to do that? He shows me this screen—he says I'll just wind it back and I'll show you. And I've got these little yellow squares on me. And the little yellow squares are here, there, there, there, there, there, there, there, there, and on my shoes.

What do the yellow squares mean?

You have something on your body. You're hiding something. And that's why you've got to be strip-searched.

When you say strip-searched . . .

Well I took my shirt off, and he bloody had his hand where you don't really want it.

But you didn't have anything on you.

No.

So they didn't find a gun.

That was with the heroin and the laundered cash, Mum.

I thought oh my God, if they start looking at that bag . . .

What was in the bag?

Eight thousand American dollars, and some cigars. I was hoping to bring them in without having to pay duty on them. But luckily, every time I go from the States back to New Zealand, I always write farmer. You've got to tick all these boxes. And when you get to have you been onto a farm I put a great big tick, so they see it. And they go oh no no, you've got to go down to the agricultural line, and the guy down there goes what have you been doing? Absolutely bloody nothing, I said. I'm a farmer and I don't go near farms on holiday. I just happened to look at this combine harvester, and these are the only shoes I've got. Look, there's nothing on them. And he goes okay, carry on. So you don't have to put your bag through that screening thing. I've done that for years. With children, it'd be ideal—kids are a bloody nuisance when you're going through that thing. Just tick the farming box. You've been onto a farm. And when you get there the guy'll say what've you been doing—oh, nothing, we just stopped and looked at a combine harvester, but since it says have you been on a farm I thought I better tick it.

Aren't the clothes babies have wonderful. Legs and things that keep them warm. Is your hair—I'm not being rude, it's so beautiful—is it dyed a little bit? I've been looking at it. It's been beautifully done. It looks quite natural. Is that a made-up thing or is it milk?

It's formula.

That's the word I was looking for. What's in it?

I don't know. I did my research.

Alice has this word that she uses all the time, and no one knows what it means. Sheya. Sheya. It could be chair.

It's not chair. It's multi-purpose. I think it means look at me, or look over here, or look at that.

It's probably French or German.

Have you told Donna?

Mum had a heart attack yesterday. She went into A&E and then last night they transferred her to a ward in Southland Hospital.

Who lives close to her? No one.

I'll have to get on the phone to Air New Zealand and see what's possible.

Does she know anything about the severity of the attack?

She said the doctors aren't saying anything.

Well that's shi—I mean, that's not good. How do we find out what actually happened? Who can tell us?

She has bruises all down her back. She must have fallen, but she has no recollection of it. She doesn't remember crawling to the bathroom to ring the alarm.

Thank God it didn't happen when she was still in her house.

Her mind must have blotted it out. I can't help but think

that this is just how Didda died. He slipped going out to the mailbox on icy concrete and he went downhill from there.

## 25

So it's *eight* twenty. Is it?
Seven twenty—oh, right.
So it's eight twenty.
I don't know. I'm not sure.
I put my clock back last night, and then in the middle of the night I realised I should have gone forward.

What's the time?
Twelve thirty. But really eleven thirty.
I'm confused.

What's the time?
Six twenty-seven. But really five twenty-seven.
She's not at all tired.

Okay, it's coming up to what she thinks is six thirty.
Which is really seven thirty.
Which is really six thirty.

## 26

I found Mum's friend online. Peacefully treasured loving adored. They posted the death notice after the funeral.

This Guest Book will remain online until 18/10/2016. Sign Guest Book. Remember this Guest Book. Keep this Guest Book Online. Keeping this Guest Book available is a wonderful way to allow those who knew your loved one to express their sympathy and share fond memories. Even if you are not a member of the family, consider keeping this Guest Book open as a special gift to the family. By doing this, you'll be giving

loved ones a place to express their feelings and share memories any time they'd like in the months and years ahead. Please note this is a US$ transaction. One-Year Sponsorship: $42.50. Allow memories to be gathered in the Guest Book for the next year. Permanent Sponsorship: $110.00. Create a lasting legacy by keeping the Guest Book online forever. This Guest Book will remain online permanently courtesy of: _____
Examples: His Loving Family, The Nelsons, Mary Smith, A Friend.

Light a Candle. Share. Home.

## 27

You are so beautiful.

This would be the song from the 1980s car ad, I take it. You're not actually telling me I'm beautiful.

. . . er, but of course. Just saying you are my sun. And yes, it's the ad earworm.

In other news, the Vengabus is coming.

## 28

She seems in reasonable spirits. It's really hard to know . . . she mishmashes the medical information so much that she could be on aspirin or she could be on opium. The Invercargill doctors want her to go to Dunedin for her heart to be checked. The echo test shows deterioration and they want to understand why. She has no family or friends in Dunedin. The hospital has to care for her. They can't discharge her. I have asked Mum to reiterate that she knows no one in Dunedin.

The neighbours' downlighting looks good on their deck. Why don't we have downlighting on our deck?

Why don't we have lighting on our deck?

Why don't we have lighting on our deck?

What about a strobe? Or a mirrorball?

It'd be nice, though, when we sit out there on summer evenings, entertaining our many friends. Having vegetarian gluten-free dairy-free barbecues. We'd have attractively lit plates of cabbage.

### 29

I dreamt that the murderer came back to the boat and discovered that the drug money was gone, and we were still there because you were fluffing around trying to pack. In your OCD manner. I was like, it doesn't matter it doesn't matter just throw it in the suitcase—

What on earth are you talking about?

A dream I just had.

Right. Some people would introduce that into the conversation.

I did. I said I dreamt . . .

No. You said we came back to the boat.

The murderer came back to the boat. Shall we check it? Shall we check the recording? See, this is the whole problem. This is the crux of the matter. Alan not listening to Catherine.

What was that?

Hmmm. And he was seeming very nice. He was seeming quite reasonable about the money being gone, but I knew it was just like Tony Soprano and Big Pussy, and we'd be sleeping with the fishes.

Not the face.

### 30

It ends with a dream sequence. Never advisable.

# [ OCTOBER ]

## 1

Did Charlie have a good sixteenth?

He did. He had a very good cake.

It looked delicious.

It was chocolate almond, dense and moist. And then it had peanut-butter butter cream in the middle and all over it, and then it had chocolate ganache all over the top.

Sounds good, doesn't it, bubba?

Hello Alice! Hi bub!

Say hi. Say hi.

Where's Aunty Helen? Where is she?

Where's Aunty Helen?

Hello! Look who we've got here—birthday boy and cat.

Hi birthday boy!

Caaaaaa.

Yes, it's a cat. That's Jubjub, isn't it.

Caaaaaa.

You've disappeared. Hello? That's cousin Jubjub. Mintiemoo, come and say hello to Jub. So is Charlie old enough to do anything of significance now? Legally?

Are you old enough to do anything legally, Charlie? Oh! Aunty Cath, that's inappropriate!

I didn't mean *that*! Oh God! Now everyone's uncomfortable.

Look what you've done to your nephew.

It was you who made it awkward. I meant like vote, or drink, or drive.

She meant like vote, or drink, or dive.

I can get a moped.

He can get a moped, apparently. But he's not going to.

Mum's pleased that you got home safely. From your holiday.

Where have we been?

Iraq, maybe? Not sure. Some war zone. Some place where there's been a terrorist attack. She said she was talking to you and you'd decided to come home a day early.

Complete fabrication.

## 2

She hates me. She doesn't want to come to me, she doesn't want me to pick her up.

She doesn't hate you. It's not personal, it's just that she wants what she knows, and that's sitting in my lap. I'm the person she sees the most. It's the other way round for most couples, where the mother stays at home. In the morning she calls for you.

She just says mamama as a sound. It's hard feeling like second best—or not even second best; she doesn't even want me to touch her.

She's tired.

I'm not a real mother and I'm not *her* mother. And she knows it, somehow. She knows you're blood and I'm not.

You're the only mother she's ever had. She doesn't understand blood.

Instinctively maybe she does.

Look how she is with Leila. There's no instinctive response at all. She's a stranger.

Well then the other answer is that I'm not very good with children and she just doesn't like me.

She's always calling for you.

3

There was a post on one of the milk-sharing pages this morning—a grandmother in Huntly's looking for milk donations for her granddaughter who's a P baby. She was taken off the parents by CYFS, so the grandmother's raising her. She said she was breastfed since birth but it was toxic. It was poison.

Where's the meal? asks hungry Seal. It's coming now, says busy Cow.

If only I'd known about the P baby angle, I could have gone with that when we were looking for milk for Alice. We're raising a P baby; can we have some donations? They would have poured in.

They break your artery, she said. I hate thinking about heart things. That time we could see my heart on the screen—I almost passed out.

Whereas I thought it was fascinating. A baby bird, beating its wings.

And the nurse thought I was weird—why would I not want to look at it? Because I can't stand looking at it. Because if I look at it, it might stop.

That's not logical.

It feeds on itself. I can see it, and then I get agitated, and then it starts going faster.

I wonder where that came from.

It's the sort of thing Mum worries about. Like—have you got cancer yet? How are you, have you got cancer yet?

So was it a heart attack she had?

I don't know. She said she'll talk to the professor guy. She said he floats in and out in his expensive suit.

Who can tell us?

When I go down to Invercargill I might get a chance to talk to a doctor then and I might get a clearer idea. Whether it's a major end-of-life problem, or whether she's just going through a bad patch—it's so hard to work out. But it makes my heart sink, the idea of travelling with Alice. The idea of being a single parent in Invercargill.

Could be worse. Could be Huntly.

I could be a P addict.

There's still time.

## 4

There's no time. I'm making impulse decisions. I'm counting the days. She got back to me and said Kim Hill's a no. I said what's happening about the photo? Because I'll have to get my brow/lash combo done and it has to settle for a couple of weeks so I'm somewhere between Frida Kahlo and Tilda Swinton. I'm having a bad feeling.

I think everyone has a bad feeling.

I'm worried it's not going to make a splash at all—it's just going to make a very tiny fart.

I don't want to bite the hand that feeds.


Everything for a long time has been about stories. It's refreshing, reading this—it's not really a story. Do you think you can get away with a lack of it?

This feels much more like a contemplation, doesn't it. A meander through her thoughts.

There's sort of a beginning, middle and end to it. But it's finding a way to make it interesting.

We read one last year that had a beginning, middle and end. It was a non-fiction story all the way through. But we're comparing two different books on frogs. Have none of you heard that before? Comparing books on frogs? You know— exactly the same but pretty similar. I mean exactly the same but completely different.

Look at the texture of the sentences. Sometimes they're really short, and sometimes they build up and up and up, suggesting massive energy and momentum and pressure.

Siri, what is creative nonfiction?

I didn't quite get that.

There's a lot that's suggested but not said. He shows her the trenches, and how to act in a combat situation—but then he gets tired of telling stories. There's a story that he can't tell. He's singing to console her.

There's always two sides. Everything's a circle. Apples and oranges.

Frogs and frogs.

She's kinda looking back at who she is, and kinda like what everything means. She's kinda honouring her past and stuff. And because of the memory, she goes back to like a kinda safe place, but then that's like a catalyst for something else she remembers, which is that she gets sent to a health camp.

There's still one, down in Half Moon Bay.

I got sent to one when I was eleven. A health camp. It was for kids with behavioural issues. My mum had just gone to jail, my nana didn't know how to deal with me, and I got sent there and I was only angry at Nana so all the people were like you're so lovely, why are you here? And I was like I don't know. It was pretty crazy. For the first two weeks you can't have outside contact with anyone. There was like this pink room and it was concrete. Because like some of the kids used to throw major tantrums, eh. If you acted up, they'd lock you in the pink room until you calmed down. It was across from the girls' dorm. Fuck it was loud. Yeah, it was when my mum went inside, and my best friend told the whole school—some best friend—and Nana thought it was better that I simmered down somewhere else. We had classes every day, and there was like this jungle-gym adventure thing. Lots of team-building exercises. And we did a show about the Egyptians.

No results found for 'two different books on frogs'. No results found for 'comparing books on frogs'.

## 5

So are there any concerns with Alice?

She does sometimes strike me.

Yes, she did the other day, didn't she. Just out of nowhere, she slapped Alan's face.

That's frustration. They know what they want to say but they haven't got the words to say it. But she'll give cuddles and kisses as well? She's affectionate?

She grabs on to Alan's nipples and she twists. To haul herself up.

Sometimes it's just teaching them—that hurt, I didn't like that. And sometimes popping them down, because they don't like to be taken away from the social interaction.

Caaaaa.

Yes, there is a cat over there. Everything's a cat to her. Because we've got cats. Everything with four legs—or even wings—is a cat.

Your speech is phenomenal, isn't it? She's got a lot of words.

She knows the meanings of words. She understands no.

And if you're talking about having a bath, or brushing her hair, she understands?

Yes, she follows the conversation. Bring me my slippers. Shall we have a book. She understands. She hasn't quite mastered the ends of words.

Last time I saw you, you were getting your donor milk. She's transitioned now?

We got through to fourteen months exclusively on donor milk. It was a military operation. Exhausting. She had milk from over thirty different women.

She's a voracious eater.

A guzzler.

But she's so tall . . . she's having green leafy vegetables? Apricots are another one. Salmon with the little bones in it. Shall we sit you on the scales, chicken?

Do you want to sit up here, Alice? Can I take a photo?

Sit you in there? Have a seat?

Oh.

Oh dear.

Not really a Facebook moment, is it? Chicken, we need to stand you up against the wall.

Are you a big tall girl?

Oh dear. Oh dear.

Torture.

We're torturing you. All done! She looks like a fine specimen to me. Beautifully proportioned. And no unusual eye movements? She doesn't run into things that you'd expect her to see when she's looking straight ahead?

She topples sometimes, if she gets too—

No, she doesn't run into things.

No.

Have you done all your childproofing round the house now that she's on the move?

Well, the garage is a big no-no—Alan's got sharp things. And mercury, for his daguerreotypes.

No, the mercury's out in the darkroom.

But she can reach the door-handle.

Hmm. So will you look at getting some locks?

Yes.

Oh yes.

Yes.


It's a nice outlook.

I actually think it's a nicer outlook than your current room. You don't have the big tree, but you do have *a* tree, and a view into the distance.

It's a much better outlook.

It will be sunnier, so in summer we'll have to set you up with a fan.

I've got a fan. I've got Gwen's. Her daughter doesn't want it back. Everything will have to go, of course.

They've put in a new basin in the bathroom. And the shower's the same as your current one. Everything's the same—it's just the mirror image of your other room. Make sure you don't get up in the night and pee in the wardrobe.

If I do I'm not going to tell you.

The sun's over there now.

I'll lose it in the evening. But I'll get it earlier.

Quite a lot earlier.

You don't need the sun at eight o'clock in the evening. At the moment I get it till it sets.

I think it's a good idea. I think it'll be much more peaceful over here.

I've made myself think it's going to be good. I haven't been thinking I'll miss my room.

You'll still see all the same people.

And the room's the same, just about. Look at all the hangers! I don't need them. They'll take all those away. No, I'm quite happy about it.

I think it'll be good.

Yes.

And they'll take all this.

Yes, this'll all be gone. Yes. Yes.

And I presume they'll clean the carpet.

Yes. And you're right by the door to outside. Yes.

It's lovely out there. I sit out there a lot. I've never seen anybody else sit out there.

The other good thing is that you don't have anyone opposite you either, because that's just a store room. On that side you've got a bathroom, so there's no one directly through the wall from you, and on that side is your bathroom, and over there is the store room.

It'll be much quieter.

I think it's a good solution.
I think it is. No, I'm quite happy about it.

Jiffy's packed on another three hundred grams. He's 6.9 kilos now—over half an Alice. The vet gave me a So Your Cat's A Fat Bastard leaflet.

Have you ever wondered what a caveman's voice sounded like? Scientists have looked at his body, at where his vocal cords and vocal tract would have been. He was found with his arm over his throat—he was killed—so they had to reconstruct his throat, and how sound would have come out of it. He has a slight Italian accent because it was Italian scientists. Can we hear it again?

6

Do fish have accents? And if they do, does it matter? Have a listen to these two recordings of cod from different regions. Remember it's in the middle of the night. What you've heard is a fishy lovesong; fish are not known for their facial expressions. Exactly what sounds cod prefer is yet to be resolved.

I know when you're in agonising situations, time tends to telescope. You wouldn't do this to a patient, would you. And you wouldn't do this to someone you cared about. You'd only do it to someone you completely despised. This is the ultimate sin; I have no interest in ever forgiving. I've already changed the name. Surely the person you're writing about must be dead. The only defence is hiding a leaf in the forest. Mothers, fathers . . . are you going to run it by them and see what they think? What if they say no, you do not have my permission to publish this? Surely my mother's going to slip on the stairs one of these days . . . but are you going to push her? You can always disappear in a cloud of ink. My brother might fall down the stairs tomorrow. We're not bold enough about telling the truth. We mask it and muffle it. Hopefully none of you have a recording device.

A witness described how Smith and the woman used a disabled toilet at Christchurch Airport for five to ten minutes on a busy Sunday afternoon, saying there was no question of what the pair were up to. The husband pulled out his phone and started recording from outside the cubicle. I myself did not have a problem with this . . . my wife, however, is protesting that it is disgusting for a public figure to do this. He was in his full All Blacks uniform and there was not an ounce of remorse or regret on his face. Prime Minister John Key said that Smith clearly let himself and those that are close to him down. I think there's no question about that. And he'll have to reflect on that, and I'm sure the New Zealand Rugby Football Union will reflect on that. That's why I think Aaron will feel pretty disappointed in himself. I suspect he'll be sitting back reflecting on the fact that he's let himself down . . . and frankly he's embarrassed himself a bit.

Why can't I stay where I was?

Because of your noisy neighbour. You were really upset and not sleeping because of your noisy neighbour.

Nobody's explained that to me, Catherine. Thank you. He was horrible.

It looks great, Mum. I think it's a much nicer room.

Well I'm quite happy now, but they just said come down here, this is your new room.

We looked at it yesterday, remember?

Yes, I do remember, but I couldn't remember whether this was the room. They forget that at eighty-five you can't remember things. Nobody explained it to me and now it's fine. If they'd simply told me why . . . I couldn't put the whole thing together.

313

Yes, I'm quite happy with the room, but I didn't know why I was put here.

We had talked about it, but maybe you'd forgotten.

Yes, well I do forget things. I knew there'd be some reason. I've been waiting for you to come because I knew.

This will be much quieter for you, and you'll be able to sleep, because there's no neighbour immediately on either side. So there you've got your bathroom, and that's their bathroom. And across the hall is a store room. So you've got no one.

No no, the room's lovely, but nobody explained. I knew it was a good reason but they forget at eighty-five, you don't remember things.

We've been waiting for one to come up that doesn't have someone right through the wall.

Oh I see. No, it's lovely. But I just couldn't understand and I thought what's wrong with the room I'm in? And I know what's wrong with it really, but . . .

That guy's been keeping you awake for months.

Oh yes.

Before him it was the woman who was wailing, and before her the one who kept knocking on the wall. You've had eighteen months of not being able to sleep.

Yes I have . . . but you forget. Or you think was it me being silly. You know what I mean. If they'd just said this will be better, I could have coped. Thank you, darling. I feel better already.

I might put these away till we can bring some picture hooks in—we don't want them to slip and knock things over before we've put them up on the wall. No, your stuff looks good in here.

It really does, but I didn't quite . . . they gave me the feeling that I'd been naughty.

No. You haven't done anything.

No, I know, but you've explained it. They didn't explain it to me. I said to the nurse, why have I been shifted? And she didn't tell me anything.

She probably didn't know.

She was the head nurse.

Mm. We'll have to get your shelves sorted.

She made me feel quite uncomfortable.

That normally goes there, doesn't it. We'll have to get you properly sorted.

Another day. Everything okay at your place? How's wee darling? Bring her in soon—I'm dying to see her.

We'll come on the weekend and get you sorted. The bathroom's a bit nicer too. The basin's brand new, the cabinet's band new. And the carpet's been steam-cleaned.

No, no, it's lovely, but . . . I didn't understand, and I thought it was something I did.

No—it's fine, Mum. No, it looks really good, and I think once you've settled in, it'll be much better for you. It's a really nice outlook.

I love looking out here, but I got the wrong impression that I was moved because I was naughty.

No. It was because of your neighbour.

Well I was hoping that's what it was, but nobody told me anything. Thank you, darling, I'm all right now. Just a word of explanation. That makes me feel so much better, thank you. They forget at eighty-five you don't . . .

We'll have to get your ornaments sorted. They need a good dust. I'll have to come and do that. Put everything out properly. No, it looks good.

Oh yes, I'm quite happy with it, but I just wasn't settled.

No, it's good. The new quilt looks nice.

Yes, I love that. Thank you so much. They forget at eighty-five you don't know what's going on.

That pile looks like it needs a sort through—but not today.

I don't know where it was before, but it wasn't in there. I

don't know whether I had a cupboard or something—I can't remember.

It might have been in your drawers, I think.

It might have been. I'll look at it in the next day or two. I don't know where it was. And where was that?

It was on the wall. We'll have to get Alan to screw it to the wall. You kept magazines in there.

Oh yes, now I remember. The screws are probably still in the old wall.

I'm not sure what he's done with them.

I'll wander down later and have a look. Thank you, Catherine. If somebody had just explained a little thing like that . . .

This is going to be much better for you. You'll sleep much better here.

Yes. Yes yes. Yes, he was awful. Actually a nurse here that I'm quite friendly with—I can't remember her name, but she's always rude to me and I'm always rude to her—she came and said to me today that I was really lucky to be shifted because she said he's going to get worse.

Yes, he will. And there's nothing they can do about it, but it's not very fair on whoever's next door to him.

The problem is, you see, they've got the upstairs, and that's supposed to be for people like him—but they haven't got any spare rooms. They didn't build it big enough. They never thought of how many people were going to live till they were ninety-five. They didn't look ahead.

Mm. No, this'll be a much better set-up for you.

Yes, no, I'm quite happy now, but if somebody had just. . .they forget that when you're eighty-five you don't know everything. Even though I'm only forty-two.

You've still got a nice tree.

Yes. I'm glad about that. And I can see trees all around there.

It's a really nice outlook when you're sitting on the couch.

It's actually a better outlook than my other room.

It is. It is.

Yes, I sat down here and I thought I've got a better outlook than I've ever had before.

Yes, you have. Yes. Yes.

Even just seeing cars going by. Thank you, darling.

We waited till a good one came up. Your bathroom there, your neighbour's bathroom there. And that door—that's a store room, so you've got no one over there being noisy either.

You see I didn't know any of that. That makes me feel so much better.

Hello!

Oh, hello. Do you know Catherine, my daughter?

Nice to meet you. I told you I'd find you, Pat. You haven't seen Myrna anywhere, have you?

No.

You haven't hidden her?

I did. I locked her in the toilet.

Oh, you can keep her then.

You're naughty.

I'm actually very nice—you're naughty.

It's the other way round. You're just saying that to Catherine.

I don't know what you're talking about.

Neither do I.

I had you shifted down here because you were too naughty.

Um—does Mum still go to the same dining room?

You can come to the same dining room if you want. I'm trying to hunt Myrna down—I haven't seen her all afternoon. There she is! I'll be back.

She's lovely. She's my favourite nurse. I don't think she actually is a nurse, I think she's a, you know . . .

Where is that music coming from?

I can hear music too.

I don't know where it's coming from.

317

There must be a ghost.

I guess it's up to you if you want to keep going to your old dining room.

Nobody's said anything. I like my old dining room. I sit with two men and one lady. She doesn't speak very much—she's foreign, but she's very nice. And one of the men doesn't speak much either. But the other man's really nice—he was a farmer, and he's just a nice ordinary man.

I think this'll be good. You'll sleep better here.

Well talking to you has made me look at it quite differently. You'll sleep so much better.

Yes.

You couldn't continue down there.

Oh no. No, it was quite awful. But they just sort of brought me down and dropped me off. It was all a bit strange.

You'll feel better once you've had a few nights of good sleep, away from him.

Oh yes. Yes. He was horrible. He's a horrible man.

And your things fit in well.

They do. They fit in really well. See, the bed just fits there.

Yes, no, it's good.

But I use the red footstool—but it doesn't matter. It doesn't really matter.

The only thing you could do would be to push the couch down. There'd *just* be room. Do you want me to try that?

Or should I wait for a while and see if I miss the footstool?

I'll have a go. It will be a bit of an upheaval, but honestly, after a night of unbroken sleep, you'll feel so much better.

Talking to you has made me feel better. It's just that nobody's . . . none of the staff . . . I feel better already. I've got a huge pile of stuff in there.

We'll have a go-through on the weekend. That's going to get a bit tight there, isn't it. How's that? It just fits.

I think that's all right. I mean I never have three people

sitting on the sofa.

You can still open your drawers. Let's try sitting here. No, that's not going to interfere.

Isn't it?

No. And you've got better access to the footstool.

And it's not sticking out in the middle of the room. Because I use it quite often. You know, if I'm sitting in my armchair. I don't always use it. I don't want it sitting out here all the time. You've made me feel so much better.

I think that'll be good. Do you think?

I think so. Yes.

Up to you.

I don't know whether I think it looks a bit funny—it's not in line with the window.

Now you're sounding like Dad. I would never have thought of that!

Remember I lived with him for thirty-something years.

I would never have thought of that. It would never have occurred to me.

Come in!

Hi Pat. Are we coming down for dinner tonight?

Yes.

Do you know where you're going?

No. I'm going to a new dining room, am I?

I think so, yes.

I went to lunch at the old dining room.

Oh, you did?

Well nobody told me anything so I just went and sat there.

They haven't told us much either. But if they've said you can go there, I don't see why not.

They didn't really say, I just went.

I'm sure it's fine for you to go down there. As long as you're getting dinner, that's the main thing.

I sit with a nice man.

You have all your friends down there, eh. That should be fine.

He used to be a farmer, and we talk about—

As long as we know that you've had dinner, so we don't bring you something here, or worry about you.

Thank you.

Well that's good, isn't it. That you can go to the old dining room.

Yes. Sorry I've been a bit silly. I'm all right now. I'm fine.

### 7

What's Hezbollah?

Hamas is the opposition force to Israel in Gaza and the West Bank—it's the Palestinians—and north of Israel is Lebanon, and the opposition to Israel there is Hezbollah.

What country is Hezbollah in?

I was saying it slowly so that you would get it. Because I knew that you weren't going to get it.

I was distracted. A dog just liked my tweet.

### 8

So we've got Mum and Dad over in the corner, the night before their wedding, and then there's my debutante ball, and then bubba in the blue dress. We want them clustered, not all scattered.

I don't mind where they go. Alan's got a good eye. Did I ever tell you Les and I did something naughty on our wedding morning?

What was that . . . ?

Oh no, nothing *too* naughty.

Good.

You're not supposed to see the bride and there was something I needed—it might have been some face cream—and I was biking down the road, and he was driving over to show his mother and father our new house. And we passed each other, and we waved, and Les's father nearly had a heart attack.

Nothing bad happened.

No, nothing happened. Poor Grandad thought we were going to be divorced in three months. And of course it was naughty enough because he was marrying a Catholic. In other words, we were naughty all the time. I remember Les very early on came and asked me for a dance. When the dance was over he stood and talked to me, and after that a guy came over to him and said do you know she's a bloody Roman Catholic? And Les didn't know him. Never seen him before. And I looked at him and I didn't know him. Of course the settlers in New Zealand were Anglicans and Presbyterians—there weren't many Catholics. And there was the Irish thing too. Grandad didn't like me for a long time—one of those bloody Roman Catholics. I don't know what Roman Catholics were supposed to do that was so terrible. But he did get used to it after a while. I seemed to improve. One night he even said to me you're my favourite in-law.

I hope Shirley wasn't there at the time.

He really meant it. I think he was apologising. I could understand it. In those days Catholics were meant to have two heads or something.

Bubba. Bubba. Those are Mummy's veins.

I've got to like this room now. It was a big decision to make. I'd been so long in the other one.

But you'd been eighteen months with neighbours who weren't letting you sleep.

I should have taken a step earlier.

Have you had enough? Have you had enough? Another bit?

I can't believe I can sit here in the evening and there's not a sound.

It feels quieter overall, this wing.

You've got a store room across from you, and a bathroom

there and a bathroom there. Plus it's not such a thoroughfare.

Yes. No, people were dashing past the other room all the time. Denise the manager told me that this was one of the top rooms.

It is one of their premium rooms, yes.

Have they charged me premium rates?

We came to an arrangement, because it was their fault that you had to move.

Mama. Mama.

I gathered it was something like that—she sort of implied it, but I didn't get involved.

Another bit?

So you've split the difference? She didn't really tell me, but she implied. They've been very good about it. There's only about two people who've been here longer than me. Ted is one. He's getting very old now.

He must be quite elderly.

Oh yes. Quite a bit older than me. He still stops in and sees me now and again. They were a lovely couple.

Shit.

I think she just said S-H-I-T. Her lunch finished and she said S-H-I-T. No no, no no, don't hit Mummy with the hammer. No, don't hit Mummy with the hammer. No. Let's get you wiped down. Shall we get a tissue? Fruit now?

Where did I get that lamp from, Cath?

I don't know—you've had it for ages.

I can't remember where I got it.

I think you just bought it. In the eighties or something.

I must have done. I don't think anyone gave it to me. No, when we shifted into the house—not our first house, our second house—I remember there was a dark corner, and we brought two or three lamps home and left our card and that was the one that fitted. One was too big, and the other didn't show any light. Doesn't the sofa fit well? Very lucky. I thought

I might not be able to have it. Oh, I love that picture. I can still remember seeing it. It was beautiful. I think it was one of the most beautiful pictures I've ever seen. The colour.

That was in Germany—in the picture gallery in Berlin. The Madonna in the Church, by Jan van Eyck.

And you bought it for me.

Where are you going, bubba? Have you had enough? Shall we save that for later? Maybe Nana can give her the bottle. But she might insist on Alan. Bottle with Nana? That'd be fun, wouldn't it?

Do you want to have your bottle with Nana?

Bottle with Nan-Nan. Oh no . . . no, don't upset her.

She does have to learn that she can't always have Daddy. Shall we try? Bub bub, what's all this about?

I bet the neighbours wonder what's going on in here. I love that wedding photo of yours. Because it's the whole family. Where's my wedding?

We need to take it home to put a hook in it.

That's right. There's the day before my wedding. That's when the family were all there. And my mother wouldn't come, because of those bloody Chidgeys. He didn't turn out so bad, did he? I was supposed to marry Arthur. You would have been an idiot if I'd married Arthur. Mrs Hight and Mum had arranged it. Mrs Hight would have liked me for a daughter-in-law because I could cook and I lived on a farm, but Arthur was the biggest drip I've ever known. Oh, that photo of Les. He loved that day. I wonder what happened to the man who took him fishing? He was so good to Les.

Dad went out for a last fish in Lake Taupo, Alan. It wasn't long before he died.

Ten days. All my friends said you can't take him, he's dying. And I said I want to take him to Lake Taupo before he dies. You helped me. And he loved it.

And he caught a fish.

And he caught a fish. And if he'd died there it wouldn't really have worried me.

Was this at Tūrangi?

Yes. All my friends thought I was mad. They tried to talk me out of it. Are you stealing my handbag?

You'll have to find a new spot for it.

There's no money in it. I never leave a lot of money in it.

Security's good here, though. I've never heard of any burglaries.

I haven't either. I never even hear of people losing clothes.

That's a relief.

At the one Myrna used to live at in Auckland—it wasn't a Mallory's—she said you were always getting back the wrong things. If you were *that* big, you got back a pair of knickers *that* big.

How disconcerting. Shall we sit this way instead, bub? Where's your leg? Where's your leg?

She's got two.

Yes. You've got the right number.

Don't those photos look lovely? I love that family one of your wedding day. Except there's one person not there. One little person's not there. I loved your wedding. It was very simple. There were no long dresses and veils.

Are you all right, bubba? You're looking a bit tired. You've got hair in your eye.

Has . . . what's her name . . . has she gone back to England?

Leila. No, they're staying on a bit longer now. She's going to be surrogate for another couple.

She's not!

Yeah, but not using her eggs, using theirs. A Christchurch couple.

What an amazing woman she must be. I can't believe anyone would be so wonderful to do that. And to do it again!

She's mad.

324

She did a good job though.

Yeah. You came out all right, didn't you bub?

Yes, you're beautiful. Good girl. I've settled into this room really well.

I think it's really nice. It's nicer than the other room.

Yes it is.

And quieter.

Yes, I was wondering what it was going to be like . . . but it's got a better view and everything. I think it's lovely out here. I can see trees . . .

It's much more peaceful.

Yes, it's beautiful. I don't know who's gone into my room. I don't think anyone has yet. He'll probably annoy them, too. He's the most terrible man. I suppose there's nothing they can do about it, is there.

Wait for him to pop his clogs.

He'll probably live till he's a hundred and get a letter from the Queen. Yes, darling—yes, it's a little picture. What's on the next page? That's where Oma lives. In Queenstown. That's where Daddy used to live.

A bit south of there, actually. Te Anau.

I wish I could remember the place I stayed at in Te Anau.

There was probably only one back then.

What was it called?

I don't know, but there would have been only one or two places.

It was a hotel and I think it was on a corner.

It would probably be the Fiordland Hotel on the lakefront.

No, I'm quite sure it wasn't along the lakefront. Because I had a job at Mackintosh Caley and I used to walk to town. And it was owned by . . . what's my cousin's name? Mary . . . Malloch. It was owned by Mallochs. And she used to get drunk every night. They were above me and I could hear them arguing, and the next day she'd come down and say you didn't hear us last night, did you? And I'd say no, no. And then she'd say her husband had a cold or something. The language! And we had other friends, and he was an undertaker there.

Cuddles? Cuddles?

I can't remember their names either, but I can always remember him on a cold night saying oooh, a few will go tonight. He was always excited on a cold night.

Your shoes are still unpacked. I mean packed.

I looked at them this morning. I've decided to do them tomorrow. Now, somebody gave me that for flowers. I think it was what's-her-name. You know, she used to come and visit Dad and bring him communion when he became a Catholic. I suppose I need to keep it, don't I?

You don't have to.

Do I have many flowers?

There are other vases you can use. It's just taking up space.

Yes, it is. And I don't have that many flowers. I had a nice meal. Roast lamb, and mint sauce, and carrots. We nearly always have carrots. The man that sits at the table with me says we've got five acres out the back. But I like carrots. And beans, and a steamed pudding with jam at the bottom, and ice cream. The meals are always very nice—I never find anything wrong with them. Of course some people do. Is there something you would love for little bub bub? You know, to keep a memory. Not now, but to have a memory of Nana later.

I've always liked the hare.

When the time comes, you take it. The room looks lovely. It's a nice room, isn't it. I think it's better than my other one. I'm still going down to my old dining room. Two very nice men sit at my table. We have sensible conversations. The other lady's quite quiet, but they talk about sensible things. They were both farmers and they talk about farming, and movies, and TV—you look around the dining room and some of them just sit there. You sometimes wonder if they're alive. Do you know what that dish is?

Yes, because there's a note inside it.

What does it say?

This is a shaving-soap bowl. I got it for Dad when I was nine. Thirteenth of June, 1940.

I'd forgotten I put that note in.

Where do you want this mirror?

I don't mind. Wherever it looks good.

Do you use it?

Not very much.

Do you want the clock here?

I like it where I can see it from my chair and in bed. Do I need that silver tray?

Probably not. Shall I take it home and put it with the other stuff?

I think so. When I was in the townhouse I used to have glasses and drinks and things, but I don't here. Oh, I love that vase. What does it say on it?

Wedding gift, Mum and Dad, 1923.

Do you not want that thing in your shower any more, Pat?

Ah . . .

The suction shelf thing, Mum. The wire thing. It's in the bin.

It's a caddy that goes on the wall, with little suction cups.

A wire shelf.

Do I need it in there?

I don't know. Someone's put it in the bin. Maybe that was you.

Is there a soap dish or something in the shower?

There is, but it's not big enough for shampoo.

I can't think. What are we looking at? Am I in your road?

This thing here, Pat. It was on the wall in your old shower.

Yes. I've always had it like that. Somebody's taken it down. I've had it for years.

A bit of Palm Sunday palm. Do you want it?

When was Palm Sunday? I always used to keep them—they used to last for a good two thirds of the year. Now they're brown in about two weeks. Oh, the pictures look lovely. It's nice to have the family photos up. That one of Les and me was at your debutante ball. And all of Les's family the day before we were married. With my father there, but my mother wouldn't go to the bloody Chidgeys'. I've never forgotten that.

Engagement diary, Listener, junk mail . . . what's this cutting? Who's she?

Now she is somebody, and I can't think who. That's why I kept it.

There's no information.

What does it say?

Nothing. It's torn in half.

Mass times for September. That can go. Do you want some lens cleaner, Alan?

Every time I go to the optician they give me another one.

She's speaking in sentences but we don't know what she's saying. Do we? Do we?

I've got no idea what this is. A cat toy? We can send Jiffy round if you like. *Then* you won't sleep. Do you use this letter opener?

No, but don't throw it away, because now and again I use it to poke something.

All these little prayer cards and things—do you still want them?

I'll have a think about it. Where did I have them in the old room?

On the shelves.

I'll look at them and decide what I want to do.

I Believe in Christmas. Do you want that?

Somebody gave it to me years ago. Yes I do. I think it was the woman that nursed Les. You know who I mean.

I managed to get the headboard in the car, just. It's crammed in the back.

Am I not going to have a headboard?

It gives you a bit more room. I think it's better without it.

Oh, so do I. Just that I'd always had a headboard. But there isn't a necessity, is there.

Dear Mum, A quick note from Tokyo, we're having a great time, it's very hot and humid so we're using fans all the time, Eddie chose this one for you, lots of love Helen and the boys. Do you still want that?

No.

Dear Mum, We are staying for two weeks in a lovely old house in a small village called Le Petit-Fougeray?

No.

Dear Mum, We are spending the half-term skiing in the French Alps? No?

No.

You've got lots of photos in here.

Who are they of?

Family, mainly.

I suppose they should be kept. It's not for now, it's for later. In time to come, everyone's glad.

Shirley's funeral leaflet?

I don't think so.

Greetings from Lapland? Dear Mum, We're having a great week skiing in Lapland, inside the Arctic circle, north of Finland?

No. It's nice, but I've read it. On the sixteenth of November wee darling was registered, and it was Les's birthday.

That's right. That's when we went to court and they said we had to keep you, bubba.

When you're fifteen Mum and Dad will say why did we? I need to go through this and look at it in case I've written something I've forgotten about. Prime TV 7:30 . . . I don't know what I was looking at. And the next week too. I must have been watching something every week. I don't know where I'm going to put the rest of my records.

They're CDs.

Oh that's right—they've got smaller. You probably don't remember the size of records.

Yes I do.

I still play my CDs. Sometimes I'm playing them and there's a lady opposite and she comes over and listens to my music. I don't really know her.

What have you got, bubba? What are you doing?

She's talking on the phone, I think. That's meant to be a phone.

Gentle. Gentle.

You know too much for a little baby.

In Flanders Fields?

Yes. I got that when I went there.

Wordsworth? From some newspaper or other?

Yes. I love that poem. Lonely as a cloud that floats on high. I kept it because we always used to say that when I was at school. William Wordsworth, 1807.

Were you at school then?

Yes.

Was he in your class?

Yes. Yes, we were friends. In 1807.

Alice, no. Don't touch that.

Send your angel to Holy Mass? Oh holy angel at my side, go to the church for me, kneel in my place at Holy Mass, where I desire to be?

Let me have a look. I can't remember that.

Is it when you can't be arsed going to church?

Yes.

A picture of the assumption of Our Lady? Shooting Spiderman webs out her hands?

I got that from somewhere.

Beauty and the Beast—Paris Opera Ballet?

That was here in the main dining room.

I don't think the Paris Opera Ballet came to the dining room at Sunset Court in Hamilton.

I think you took me to it.

I don't remember that.

Where do you want your jewellery box?

I don't know where I normally have it.

It used to be on the chest of drawers, but if you're putting the water jug there now, maybe it could go here. Though Alice will grab it every time.

She can do anything she likes, she's so lovely. You're not going to have an idiot there. She'll be telling the teacher what to do.

And this is a book from Myrna.

She loaned it to me to read. I don't think I'm going to, but I'll keep it for a couple of weeks. She reads the oddest books. What's the year now?

2016.

This is 2014. I'm sure I don't need it. There's no use looking through it, is there? I probably just stuck it in a drawer.

Things have been piling up a bit.

The last few weeks have been terrible.

Well, you haven't been sleeping.

No. That was the whole trouble. I'd get up in the morning and I'd be so tired I couldn't do anything all day. But I just feel completely different. Terrible man. I might throw something through the window at him one day.

Right, it's looking good.

It is. It looks so good.

It's really nice.

It is nice. It's a very nice room. I reckon it's nicer than the one I was in, to be quite honest.

It is. It's a nicer outlook, and it's much quieter.

It's just beautiful. It was very good of Mallory's—I mean usually once you come here and rent a room, that's it.

Do you want me to get rid of these old magazines?

No, I put them down in the lounge room. I'll take them down. People here like to read them. They don't know what the dates are.

What are you doing, bub? No. You've torn out a page from 2015.

It doesn't matter. I just love her. Goodness, look at the dust.

I'm going to have a nap now and pretend I don't exist.

### 9

Iconographically, too, she follows Byzantine types: the Mother of God as Queen of Heaven, and the Madonna of Tenderness who holds her baby gently by the foot as he reaches for her neckline. Notice the Madonna's head: light passes through the transparent flesh tones and bounces off the white underpaint like light passing through stained glass, so that the Madonna's face is lit from within. But this is no ordinary daylight.

### 10

You think oh, he sounds promising, he has good reviews, he seems to get results with his patients—and then you google, and he's a chiropractor wearing a white coat and stethoscope, or he's a vet, or he is an actual doctor but he's been struck off.

### 11

I'm going to see the . . . the . . .

Neurologist?

The neurologist tomorrow. Auras all over the place. Maybe he'll remove my brain. I didn't go to sleep till two in the morning.

I went to sleep at one. And then my bloody deaf cat started screeching just before six. Alan and Alice are away—they're down seeing Alan's mum. I've got to make the most of the time. I've got to make the most of the time.

I haven't even been to look at schools yet and there are only a few weeks left. She's telling me every day she doesn't want to go to a new school. I know if I come back this afternoon, I'll be here for ages. It's insane how much I over-prepare. I'm sitting in the lecture and I've got eight things to do and I'm up to number two and there's half an hour left. I've got to stop it. I've forced myself to write my lectures in an exercise book. It takes me less time and it doesn't make me quite so OCD. Something about handwriting. I end up talking about things that I haven't planned anyway.

You don't need to prepare at all. Just go with the flow. Go wherever the students are going. Let them lead it.

And call it responsive Pasifika pedogogy.

## 12

She's looking for you. She seems genuinely sad. You're backlit. We can't see you. Bubba, who's that?

## 13

Do you sell talcum powder?

Talcum . . . powder. . . ? Ah . . . I'm not a hundred percent sure what it is, but someone asked before and the answer was no.

She was in tears this morning—she hates the room, she's lonely, she wishes she never moved, she can hear when the lady next door is doing a poo. Give me fucking strength.

I keep telling myself just tackle the elephant a bite at a time. I've got this buzzing circuitry at the front of my brain. That's what keeps me awake at night—as well as getting jammed on every bad song I've ever heard.

Oh God. I'm still on the Vengabus.

Get your glittering hotpants out.

I don't think Hamilton's ready for that.

Facebook can't decide who I am. It sends me silver-fox dating sites and cruises for the elderly, but it also sends me punk burlesque rock stuff. I must admit, I don't get all those old-fashioned emails like I used to, asking me if I want to increase my cock size.

I don't get those any more either. I miss them.

I miss the Russian women.

I had spam from a dead person this morning. Harvey Zucker—Alan's old friend from New York. Re: nothing. Re: blank. The message said what a surprise! Isn't it incredible! I didn't click on the link, but I'd like to know where it would take me.

What's the best thing to do? Leave it and hope?

It gives you a jolt to see the name. He was my diamond mule for a while. If there were eBay sellers who wouldn't ship diamonds to New Zealand, he was my man.

You were thinking of interviewing him at one stage.

I was. I would have loved to interview him. And now it's turned into *this* thing.

Where I'm the most exciting person you've got to come and talk to today. You've hit rock bottom.

Fergus was comparing me to international experimental writers I've never heard of. I'm not looking forward to staring down the blank page again.

I'm still so torn. Should this just be memoir? Maybe it's because I'm teaching memoir.

Embrace the autobiographical first novel.

Maybe it's not autobiographical enough. I'm too tangled. I can remember my grandmother in pantyhose at the beach. It was happening all over the show, in a million disjointed fragments.

I put a call out on two Facebook groups. This is the situation. I'm in despair with my health. I can eat four things. I've exhausted the possibilities in New Zealand. Does anyone know of a *doctor*—I was very specific about that—who does international Skype calls and can help? One woman said I'm based in New Zealand and I'll treat you for free. But she's not a doctor. She suggested a homeopathic approach. I thought, that name seems familiar—turns out she friended me a while ago. I think she has literary aspirations. I don't know how to reply to her: really nice of you to offer to help, but . . . this is bullshit. It's water. I don't believe in water. So now I'll close my eyes and stick a needle in the page.

### 14

Have you ever considered taking an attitude of gratefulness? I know it's painful, exhausting, confusing, isolating and difficult, but we have a condition that REQUIRES us to slow down, manage stress, detoxify, and supplement nutrients. Essentially, we must seek health to feel well! Our bodies are telling us to take action. It's hard to be thankful for hardship, but as we recover we can become mentally and physically much better than we were before. I hope this encourages you. You are strong! <3 <3 <3

Catherine Chidgey?

Unlike. Unfollow. Unfriend.

### 15

All the cherry blossom will be gone by the time you're home.

### 16

Chocolate Santas spotted at The Warehouse. And the fifth angel sounded, and I saw a star fall from heaven unto the earth: and to him was given the key of the bottomless pit.

\*

Bubba! Hello!

We've only got four percent power.

How's my girl? How's my sweet pea? Hello darling! Did you just have a sleep? Not really? Your hair's growing, bubba! Even in a few days!

Dada. Dada.

Yes, that's Dada. How's my little sausage? Mummy misses you. I miss you.

Bubba. Bubba. Bubba. Bubba. Bubba. Bubba. Bubba. Bubba. Bubba.

Yes, that's you.

We're down to two percent.

Kiss? Kiss? Blow a kiss? Hello sweetie. Don't let her delete anything.

Down to one percent.

Bye little sausage. Bye darling. Love you. Mummy loves you. Bye bye sweet pea.

## 17

What was I saying before that?

Faecal transplant.

Oh yes. I have read success stories. I could go to Mexico and swallow some crapsules.

Is that how you have to do it?

Either that way or *that* way. But in New Zealand I'd need to get onto a trial, or find a willing donor who's been screened for everything, and then get pieces of hosing and a blender—well, you don't want to be googling the DIY method.

You're not that much of a hippie.

Or you get the capsules and fill them yourself. And then double-capsule them, and then dip them in wax so the stomach acid doesn't destroy it before it gets to where it needs to be.

I think that's something you'd only want to do under proper medical supervision.

And how do you approach a donor? The farmer across the road is pretty hale and hearty—perhaps I could go knock on their door.

No.

Mm. Anyway, I thought you might want to see some of my jewellery.

I do! I don't know that he does, but I do. I'm nosy.

This is a book ... it says SOUVENIR. Souvenir as in mourning rather than souvenir as in souvenir. And then you open it out and it's a bracelet. There's a little compartment for the hair of one's beloved.

Where does it come from?

EBay.

But before that.

Don't know. The UK.

Look at that. That's a serious bit of earring.

Coral and onyx and diamonds and platinum. From eBay Australia.

Do they often come with provenance, or do you guess?

Hardly ever. This is my oldest piece. Pearls for tears, and a diamond forget-me-not. In memory of the Reverend William Williams, ob. 17 April, 1793, aged 58, and also Mrs. Sarah Williams, ob. 6 February, 1793, aged 62. This looks like a normal ring but you open the buckle and there's a little compartment for hair. This is French. Turquoise and a cross, and a compartment on the back for hair.

Mourning jewellery mourning jewellery mourning jewellery.

This is Cupid. Have you heard of acrostic jewellery? It has a code hidden in the gemstones.

Lots of hands.

Yes. Hands. And if you take the first letter of each gemstone, it spells out a word. Diamond, Emerald, Amethyst, Ruby—

Dear.

—Emerald, Sapphire, Topaz.

Dear. Est.

Dearest.

Dearest. Dearest.

The hands are fantastically creepy, aren't they.

A marcasite lizard bracelet. A stylised dragonfly with sapphire head and diamond wings. A deco pendant watch with fine enamel work. A bracelet of real butterflies and a fake bird. A pair of deco diamond dress clips. An art nouveau aquamarine and diamond brooch.

Your eyes are so strange, aren't they. Are you the young one? I'll give you your beautiful butterflies back.

I've seen what I want to buy with some of my Wish Child money. Although the condition isn't great, so I'm torn. It's hard being a perfectionist and liking antiques. It's a mourning ring with a lock of Byron's hair in it.

That's a bit exciting!

It's black enamel and gold. There's a central rock-crystal panel with the hair, and around that it says George Gordon Noel Lord Byron, and the date of his death on the back. But the black enamel is in quite bad condition, and enamel repairs are very very difficult. And then there's the whole question of . . .

Is it then authentic. Or do you leave it alone.

I'll let you out. I will. I will. I'll let you out.

Where is the Byron ring?

Be good.

In London. It's so cool.

It's *very* cool.

And that would mean I wouldn't have to change all my pounds into New Zealand dollars. Though there's also the question of is it really Byron's hair.

You're not going to be able to prove that, are you. Unless you did the DNA.

He died in 1824, and the ring is hallmarked 1822. But that's not in itself suspicious, because jewellers would have had blanks of mourning rings in stock. I don't think that's an issue.

Is it just a claim? Does it have a provenance?

Not as far as I know.

You probably could get DNA done.

No, you'd need more hair than is in it.

And then you'd have to open it. He's on the move, isn't he. I can see him in the glass. He likes sitting on the fence, but he likes sitting just a foot that way, to the left, where we can't quite see him and don't know if he's going to leap off and chase cars.

Do you have to keep him in? Is he a bit senile?

He's deaf. Go and sit with Fergus and Elizabeth.

I'll see if I can show you a photo of it—my poor old laptop needs a serious clear-out. I keep getting this worrying message. I'm wary of the cloud. It's thinking about it; it's taking its time.

Ohhh. That's a beautiful ring. I quite like the damaged enamel.

Do you? It's damaged along there, and gouged on the shoulders.

But that just makes it look like it's old. His hair is faded.

If it really is his hair.

I'm sure it's his hair—well, I'm not sure it's his hair, but it could be his hair.

It's quite likely.

Lots of people snipped off his hair.

Did they?

Well they must have.

Or someone's hair. It could be from a cat.

Or any of his friends. My aunt spun cat hair into things. It's pretty cool though.

It's pretty fucking cool.

It really is.

I want it.

Sounds like a done deal.

It's at auction, so it's definitely not a done deal.

But in terms of the wanting.

Shall I tweet that photo of you showing Elizabeth the jewellery?

You have to show me first. Let's have a look.

That's a good one of hands. You're explaining the hands.

I suppose so. I'm doing something weird with my mouth. I often do that in photos, I've realised.

You do the thing I do. Which is you talk slightly out of the side of your mouth.

I do. I never realised until I saw myself on TV.

I used to get hell from my father for it.

But it's genetical.

It is. There's nothing I can do about it. Nothing I can do. Totally out of the right side of my mouth. My right eye's bigger than my left eye. I'm deeply asymmetrical.

We all are.

We're all asymmetrical.

I wrote myself a note—there was something that I needed to ask you. One of the questions was should I buy the Byron ring.

We can't help you with that one.

It sounds like a good thing to do, but—

Okay. My publisher says yes I should. Shall I do a selfie of us?


## 18

We have achieved a degree of stability over the past hour.


I was thinking how am I going to get the five steers down the road to the neighbours' paddock? And all I had to do was tie the goat to a lead, and they followed it. They lick it all over. They think it's a calf.

What's a steer?

That is a calf that's been born, and it's had its . . .

Yeah.

Taken off.

If your bits are gone, you'd think that might stop the nurturing instinct. But no.

No. They do not like to be separated. They absolutely love the goat.

You chose to get a goat as a pet.

I had one previous. They're very lovable to people. But I don't think you'd have them inside, because when they pee, it stinks. It is absolutely putrid. You would never ever house-train a goat.

But I wonder whether you *could* house-train one.

I'm going to say no. I know you can train rabbits and dogs but I don't think you could train a goat. I really don't. A pig you can. A pig, when he goes to the toilet, goes in the same spot all the time. So if you brought a pig inside and he was in for an hour and he wanted to go to the toilet, he would actually go back outside to the spot that he's used to.

Wow. Hey Heather—

And very clean.

Let's go to Brendan.

Goats. Yeah. I had pet goats when I was a kid. My first ever pet was a goat. Her name was Floppy. I took her to pet days. When you used to have pet days at school. I was on a farm in Taranaki. Dad mainly had goats to keep the roadside tidy. They will eat absolutely anything. They will literally eat the clothes off your back. I recommend if you are going to have one, have a female one, because billy goats have a nasty habit of weeing all over their faces.

What, their own faces?

Yes, their own faces. They will literally put their heads down between their front legs and urinate on themselves.

I want to widen it out. What other unusual pets have you had? I like those bearded dragons. Apparently they're quite affectionate. They like being handled. But there's a limit. I used to worry about people with huskies. It's lighting up like a

Christmas tree at the moment. Let's go to Carolyn.

Has it been used for Hitlerian pilgrimage purposes? Yes. I've been there. I tried to speak to her; very very secretive. They drop into a whisper. We live with this legacy. People are still going to know it is the site where he was born. History is history.

### 19

Catherine, we're building hope. Are you in?

Did she really point to a statue and say Mama?

### 20

That was a godawful flight. She screamed the whole way. I can't do this parenting thing any more. I'm so tired. I've had it. I'm fucked. The whole time she's fighting me.

What can you do?

Cry. I had some pissant little adolescent steward who tried talking down to me—he looked thirteen. He gave me a seatbelt for Alice and it wouldn't fit around her middle. I said well you do have them, Air New Zealand has them, because I used one on the last flight. He said no, this is an *infant* belt. I gave him a look and he didn't talk to me for the rest of the flight.

Did you go on the plane with Daddy? Did you go on the plane with Daddy?

That was the hardest ten days of my life. Fuck. Oh my God. I didn't think I could hold her. Mum's not in a very good way at all. Bubba needs a bath but I don't know if she's going to tolerate it. She's been hitting my bollocks an awful lot lately— she's kicked, kneed, punched, and on one occasion went to bite me. I had trousers on.

Bubba!

I shout and she gets frightened. Why does Daddy act all

hurt when you punch him in the nuts?

What's the diagnosis?

Congestive heart failure. She has heart disease. Her heart isn't in very good shape.

That dress is shorter. You've grown, bubba. So it *was* a heart attack?

Apparently. Everything's been stripped back.

She needs to put it in writing.

She kept on saying oh yes, I'll tell him. But if you don't tell him now and you die, then it's a problem—I couldn't say that. Whenever she's alone, she's scared that she's going to . . .

Yeah.

She digs a hole and throws herself into it. Anything could push her over the edge. She asked about the metronome again— have you got the metronome? I said yes, you gave it to me. Oh, she said, I don't know what I was doing.

Did she have a music box for when Alice was going to sleep?

No, she had a creepy clown doll. A vaguely Florentine porcelain thing with a clown face and a music box inside its body. It made jerky movements like a Blade Runner replicant. But even creepier was this doll she won in a raffle in the 1980s. It was at a Mathieson gathering and my grandfather's sister made it. It looks like a scarecrow and it's larger than Alice. I brought it out for her and it was sitting on the couch and staring at Mum. Like it had been in a car accident and its head was on an angle, but it was still staring at her. She got increasingly wigged out during the evening. I was saying *Beryl . . . Beryl . . .* under my breath.

You mother's just had a heart attack.

She was laughing, though. But then she made me take it out of the room. So I hung it up in the wardrobe—I put its head through a coat hanger. Oh my God, it's good to be home. The house looks nice.

I changed it round.

Bubba, come and have a story. Daddy needs to slip into a coma.

The ivy's out of control. The cherry blossom's all gone.

## 21

I keep looking up and noticing the shadow of an eyebrow hair that must be one of those long wiry old-lady ones. I've been trying to flatten it but I can still see the fucker.

I've got them growing out of my chin.

No!

Don't worry, I pull them out.

When did that start?

I don't know. I'm a bit older than you, aren't I?

Four years.

Four years is a lot. A lot of things have happened in four years. Look. I never used to have this. This has happened literally in the last year. It's awful. It's really turkey. And this used to be up here. My eyelid. That happened two or three years ago. And the bags under my eyes are new—I never used to have them.

That's possibly because you're overworked.

Possibly.

It's reversible, Tusiata. I refuse to believe that we can't turn back time. I don't accept that this is my face now.

I really struggle with it. It's one thing being overweight my whole freaking life, but now getting old . . .

I'm getting exactly the same lines between my eyes as my mum. Exactly the same.

This is my mum, her sisters, her uncles—everyone on my mum's side. I seem to have inherited all the shit stuff from the palagi side of my family—the thyroid issues, the sticky-out eyes, the big boobs. But no doubt I'll get diabetes and all the other shit from my dad's side eventually as well.

I never worried about getting old—it was always my weight,

344

my weight, my weight. And now it's happening—shit, it's way worse, because you can't change it. There it is—the eyebrow hair. Look. Look. Can you see it?

No . . . where? Oh, I can. It's really small. It's a really small fine one. It's just sticking down. It's not a big old-lady wiry one at all. Can you still see it?

Yes. I'm having them done tomorrow because I'm having my photo taken on Wednesday. I want to do a smoky eye and I don't know how. It just looks like I've been punched.

YouTube tutorials.

I did one of those. It still looked like Alan had given me the bash.

So the . . . the . . . what's his name?

The neurologist?

The neurologist sent me a letter and told me the name of the thing in my brain that I've never known.

What is it?

I can't remember. Um . . . it's called . . . hypothalamic hamartoma.

Haematoma . . . is that a blood clot? Like your book?

I don't know.

That would be freaky, wouldn't it.

Very freaky. I don't know what it is, and I don't want to. I actually don't want to google it. I freaked myself out badly when I first found out about it.

You thought you were dying for five months.

I thought I was dying for five months. He also says—in the letter—I did not remind Donna that it is against the law to operate a motor vehicle for one year after a generalised convulsion.

So he's saying he forgot to mention it?

Yeah.

Is a generalised convulsion like a grand mal seizure?

You know I've had two, right? I had one in July where I

wet the bed in my sleep. My two-and-half-thousand-dollar bed. And I told you how I peed on the floor at the rehearsal of my play.

I'm not laughing.

It's funny. It is funny. Apparently they were all really nervous about me coming to the rehearsal.

You put them at their ease.

They all had these long black skirts on and two of them took them off, to mop up . . .

To mop up the pee.

Yep.

That's nice.

Isn't it nice.

I'm not laughing. Do many people still call you Donna?

A few in Christchurch do.

I can't think of you as Donna. You don't look like a Donna.

No. I always flinch when people call me Donna. My mum does. I don't flinch when she calls me Donna. Actually my mum always liked getting older, except for when she started getting unwell. But I find it a struggle. I find it hard to accept. I've had the Botox fringe for a while now.

It suits you.

I wonder if I could just grow it all the way down to my collarbone.

Well your chin hair will take care of that.

Oh fucking hell.


## 22

I called him a cock and that's all he can focus on—never mind the other stuff that's wrong. Now we're ignoring each other and the cat's thrown up on the carpet.


## 23

So raw. We can't go home now. We've got to keep moving

forward; this is all about the future. It feels exposed.

The darkness at the end of the tunnel has not been easy. I don't think we've had three days together since our honeymoon. We keep running into problem after problem. You've got to get all that perfect. This white wall is not white. It doesn't feel finished.

I never wanted to leave.

A little bit of honesty would be nice. Our zone this week was the master bedroom, and it feels enormous in here. We really hope that all the love we put in will get us over the line. The only thing I'd say is that there's quite a lot of blankness around it. I think there could have been more. When you compare them side by side, it feels lacking. We've taken a risk with the void.

It looks really raw—and then you go under.

We need to be functional; seriously multi-purpose. I think it's going to get messy very quickly. There's a relationship and it feels like these are things that have been salvaged and repurposed.

We chose to expose the sewerage pipes and make them a feature. It could be a big fail, but I think it's paid off. I mean check it out. That is an art piece. It's an installation. (I'm not an artist.)

They're lacking vision; there's no function to them. They started with good bones, but they just don't seem to be making consistently good choices. It's a shame. It doesn't have that big wow. Nothing feels enclosed. The scene is picture-postcard perfect, but there's a glaring problem. It's a veneer. It's faux. It's not real. Not wanting to play it safe, they've put this big telly in here. That's gutsy. That's risky. That's raw. They felt the pressure to get it right, and it cost them major grief. They've painted it so it *feels* authentic, but this massive industrial chain is just sitting here. You couldn't sleep at night.

*

We are definitely in danger.

Everyone's in danger. We've taken a lot of big risks.

You topped it off with punches. What possessed you? I was barely holding on. I won't ever be coming out of this bedroom now.

Unfortunately your choices just weren't quite right.

The exposed pipes were never meant to be elegant. They're exposed pipes for a reason. This is raw, not a fairyland.

Our interpretation was off the mark. Someone's going home; I hope you haven't left your run too late. This is about to get very real.

A little bit of hope here. We've pushed ourselves to the limit. Let's see where we currently sit.

I'm most worried about the sewerage pipes. They could be our downfall.

Unfortunately they were another disappointment. They felt a little forlorn; the overall concept didn't work. It didn't have a purpose.

Anything that doesn't have a purpose is art.

I can't get past my first impression that it feels unfinished. I picture myself sitting in there, getting away from you for a few hours. Locking the door.

It could be anyone. There's not much in it.

But is it enough to keep us safe? The fact that we didn't finish really puts us at risk.

We're safe. We're definitely safe.

It's so close. Everyone is so close and I am sick to my stomach.

You are safe.

My heart is pumping. I'm so scared.

This week I'm giving you a seven.

It's not finished well. We gave it a crack; I'm a bit gutted.

I'm going to cry. This is out of control. We left our child; my heart's coming out of my chest. Do you know where we are? I cannot believe this is our house.

### 24

Would you live in a city made of bones? Bones may break, but they can self-heal. In the future you might not have a choice.

### 25

I hate seeing roadkill when I'm driving. I find it very distressing. So I close my eyes.

### 26

The phone may ring at midnight.
Someone from the other side of the planet?
Yes.
Anyone I know?
Um . . . that depends. Do you know Christie's auction house?
Oh my God. All of it?
All of it?
The advance.
Don't be ridiculous.
It's not without precedent.
Are we talking about the Florentine cross?
Yes.
I was insane then. No, I have my limit set.
So what is it?
A memorial ring containing a lock of hair from Byron.
For real?
There's no certification, but it's a memorial ring from when he died.
I thought they came in a set of ten.
Like the finger bones of Christ . . .
So there are no diamonds involved?
No diamonds. Just enamel, gold, rock crystal and hair. It's a

really small finger size. And there's no certification saying this is definitely from Byron, but how would you know?

DNA testing.

That's what Elizabeth said. But a) I don't know if he has any living descendants, and b) you'd have to destroy it.

You'd only need a tiny bit.

But you'd have to destroy the ring to find out that it was genuine.

It couldn't be opened up and a little bit taken out?

No. It's woven into a design. It's so small—I don't think it will even fit my pinky, and it's impossible to size, because it's enamel, which is like glass. It would shatter. And also, there is enamel damage, which I could have repaired, or restored. There's a difference. I got onto these Russians in LA—

What could go wrong?

—and I've been corresponding with Polina, and they do museum-quality restoration, so it's reversible. I don't think it's going to fit my finger, but I thought I could wear it round my neck. I assume it's genuine. I asked and asked and asked if it has any provenance. I finally got the man from Christie's to answer, and he said all we know is that it came from a private collection and was bought in the 1960s. Byron died in 1824, but the ring is hallmarked 1822.

That's not unreasonable.

No. I don't really think that's an issue. I'll show you a photo. It's got a central panel of woven hair under rock crystal, and then around that is black enamel, and his full name in gold. And the underside is engraved with the date of his death.

What's the reserve?

The estimate is I think £2000 to £2500. But I imagine there could be a lot of interest in it and it could go way higher. I've decided my limit is £3000.

I think it's a very good thing to buy for the fourth-novel celebration. Commemoration.

I really want it. I really really really really want it. But there would always be that question—is it Byron's hair? It's a genuine piece of the period . . . there's just no way of knowing.

On the balance of things, you'd have to say that it's probably legit.

About two years ago one in much better condition and quite a different style went for £6500. The thing that might put people off this one is the tiny finger size.

Could you have it set into a brooch?

God! Why would I do that? You know who you're talking to, right?

All right, okay. Necklace it is. I'm very tired.

The phone will probably be going between eleven and eleven thirty, but midnight sounds cooler.


We're up to lot ninety-six right now. Your lot for today is ninety-eight. Another couple of minutes . . . I'll put you on hold. You can hear the auction. Stand by for me.

Okay.

Is that okay?

Yes.

Are you still with me, madam?

Yes, I am. Yes.

Fantastic. Can you stay on the line for me for another few minutes?

Yes, that's fine.

Fantastic. Thank you very much.

Okay.

Okay, madam. We're going to lot . . .

Are you still there?

Yes, I am with you. Can you hear me?

Yes.

Fantastic. The auction starts with one thousand three hundred . . . one thousand four hundred pounds. It's started.

It's fifteen hundred, sixteen, seventeen eighteen nineteen. Two thousand. Two two. Two four.

Are you there? Hello? Are you there? Ah fuck. Fuck fuck fuck.

## 27

Byron memorial ring buy
Byron mourning ring buy
Byron death ring buy
Byron death ring hair buy
Keats mourning ring buy
Keats mourning hair buy
Shelley memorial ring
Hair mourning poet buy
Famous death hair buy


I'm ringing about my mother's bank account. I already had signing authority on it but I've organised recently to have full access to it, as I need to be able to see the statements online. I did that a week ago but I still can't see them.

Okay, let me have a look. How's your day been, is it going okay? And Mum, is she doing okay? Can I put you on hold for a couple of seconds? A couple of minutes, to be frank.

All right.

Okay, so physically even though you have signing authority, we could only send statements to you—we can't get them online. The reason is our system won't support in order to attach the individual person. For example if it was a trust it would be okay, but if it is a individual person we can't attach that to your internet banking, even though you can see the account information, our system won't support us to generate online statements for individual persons like your mum. You have full authority but you are not account owner.

This problem has been going on for weeks. I need the

statements for WINZ so her income can be assessed. How do I do that?

I'm more than happy to send the statements to you shortly, but online you won't be getting the statements online, unfortunately. I tried, but it is not letting us. A colleague double-checked, and then my manager tried too and he got it double-checked with the system and they confirmed that it's technically not possible.

When I rang about this a couple of weeks ago I was told that I need to bring in all the paperwork including the power of attorney to the bank and be signed up for full access, and then I would have online access to the statements. That's what I was told. And so I've made two trips into the bank—I've had to come in twice with various bits of paper—and now you're telling me that it was all for nothing?

I do understand. My apologies. I can see the information, I can see exactly what happened at the time. You were speaking to one of our tellers. But what happened in here at the time, somehow your mum's account was attached to your internet banking. In first place, they shouldn't have attached that account. That's the whole reason why to fix that problem, I'm not sure whether or not he clarified you, but that's the whole reason we're asking you, since you have that account already attached, we wanted to make sure, just legislation-wise, you need to have a signing authority, like a full signing authority to be able to see Mum's account online. But technically if you want to get a statement, you can't get them. You could get statements for your relationship accounts, like a trust account, but not a actual direct relationship like Mum's or a individual entity.

And so whenever I want a statement, how am I meant to do that?

You would be getting paper statements only. It's something we could arrange, but it goes to Mum's place, but because you have full authority we could send it to wherever you would like.

But you can't get them online.

But whenever I want a paper statement, do I have to request it?

It will be a monthly statement. We will be generating the statements monthly.

But I was told last time I rang that paper statements were no longer being sent.

Um . . . I'm not sure what mixed information you've been given, but tell you what, in the past, at the time, with the additional signing authority, you have very limited access on this account. Because now you've placed yourself as full authority—

No no no. No. I was told that paper statements were no longer being sent at all for this kind of account. Either to me or to Mum.

Um. Not really. That's not true.

I was told that happened back in June, and I haven't had any statements since then, which is why I've had to go through this process. I don't know why the paper statements stopped. They came to my address anyway. So why have they been stopped?

I'm not sure exactly how they have set it up as a additional signing authority in the past. You shouldn't be getting that information sent to you, actually, unless your mum was living with you, whether or not it might be directly addressing her—

My mother has dementia, which is why I had to bring in proof of power of attorney. That's why the statements are sent to me.

What I can do for you at the moment, just to prove to Work and Income, or wherever you want to submit this document, I should be able to, or even if you wouldn't mind coming in—

I don't want to make another trip into the bank. I'm not making a third trip into the bank to try to sort this mess out.

Sure, that's all right, I can understand your frustration there too actually. So I could send the statement for you. That's all I can help you with today. I can understand where you're coming from, but unfortunately there is nothing I could do just to attach that account to be able to get online statements. You can see that account, but unfortunately our system won't support in order to get online statements for a separate entity.

Will you be posting the statement today?

Yep, if you would like. I'll just double-check when was the last statement for Mum. Just give me a second. Okay, all good, the last statement was generated on the tenth of October. Up to tenth of October, I should be able to. So how far back statements were you after?

Just the most recent one.

Are we sending it to the same address?

Yes.

I should be able to send that today.

And then after that, paper statements will be sent regularly?

Oh yes. Yes. Because Mum doesn't have access to the online statement, so that's definitely the paper statements from now on. Do you have by chance any idea how many statements were you after?

Just the most recent one.

I will be able to send that one. And just in case, in emergency only, I know you don't like to come into the store, but they can also give you a print-out immediately. It is available through their system as well. Just remember that. Now what I've done here for you, I've just made sure that Mum's account listed as a paper statement. So every month statement will be closing off tenth, or you would like any time, but if it's a monthly, statement will be generated and sent it to the same address where you have listed for Mum.

Okay.

I'm sorry about that actually which we could not help immediately with that.

*

I was bidding by telephone on this last night. It ended up selling (not to me) for £7000—so a total of £8750 with the buyer's premium added. Isn't it wonderful?

Oh the beasts! I think it's the closest we get to the highs of a P addiction.

I was very anxious—and once the telephone rang and the bidding was underway it was racing along, and passed the estimate in seconds. And then I was cut off! They rang back straight away but when I answered it was dead. Very strange—and I was so disappointed. By the time I managed to get someone on the phone the hammer had already come down. Perhaps the ghost of Byron was preventing me from catching auction fever and bidding far more than I could afford.

Oh how interesting re the phone cutting out. That is rather spooky, especially dealing with an object with—I suppose—an intense wairua. Douglas has often had that experience—seeing something that captures his curiosity—entering the fray—only to have the estimate swept by in seconds. The consolation prize is that you have excellent taste and acumen in even spotting the object and seeing it has value. And as Douglas always says—there's plenty more to come.

Well I'm not sure that there *is* plenty more of Byron's hair to come! Anyway, who knows if it really was his—apparently when ardent fans sent him a lock of hair and requested his in return, he'd sometimes send a sample clipped from his dog.

## 28

This still feels very non-specific. What would she *say*? How? Such as? Such as? This is abstract. Perhaps some indication in the very first sentence that it's NYC, eg yellow taxis. Repetition. Incomplete sentence. Repetition. *Show* this. Cut. You need to be *much* more specific and detailed in order to bring your work to life. Show this—how did you know? What did she say? Again, this addition doesn't add the specific detail required—it doesn't *show* me the gratitude. Incomplete sentence. This is a cliché, but it captures the teenage voice. Disappointing to see the same typo that I corrected in the earlier version. Still very general. This is *summary*—we need a detailed *scene*. Perhaps linger on this a little longer—it seems so important, but is very rushed. Repetition. How? How? How did this manifest? How? How? I'd cut this, and some of the other lines like it—they start to get a little intrusive. Such as? Such as? Can you show this? Can you be more direct? *Not* literally, though. What was said? *How* did this feel? Vague. Not a question. *This* is your final line.

## 29

That was less interesting than I remember.

## 30

The first thing she said to me was she found it hard to see how it all fitted together. This was right before I was due to go on stage and talk about it. The lights were so bright. I was using the clicker to move my slides along, and I wanted to point to particular bits. I'd taken the cat laser toy but I'd left it on the table, so I said Carole, could you please pass me that laser pointer shaped like a cat's paw? I lasered the audience at one stage. I was waving it around and I didn't realise. It wasn't until the second half, when someone else was pointing out features on their slides, that I realised the clicker also has a laser on it.

What was the crowd like? Ladies who lunch?

Pretty much. There was one guy in the auditorium. *One* guy. The personal essayist was tweeting on stage. The novelist who had breast cancer sat with her eyes closed, rubbing her sternum. One of the poets was drawing birds; another drew a cross-hatched heart. Another asked me did you marry that doctor? I said no, I married an artist. She said do you have a family? I said we have a daughter. She said how old? I said sixteen months. She said oh, but you're so slim! I said we had her via surrogacy. I could tell she didn't understand. She said did the surrogate *have* the baby?

What does she think . . . ?

I don't know. I don't know. The comedian started to cry. The poet who was drawing birds said stay away from me. The short-story writer said she grew up in a lighthouse. The comedian said okay, I was exaggerating a bit, but that is something that *could* happen to me, so as far as I'm concerned it's a true story. Carole got a standing ovation from everyone. The writers might have got one too—I'm not sure. There were three people standing. Then again, they might have just been leaving.

## 31

I've been thinking more about that. I think we probably should get her baptised. If we're still here in Ngā, the best that we can do for her is bite the bullet and . . .

Praise Jesus.

And go along with it. I wonder though—will they be teaching religious instruction in the school?

They will have some, yeah. But it's just another fairy tale.

Will there be creationism?

No, dear. Catholics don't teach creationism.

Well, some of them get a bee in their bonnet about things, and they might get a bee in their bonnet about evolution.

You walk up to the house on top of the hill and there are all these dead bodies and arms and coffins. People lying there, grabbing you. They keep an eye out for who's coming—those that can be scared and those that can't. You go to get your sweets, but from beside a coffin an arm grabs you.

Do they do the same thing at Christmas? Not with the dead bodies and coffins. Not with zombie Baby Jesus.

Poor neck. How comfortable do you think you'll be lying face down? I think it might be nice to at least have a discussion with your upper back.

Nobody does that.

We did dissection right in the centre of London. It was fantastic. It was the real thing. It didn't half make you realise how quickly we become meat.

It's like reviewing a movie and telling everyone how it finishes.

The undefinable bit that's missing—it makes that very clear. You see anatomy books and it doesn't look anything like that. All the stuff that they've taken away to make the photo look good is important connective tissue. And there's no space between organs—not a millimetre of space.

I couldn't do that.

You'd be surprised. I was grateful, I think. Some of the noises you might baulk at—when you take the brain out there's a pretty disgusting noise. We had three people faint.

What sort of noise?

The noise you would expect.

A squelch?

A suction/pop. It's quite connected, the brain.

It usually works best if it is.

You tended to start with them face down. The biggest problem was the formaldehyde—but now they plasticise the body. It's like cutting through Play-Doh. It makes it much easier to dissect, and they last forever. Unfortunately we still refer back to the same old textbooks, which are beautiful, and a lot of effort went into them, but they're wrong. Most of the corpses were poor people. There's a gland here called the thymus, and it decreases in size with stress. If you looked at an anatomy book, the thymus was tiny. And then cot death was starting to get bigger and bigger and they found that all the babies that were dying had an enlarged thymus. So they started irradiating the thymus, to make it smaller. But it wasn't an enlarged thymus, it was just that the babies that were dying were often wealthy kids who weren't stressed, so the thymus was a fine size. They got the norm wrong. So they'd given tens of thousands if not hundreds of thousands of kids cancer that they all died from. And if you look at the brain, there's a thing called the amygdala, which is our anger and fear and unforgiveness. In poor people it tends to be larger, so the average amygdala was thought to be bigger than was often found. Someone said oh, that's interesting, and then they started looking at left- and right-wing people. And right-wing people have a bigger amygdala, and left-wing people have a larger . . . whatever area of the brain is associated with empathy, which I'll remember in about ten minutes. So you start off being angry and annoyed and racist, and then you end up voting for an angry annoyed racist person, which encourages it, which means your amygdala gets bigger, which means you're better at being angry and annoyed and racist. There's no way of convincing a Donald Trump supporter to vote left-wing, because their actual anatomy is different.

So we need to irradiate the brains of Trump supporters. That's the logical conclusion.

Yes. A quick trip to Chernobyl and they'll all be sweet.

We're in Cornwall—you can't tell really. I've had to go to the bedroom because they're watching some Indonesian martial arts gore-fest instead of my preferred DVD, Dirty Dancing. The clocks have just gone back so we're all tired but it's only half past eight or something. Fred gets up at five thirty. He's a lark.

I used to be an owl, but I'm neither now.

What are you?

I don't know.

I can hear gunshots from the other room.

# [ NOVEMBER ]

## 1

Are you from Hamilton and do you dream of long and beautiful lashes? What you are about to read holds tremendous potential to radically change the entire world in many positive ways.

## 2

I'm not an expert but this is what I was told.

## 3

We need to stop saying fuck. Shall we say fridge instead?
Fridge.
Fridge.

## 4

Today we are making some announcements about proposed changes to the Faculty. These proposals underline the ever-changing environment we work and live in. It goes without saying we need to constantly evolve and adjust to what's happening around us. I want to acknowledge that some of these proposed changes are not easy on our people and I recognise the contribution that we all make. These changes are part of the steps we will be making as we take opportunities and respond to the movements in funding, the industries we engage with, the local and regional economies and our communities. Have a good weekend everyone. I'm really looking forward to watching the All Blacks play Ireland.

## 5

Bomb threat on a flight from Palmerston North. Seems unlikely, doesn't it. Probably some Guy Fawkes prank. I used to love Guy Fawkes when I was little. The smell of it.

We always had a token amount of fireworks. Mainly sparklers. Mum was her usual paranoid self—I'd stick one in my eye.

We used to light a sparkler and try to run round the outside of the house before it went out. Never could.

Dad stood the sky rockets up in an old milk bottle. In Ōtautau there were two trees—a big oak out the front and a little one to the side. I always thought of that as my tree. I remember Dad put a pinwheel on it and singed it. I don't know if those trees survived. People built a modern place over the shell of that house, which was late-1960s, pitched-roof, blue patio—that swimming-pool blue. They built a whole new modern house over the top, and chopped all the trees down. Across the road was Bill Forbes. He had raspberries and boysenberries growing over a hillside. We used to ramble through them and get all scratched up and completely full of fruit. He had an old villa—quite small—but then he had these little sheds outside—singleman's quarters. One of them was full of newspapers. He'd go out there and throw the newspaper in. He'd been doing it for so long—Ian climbed in and dug down through the newspapers, and he got down to 1964. Bill Forbes had all these cats, too. And he had a distinctive look to him—short and quite rotund, and a sharp goatee, and big thick glasses so you never saw his eyes. He looked like he could have been a Russian politician in the nineteenth century.

I remember we were letting off fireworks in 1987 when we got the call that Grandad had died—Dad's father. And I remember when we were little, going out onto the streets the next morning and looking for dead sky rockets. Smelling them.

I used to let off tom thumbs.

Those were the stupid ones that just went bang.

The little red ones.

That boys liked.

We were always putting them in mailboxes.

Double-happys. Are they the same thing?

I don't know. On the farm we made our own fun. I remember one time at Centre Hill—

Do you know how old you sound?

—one time at Centre Hill I found a .22 bullet. A live one. I put it on top of a rock and I threw another rock at it, and it went BANG, like a gun. And then I thought hmm, that was really unpredictable.

You could have killed yourself. I bet you didn't tell your mum.

No. I don't think I've ever told anyone.

Is that rain?

That would be good. Rain out the bastards.

So it was all right for you to set off the tom thumbs and have your special pinwheel on your special tree . . .

I was too young to know any better. But the stupid yobs down on Te Rapa Strait—a shipping container appears out of nowhere, full of fireworks, and you see all the yobs going and buying them.

It's weird when people like Facebook photos from years ago, and then everyone else starts liking them as if they've just happened. Oh, and we may be getting a phone call from a solar panel company. The phone rang, and I answered it, and it was this recorded message from some solar panel company saying if you are interested in a scheme whereby we install panels for you and the energy they collect pays for the panels, press 1. If you're not interested, press 9. And I thought—are we interested? I don't know. Panicking. Um. Um. We might be missing out on the deal of the century—and only fifty will be selected, he said—so I pressed 1. And then after I hung up I realised that you still have to pay for the panels.

I think on the next house. Not on this house.

You have to stay there for ten years to get the benefits.

Hopefully our next shift will be permanent.

It would be nice.

All my dreams and aspirations have dried up. All that concerns me now is emptying the next nappy.

That's the spirit.

## 6

I have to stop calling it Nutsack. I didn't even realise it was a retelling of Hamlet.

Is it?

Yeah.

I didn't know that.

It makes a lot more sense when you do.

What's it about?

It's told from the point of view of an unborn baby, and his mother and his uncle—his father's brother—are scheming to kill his father.

And so the baby hears all this through the womb.

Yeah. He doesn't realise his uncle is his uncle. For quite a while he thinks it's just a guy. And then he suddenly finds it's his uncle.

I better have a look at the blurb. That's not familiar at all. I probably would have been interested to read that.

The voice is so laborious. It's like a little professor. I think I got to like ten percent and I was like I can't do this. I found that I was skipping.

It was interesting but weird.

I'm going to go home and delete it off my Kindle.

It was quick to read, though.

Yeah, it was. It's quite short. And once I got into it, actually, I did start to enjoy it. The first section where the voice is establishing itself and it's ponderous and you're not really into the plot . . . I found that heavy-going. But when it gets into the actual murder—

Ooh. Do they go through with it?

They go through with it. And the police investigation— that's when it started getting much more interesting for me.

I didn't get that they lived in a hovel. I thought that seemed a bit weird.

It did. There was no real reason.

It was an absolute derelict mess of a house. And they were so filthy.

Maybe it's meant to echo something is rotten in the state of Denmark.

I'm going to have to read Hamlet now.

It left me wondering . . . but why? You're just being clever-clever. You're just showing off.

It didn't feel clever, though.

In the bit I was reading he was thinking that he had to foil the plot. The foetus. How was a foetus . . . like was he going to try and make himself be born or something?

He does. He tears open a hole in the amniotic sac. But at one stage he tries to kill himself—

What? The baby tries to kill itself?

Once I realised it was Hamlet I thought oh, okay, to be or not to be. He tries to strangle himself with the cord because he thinks that if he's stillborn . . . I can't remember the reasoning behind that. It would somehow foil the plot or save his father or . . . I can't remember.

It was all really weird.

It was just really forced, I thought.

It lurched from one thing to another.

But it's got good reviews.

Has it?

I couldn't find one bad review. Everyone's falling over themselves.

And so does the mother get caught?

They turn on each other in the end.

They try and do a runner.

The uncle was going to drop her in it, wasn't he. He was going to take off and leave her.

They don't make their train that they need to make because she is insisting on taking a framed portrait of her mother. Which I assume echoes Hamlet as well, but I don't know. She's taken a framed photograph of her mother and it's too big to fit in her luggage and that all just felt like . . . plot device, plot device.

Weird.

So what would you rate it out of five?

It wasn't onerous, because it was so quick. Five? It wasn't horrendous.

Out of five?

Out of ten.

Oh, out of ten.

I thought you said ten.

I said out of five.

Oh, out of five. Oh God no. Two.

You're allowed to give halves.

One and a half to two.

Really? You're harder than I am. Because it did pick up for me—I did start to enjoy it much more—I would probably give it a two and a half.

It was short.

I got quite irritated by it. He'd talk about things that he saw and knew. And then other times he'd specifically say well I couldn't see that.

I found that quite irritating too. The need to be constantly reminding us of course there's no way I could actually describe this but I'm going to anyway. It felt like he'd come up with this gimmick, and he wanted to shoehorn the story into the gimmick. I did like it more once the police got involved. Once the deed was done and the police were on the scene. It felt like there was more urgency and something was actually happening.

## 7

He turned up in the final minutes of the first class and wanted to know if he'd missed anything. So I had to go over everything I'd just spent three hours talking about, and tell him when his seminar date was. And he got out his phone and was laboriously trying to enter in the date . . . just write it down, mate! Just write it the fridge down!

Students laugh at me when I pick up my diary to write a date down.

Like a real actual diary?

It's a folding thing with papery pages inside. And several times this year I've been in a meeting with a student and we'll be arranging for the next meeting, and I'll pick up my diary to write it down and they actively laugh. They're amused at what a relic I am, shuffling my little pages. I just can't get with recording life on that tiny tablet. It doesn't compute. It's not mapped into my sense of how days work.

I don't even know how to use it.

If I plug dates into my diary and don't write them anywhere else, I lose those days. They're gone; I forget to check. Whereas I will check paper. Paper is where I live. I can't live on those little sliding screens of light. It won't fix. It won't take.

There's been endless confusion with the workshop rooms. You know how I said they'd given me two that had fixed seating?

Even though we fill out forms over a year in advance asking for movable seating.

I thought okay, the easiest thing would be just to put a half-dozen chairs facing the front row of fixed seats, so we can kind of make a circle. I apologised to the students—I said a couple of you, just on Thursdays, will have rooms with fixed seating, but this is a way round it, I'm sure it'll work. So I get back after class and there's an email from Alison saying that timetabling have got back to her and said that unfortunately we can't put six chairs in those rooms because of safety concerns.

Safety?

Yep.

What are the six chairs going to do? Stage a fucking coup? Will the students start breaking them and bashing one another with the legs?

Yes they will. So timetabling gave us two temporary rooms for this Thursday, and then after that we have to use different rooms. That's the only option. I sent round a group email saying really sorry to have to change plans, but because of safety concerns we can't use the lecture theatres like I thought we could, so just for this week, groups B and C have to go to these rooms, and after that it'll be *these* rooms. And then after I've sent the email I get a message from Alison saying actually, timetabling have got back to me, and just for that week he can move us a lot closer. So I said can I stay with the ones I've just emailed them about? But no, it was too late, he'd already allocated them to someone else.

Oh my God. They should have safety concerns over the fact that you will fly into a million fecking pieces from the stress of it all. That you will spontaneously combust, and the six chairs will block your students' safe passage to the fire exit.

Here's an email from one of them. Thought it started on Tuesday—I was wondering if I missed out on anything? No, I just talked about my cat Mintiemoo for three hours.

We frequently have first lectures and say absolutely fucking nothing.

## 8

Generally, when you've got white space, that's time itself.

## 9

I don't want to mingle. I don't like people.

But you're the person everyone's here for.

No, they're here for the wine.

You need to go and bask and . . . hi!

Was that you texting me, saying we have oarked? I didn't know what that meant.

I thought you would have had my number.

Alan's apparently stuck in traffic as well.

There's a lot of traffic out there. I think people are driving round in hopeless circles.

I'm trying to drag her out to make her go and mingle and bask.

Except I don't like people and I don't want to mingle.

That's no excuse.

Now I'm in the Listener saying I'm infertile.

I didn't pick up on that.

I thought I might as well say it, because people are going to keep asking why did the novel take thirteen years. I thought all right, let's just get that out of the way, and then maybe they'll stop asking. Because it's too uncomfortable. They changed a completely to a complete. It was meant to say how completely evil can penetrate blah de blah, and it now says how complete evil can penetrate blah de blah. Which is different.

But it makes this book an incredibly timely book—a book for today—because one of the key themes of The Wish Child is the way that the decay of language and the decay of truth and the decay of morals can lead a civilised society right into the abyss. I had no idea. No one thought that today had any other significance than Catherine's launch. [laughter] No updates, and please all turn your phones face down. [laughter] America, as we know, is teetering on the edge of the abyss. [laughter]

Is it Trump?
It's not pretty.
That can't happen.
Ah, it could happen.
Jesus.
I know.
It's not over, but it's close.

I like how the VC rocked up just as you were talking about the manipulation of language to make everything seem better.

## 10

A lot of these photos were Nana and Grandad's and they were just in boxes. And because Mum was living with Grandad, she ended up with them.
That was the day before our wedding.
Yes. And we've worked out who that person is.
Who is she?
She was a next-door neighbour, and she just came over and sat on the end of the photo. She was really nothing but they were taking the photos and she jumped the fence and came over and nobody noticed. Which are Phil and Rhona Coull?
That's him there—Phil Coull—and that's Rhona.
Who were the Coulls?
Aunty Leila, who was Nana's sister, was married first of all to Alec Coull. And Phil Coull is his son.
And what happened to that marriage?
I don't know. It blew apart.
So no one died.
Oh, you mean Alec Coull and Leila? He died. Sorry. He died, and then Leila was—

Leila was killed in an accident.

Leila was killed in an accident.

The car accident?

Yes. Yes. They were going—

I think it was to my wedding party.

No it wasn't. It was to—

It was something like that.

There was a wedding involved.

She was married to Fred Austin, and Fred had two daughters—Mary and Elaine.

That's right.

And it was Mary's kitchen tea they were going to.

That's right.

So this was Leila's second marriage?

Yes.

And they were going to her stepdaughter's kitchen tea?

Yes.

Yes. Her stepdaughter's kitchen tea. And they had the accident. I've read all that in Grandad's diaries.

I think I remember it too.

I'm gradually transcribing them. When I photocopied them donkey's years ago I just copied pages that had any connection with my family, obviously. They are interesting, in spite of all the things he said about me.

Mm, he didn't hold back. Have you got this week's Listener, Mum?

Yes.

Because I'm in it.

You said you had it, Pat, when I rang the other day.

Yes, yes I have got it. And I have looked at it. Only this morning.

I think you've got the wrong week, Mum. Show me the cover?

When I talked to her on the phone the other day, she actually opened it. That's what she told me, anyway.

What are you saying? I didn't hear what you said.

I didn't want you to.

No, no this is October.

No, not that one.

No. No no. There was something in it I was going to read. I've no idea what. But if I've put it there, that's to read.

She said she had it here, so . . .

It'll be around somewhere. I'll know the cover, if you show me the cover.

It's all screwed up.

I can't even find the cover.

What have you been doing to it? Eating it?

Yes. I didn't get morning tea the other day and I ate it.

Books and Culture . . . no, that's definitely not me, that's Margaret Atwood. It's not this one.

It must be somewhere.

Did I see it?

Well you get the Listener.

Yes, but I've a feeling one week I didn't get the Listener.

When I talked to you on the phone I described what the cover looked like and you had it then.

Did I?

You said someone had just put it on your bed.

I don't know what you've done with it. Maybe someone's borrowed it, to have a look. Maybe Myrna's taken it.

I don't know.

That's not it.

No. October the fifth. Well that's funny.

Gosh, I haven't seen some of these photos for a while. Aunty Joan made that dress for me, and I've still got that doll, and the dolls' clothes. That's Judy—my walkie-talkie doll, which I loved. I got it fixed up a while back. I got new hair on it.

They were beautiful, those dolls.

I was really disappointed with what they did. It cost me

quite a bit. It had stopped making a noise, so that's all going again, but the hair—I was so disappointed with the hair. I still look at it.

There used to be a shop in Christchurch that was absolutely amazing. It was off Regent Street.

What was the problem with the hair?

It was just straw. I didn't like the colour, and it didn't sit nicely. It wasn't as I envisaged.

I had a doll a lady did, and the hair was beautiful, and I could comb the hair.

The original hair was wavy but this is straight. He reckoned he told me exactly what it was going to be like. I probably was silly getting it done in the first place.

I've seen none of these photos. I wonder where you got them from?

As I say, they were all in a big box. They were Grandad's, and I've just put them in an album.

Well I know how Grandad got them. He always asked Les for the photos, and he never gave them back to us.

Oh.

That's how Grandad got them. And Les asked him for them lots of times. You know what Grandad was like.

Have you been down to Christchurch lately, Linda?

No—the last time was when Ron died. That'll be two years ago. I don't know what date it was. We don't have a date because we don't know what day he died. I think it was probably the twelfth. That's going by the last time he was on his computer.

I can't remember anything about that—why you don't know when he died. I've forgotten.

He wasn't found for several days.

Oh yes, now I remember.

Mm.

Mm.

That was horrible, wasn't it.

He'd even said to his next-door neighbour, look, if the curtains are closed, don't worry about it; if you don't see any sign of life, don't worry about it. He would say that sort of thing to her. But she got a bit suspicious when she hadn't seen him at all. She went to his GP—how she found out who that was, I do not know—she didn't even know his surname. But she went there, and said she was concerned about him, and left it in the doctor's hands. He'd had nothing to do with Summer, his daughter.

That's very sad.

She annoyed me, though.

Oh, I didn't know her that well.

It was over that jolly grouper's head. Do you remember that fossilised grouper's head?

Yes, I knew there'd been a big thing about that.

It wasn't a *big* thing . . .

Well I did hear about it.

What happened?

Originally Ron and Bill found it. That's never been disputed. It's always been in a glass case and it's always been Ron's, so it was always at Mum's place. Then when Mum died, Ron got it, obviously, because it belonged to him. So when he died and I went down there and we cleaned out his place, I said to Summer there's nothing I'm interested in except perhaps any personal things that were my parents'—but the only thing I'm serious about is the grouper's head. I said that should go to Bill, my cousin, because he found it with Ron.

I can remember when they found that.

It was in the paper wasn't it?

Yes, yes it was in the paper.

Grandad had a clipping in his diaries.

She said nothing. Absolutely nothing. And the next day Pam came down with me to help clean out the place, and as soon as we got there Pam saw Summer take the grouper's head out to their car. And so I just confronted Summer about it. I said that's the only thing I feel very strongly about. I said that belongs in this family. She was moving to Australia in three weeks—what was she going to do with it?

And she wasn't really one of the family.

Did she decide it was worth something?

I think so.

Was she going to sell it to a collector?

I think so. She saw dollars. She said she thought Kayden should have it. Kayden, her son.

Why Kayden?

And Kayden was there, and I said to Kayden, you don't want that, do you?

It would mean nothing to Kayden, would it.

Of course not. I was furious. I never saw it again. If she wasn't going to Australia, I could understand it a bit more, but she'd packed everything up—what was she going to do with a great big heavy fossilised grouper's head? For quite some time I looked on Trade Me—I did a search on grouper, spelled both ways, in case she didn't know how to spell it. Nothing came up. After that I took whatever I wanted. Up till then I was checking things out with her.

Well she was really nobody's . . .

Joanna calls her white trash.

I'm trying to remember . . . was she Pam's daughter?

Yes, Pam's daughter.

And not Ron's biological daughter?

No. Pam had her when she was sixteen.

But she grew up with Ron?

Oh yes—he adopted her when she was about two, I think. So legally, yes, she's his daughter. His next-of-kin.

Who was the father?

Some guy called Richard.

I'd never heard that before.

What happened to Pam? Her mother?

Pam died.

Did she?

Oh, about five or six years ago now.

I don't know if I knew that. You probably have told me and I've forgotten.

She was only forty-eight or something like that—she had breast cancer. She'd had it for years. I liked Pam. I always got on well with her.

Yes, I did too.

Did I get in touch with her? I can't remember now. I think I might have sent her a letter—

I did too.

And she rang. We had a really good talk.

When Ron died.

Yes—no no, this was a long time ago, before *she* died.

Oh yes. I've got my time mixed up.

I wrote to her. I remember. What's this church made of polished stones?

I've got that at home.

It was in Grandad's house.

I remember it, and I'd never have remembered it if I hadn't seen the photo.

I've got a table of stones, too. I've got a few crabs and rocks . . . not much, but enough.

We're nearly finished, Cath.

Apparently Ron blew all his money on a Filipino woman online. Bill rang Summer and tried to get her to give him the grouper's head, and in the course of conversation she told him that. About the Filipino woman.

So when you say a Filipino woman online, do you mean she was asking for money and he was sending it?

Yes. It was a scheme. He was always getting into schemes where he was going to make a lot of money.

So she probably didn't exist . . . ?

Possibly not.

Living down in the South Island, I used to hear all this, but I never hear anything now.

Mrs Bullen—here's a photo of Carol and Mrs Bullen—was she something to do with Bullen's Rock?

Yes. Lived in the house up above. That's why it was called Bullen's Rock.

And she used to play the piano at night.

Did she?

Were you never up there when she played?

I don't remember that.

You'd go outside about ten or eleven o'clock and she'd be playing classical music on the piano.

Would have been beautiful.

Oh, it was beautiful.

And you could hear it all? How lovely.

And you know where her house was—right up the very top—and it echoed down to us at the bottom. Les and I used to go and sit outside to hear her. I think the Chidgeys thought we were nutty. But it was beautiful.

I remember where the house was. A long way up.

Is it still there?

I haven't been down that way for so long.

I used to go up when my sister lived in Kaikōura, and it was still there then, but that was years ago.

I can't remember the last time I went down that road.

I don't know when I'll ever get to Christchurch again—I haven't got anything to go down there for now.

I went down for my sister's funeral. Catherine came with me. And I think that's the last time I'll go.

I'd only go if Aunty Joan died. Oh that one was at Bill's first wedding. I never went to that wedding.

I don't know whether I went to that or not.

I don't think you're in any of the photos. That's how we usually figure it out. He married Carol. Carol Ainsley, she was.

No, I don't remember that.

I always got on all right with Carol.

There's too many Pams and Carols in this family. It's confusing.

I'll be just a minute, Catherine.

How does Drummond McMeekan fit in?

He's our great-grandfather. Nana's father.

He was very handsome, wasn't he.

Wasn't he. Isn't that a great photo?

And that's why Dad's middle name was Drummond.

Exactly.

And they were Irish, weren't they?

No.

Yes, they were. From Northern Ireland. Bangor.

But it wasn't him, it was a generation before. It wasn't him.

Well, his family.

Like me.

Yes. Though from Protestant Ireland.

Northern Ireland.

Yes, Protestant Northern Ireland.

Yes I know. But my family were Catholics.

Yes.

Do you remember when Christchurch used to have the displays on Saint Patrick's Day? The Catholics in the morning, and hosts and chalices and holy prayers. And then a little stop, and then the Anglicans came along. And we all used to clap the Catholics, and the Anglicans would boo them. And then we'd boo the Anglicans and they'd all clap. It was only in fun. It was never unpleasant.

Remember that place?

Saint Martin's Road. Yes, I do. I'd forgotten about that house.

It was a cold house.

Wasn't it cold.

Freezing. All Grandad's stones and fossils seemed to suck out every bit of warmth.

Why did they ever go there? Because it was smaller, I suppose. It made you feel cold just looking at it.

Before that were they in King Street?

They were in King Street, with a huge section.

That doesn't look like Syd and Ida.

I love that photo . . .

Yes, but they're not as I remember them. Not as Nana and Grandad.

I don't know when that was taken. Unless it was at Carol's wedding.

It might have been. Because Ida's definitely at a wedding. And it wasn't ours, so it might have been Carol's.

Do you know if Grandad's house is still there, or if it was damaged in the quakes?

Saint Martin's Road? It's still there. I always drive past these places when I go down.

My little house in Christchurch is gone.

Oh, look. Helen two months, Catherine seven months.

Two *years*, it must be.

Two years! I was going to say, that's not right.

You can't read my writing.

Does that say two years?

No, that says Helen twenty-one months, Catherine seven months.

Oh, twenty-one months.

It's what was on the back of the photo, obviously.

I'm not very good at reading.

Remember her?

That's Joan.

Your mum's penfriend? In England? She stayed with us once.

I've got to ring her. I hope she's still alive. That sounds terrible.

I don't know if she's alive either. We used to send Christmas cards, and then she stopped.

I won't know until I ring her.

Did she marry?

No, never married. I saw her when I was in England. Her sister and Joan—Aunty Joan—were penfriends too. My friend, who I was with, said have you got any other family, and Joan said no. And I thought well I know she's got a sister.

I wonder what the story was there?

Syd Chidgey's funeral. Gosh, 1981.

'87. My writing again.

It was his anniversary on Guy Fawkes, because I always remember we got the call to say he'd died as we were letting off fireworks.

I don't remember that.

I do. We were at Frederick Street.

Yes. But I don't remember it being Guy Fawkes. Catherine's got a good memory. Peter, two and a half.

Peter completely outgrew his epilepsy?

He did. By the time he was four and a half.

What was wrong with him?

Peter had epilepsy.

I never knew that.

Oh, you did.

Did I?

At the time.

I suppose I did, but I'd forgotten.

He was on medication till he was about eight. The only time I was ever concerned about it in later years was when he started playing rugby. And we were concerned when he was living in Corfu, and he was riding a scooter, and he skidded on olives. We thought that could bring it on again.

I remember when you were visiting us once and he was wearing the little padded helmet.

Well I don't even remember that. My memory's not what it was.

Mm. I always regret not asking my mother what time of day I was born. No one knows. It's just something I don't know.

Catherine was born in the morning, I think.

I thought it was twenty to seven in the evening.

Oh yes, it was. No. Yes. It was, because in the morning I started, and then everything stopped, and they didn't know what to do with me. And your head was coming out and it had stopped, and I couldn't push. And so in the evening they said to Les I think we've got to do something, and Les said well I think you better. And so they rushed us down, and I can remember Les running after the . . . thing I was on. You know. The nurses were pushing it. The doctor was running, I was being pushed, and Les was running too, and he had my handbag, and I can remember him running along with the handbag. He didn't remember it, because I can remember asking him later how did you get the handbag, and he said what handbag?

And then he had a cigar and vomited.

Yes. He didn't even smoke. But the neighbours were celebrating this baby—they were all lighting cigars and they had a drink of something, and Les was sick.

Oh dear.

Because he never smoked.

No.

Alan did the same when Alice was born—he had a cigar with Rikk, Leila's husband. And Leila's brother Owen, who was staying there too. They went outside and had whisky and cigars. This was when we were back at their place. And then he was sick. It may have been the whisky rather than the cigars.

And he doesn't even smoke. Les never smoked, you see, and when we had visitors come they sat in the lounge and smoked, and I always gave them ashtrays, and Les grabbed them and threw them outside and we opened all the windows.

It's just after quarter past four, Mum.

My watch says twenty-five past two. I obviously haven't wound it. I wind it at ten o'clock every morning.

Oh, you need to wind it?

It's fifty-odd years old. And I forgot to wind it this morning—I knew I did. Les didn't smoke, and my father didn't smoke—only a pipe. He had one pipeful at night. Pipes don't make the awful smell that cigarettes do.

How's David's health these days?

We had a bit of a scare earlier this year. We honestly thought we were going down the same path. But no, everything came right.

What are you talking about?

David. He's got B-cell and T-cell lymphoma. B-cell's the bad one. He's still got T-cell—these lesions come up on his skin now and again. It's considered not serious, but it can lead to other things. He still gets checked. Monitored.

How long has he had it for?

About 2009 I think. He's always felt all right. But you never know. He's as skinny as ever—he'll never be any different. He just knows when to stop.

I remember the afternoon teas at Aunty Shirl's and Aunty Lena's. Cream cakes and custard squares and sandwiches and sausage rolls . . . the table groaning under the weight.

Remember when I think it was Helen put the custard squares in her bra? Was that you or Helen?

It was Helen. We were at Aunty Lena's and she couldn't eat any more, but there was the expectation and the pressure . . .

Yes, the pressure.

You couldn't say no. So when Aunty Lena was out of the room she wrapped the custard square up in a paper serviette and put it in her bra.

And coming home in the car, you two were screaming with laughter in the back, and Les and I were saying what's going on? I don't know whether we didn't find out till we got home or whether we found out on the way—I can't remember—but I think Helen must have shown you that she had cakes in her bra.

I can't remember now. But I remember another time she came home from Aunty Lena's with honey toast wrapped up in her suitcase. That inch-thick butter.

Oh yes. Yes.

And another time we were there, Aunty Lena had given us a plate of vanilla ice cream each, but it must have been in the freezer for ages—you know how ice cream goes gritty and horrible? We couldn't eat it. We were thinking what can we do with it, what can we do with it? We went to the loo and tried to flush it, but it just kept foaming. Every time we flushed it doubled in size and foamed up even higher.

She used to annoy Les—have another cake, Les. She was the same with the girls. And she used to buy them the most hideous Christmas presents.

She used to knit them. Big scratchy jumpers that never fitted us and felt like cardboard.

Well Lena knitted for her five sons who worked on the farm. On Christmas Day Helen and Cath would put them on and we'd take photo, photo, photo, photo, and then I'd post the photos to Lena, and then I'd give the jumpers to the Saint Vincent de Paul. Oh, remember that terrible man at Carol's first wedding?

What terrible man? Her husband?

Yes.

David Bicknell?

Was that his name?

Yes. He had beautiful handwriting. Nana told me to beware of men with beautiful handwriting.

Grandad had beautiful handwriting.

David had beautiful handwriting—my David. I think that's why she said it.

Les didn't have beautiful handwriting.

Oh, hi! Can I just interrupt for a while? I'll just give Pat Chidgey some medications.

Lollies, please. Where's my chocolate? She always teases me.

The other day at home there were big headlines about a farm owner and his wife who were fined I think a hundred and forty thousand because one of their workers rode a four-wheeler, wasn't wearing a helmet, went over a bank and died. If Campbell goes over a bank and kills himself are we going to be liable for it because he decided that day not to wear a helmet? He knows he's supposed to, but no one does. We've done all the health and safety. It's unnecessary, really—there aren't that many accidents. They try to make out that there are, but a lot of the time it's just stupidity, or something unforeseen.

Even here they say the silliest things. We get an announcement at dinner: don't swallow your fork. Absolutely stupid things. Perhaps upstairs it might be a different story, but down here we're all reasonable people.

I better make a move. I've got to do some work. There was a magazine published late fifties to mid sixties called Hawkes Bay Photo News, and we've got them all scanned and ready to go online. Some people won't be very pleased. I came across quite a few wedding photos of couples who are no longer together, but what can you do?

It's part of history.

That's exactly right. Part of history.

In our parents' time they stayed together. They didn't run away with someone else. Though Mum's sister did.

Who was that?

Aunty Annie. And nobody saw her for years. She ran away with this man.

She left her husband?

Yes. She left her husband and ran away with this man.

Did she have any children?

I don't know. She came and saw me when I lived in the other
. . . you know . . . the house. And she wouldn't tell me how she
knew who I was. But she knew I was a McGough. She was a
bit weird. She chatted for a while, and I made her a cup of tea.
I never heard from her again. She just wanted the contact, I
think.

Family's important, isn't it.

Yes, and there's no McGoughs now—there were only the
girls, and we all changed our name.

So it's died out?

It's still in Ireland.

Except it's McGeough, because somehow we lost an E on
the way over.

I think that was my uncle—he couldn't read or write.

Uncle Owen?

Uncle Owen. Yes. I think he was something to do with it.

The McGoughs here sent back a marble obelisk to the
McGeough family grave in Ireland, and they put McGough
on it. That must have been disappointing when it arrived. And
when we went to see the cousins in Ireland, they took us to the
family plot, and there was this big marble thing with the wrong
name on it.

Huge thing.

I'd love to spend more time doing family history, but I don't
let myself. You can get so involved in it.

I imagine once you start something it gets bigger and bigger.

That's the thing, it does. It would be nice to go over to
England and go round some of these places, where people have
been. One day. Yeah, no, it won't happen.

I'll get a photo of the three of us together. Hold on.

Oh, Mum loved that jersey. See this one she's got on here? It
had frogs on it, and mushrooms. And when Mum died Joanna

took it and sold it in her shop, and for a long time afterwards she saw this person walking around wearing it.

## 11

The SuperValue's offering 'chicken' drumsticks. What does that mean? 'Chicken' drumsticks.

Eyes and arseholes?

Leonard Cohen died.

## 12

Those sheets are too fridging small.

Are they not super king?

They are super king, but I just about broke a finger trying to stretch them over the mattress. It's because modern mattresses are so thick. You have your springs, and then your elephant foam, and then your memory foam, and then your topper, and then your overlay.

It's not like the Russians are dropping cluster bombs on our house, though.

No . . .

No.

I guess I'm pleased with that first review.

It's a good review.

Mainly I'm pleased they used the hot author photo. In case ex-boyfriends see it.

## 13

I create illusions by cutting paper. I make jewellery pieces inspired by nature and fantasy. My paintings portray the magic that lies all around us. I create surreal illustrations to show how different ideas co-exist. All this pug needed was a pair of socks and his life totally changed. One anagram of my name is Hyena Held Laser, disappointingly I could not work that into a poem.

## 14

Did you feel it?

No, but Paul and Joel did. It just goes to show how bad my husband's snoring is. I can sleep through an earthquake but not my husband's snoring.

I slept through it too. Alan said the blinds were clacking, and I noticed that a few pictures in the hallway were crooked this morning. He woke me up at six thirty to see if I felt it. I was fridging fast asleep! I was dreaming that Barbara Else had written a horrible review of The Wish Child in an Australian literary journal—a really influential one—and I'd just found it online. I was saying to you look, that bitch, she's fridging ruined it for Australia. That's Australia gone. *Gone.* And I was hoping you'd say nobody reads that journal, but you were going yeah, no, that's Australia gone.

I was wondering why my bed was spinning when I woke up, and then Justin started yelling earthquake! Get in the hall! We had to go stand in the doorway.

Is that the right thing to do? I thought you were meant to get under a table.

I think you're supposed to go outside, if you can.

I thought you're not supposed to go outside, because masonry will fall on you. The chimney will topple on you.

Oh. I made everybody go outside.

No. That's totally the wrong thing to do. You just put your family in danger.

So that's two wrong things. First we did the first wrong thing, which was get in the doorway, and then we did the worst wrong thing, which is go outside. So we didn't survive.

No.

But we have no chimney, so there's hope.

Maybe.

It felt like we were on a ship, going up and down. I've lived on a ship, and it felt just like that. I've been in a shaking earthquake before, too, and it's fast—but this one was so slow, like being on a ship, and then I could feel the waves, and something was clicking. There was a weird ticking rather than a rumble. It sounded like it was outside. An even tick, like a clock. We'd gone into some fantasy world; the clock had signalled it was time for the ship to take off, and you could hear the clock ticking, and feel the ship moving.

## 15

This is a gradual event. Look at the night sky; the moon may appear larger than you remember. Ghost earthquakes show up in reports, but don't exist. The fact that we have a full moon and tides is not enough; we're surrounded by water and hills. We need to be very careful not to make retrospective forecasts of what's going to come. It's so close.

I guess I'm not going to see the super moon. I meant to look last night.

Last night you couldn't see anything. I went out at midnight—it was all overcast. Obviously there was a moon because it was quite light, but you couldn't see anything.

I was falling asleep and I thought oh, I forgot to look for the moon; I should get up.

It's just a moon. Just a little bit bigger.

But there won't be another until we're sixty-something.

I remember seeing Halley's Comet in the 1980s.

I do too. A tiny smudge.

My grandfather saw it in 1911. He died in 1982 and it was odd, thinking he saw that as a boy.

## 16

I just rang Mum. We chatted for a while, and then I said it's Dad's birthday. Yes, she said, that was the first thing I thought about when I woke up this morning—but we don't need to do anything, do we. We don't need to buy anything. No, we don't need to buy anything, because he's dead.

## 17

You have to say it all again.

I can't. That's the stupidest thing ever.

Well Melody did the other day. Melody did that for me. Maybe Melody should be my new BFF.

Maybe she should. I have to go, anyway. What's the time? I have to be somewhere.

Two forty-nine. Plenty of time.

I can't remember what I was saying.

You were telling me about the disgraced headmaster.

Okay, so I would gather flowers for this little old lady, and I can't remember—

She did the church flowers?

She did the church flowers. And she was a painter, too, and she was doing a big mural for Saint Francis Church. Saint Francis with birds and bees and wildlife scampering around, and two children—one little Māori boy, and a little white girl. She needed a model for the little white girl, and I sat for her. But the child looks nothing like me at all—she's blond, and nothing like me.

But it's not as bad as the fresco the Spanish woman fixed . . . have you seen photos of that?

No.

I haven't got time to show you now. It was a beautiful but crumbling fresco of the face of Christ. She made Him look like a cartoon. It went viral. Wait, here it is.

Oh Lord. It's kind of . . . hedgehog.

What about the headmaster?

Her husband had been the headmaster at the local primary school, and he'd been dismissed in shameful circumstances—

for caning a child. He'd caned him across the face and opened his cheekbone up. So you never saw him—when I'd go round to deliver the flowers, he was hidden away like some dirty secret.

That's fantastic.

What time is it?

## 18

I'm having to tell a story about the telling of the story, because telling the story isn't enough these days.

## 19

(Oh, and towards the end, please replace 'detective' with 'defective'. Sigh.) (You may have to zoom in.)

## 20

Imagine how many more Thai girls you can meet if you know some Thai vocabulary and phrases! You will have a repertoire; it does make sense to know how to ask her if she's horny or tell her to undress. *It's hot here, isn't it? Do you live alone? I love your skin.* Thai girls let you make the decisions. Thai girls smile more than Western girls. Thai girls know that housework is their job. Western women just seem to wait for reasons to get mad at you and they are also a lot more resentful than any Thai girl. *Don't be shy. What is your favorite position? Does it hurt?* Statistics prove that western countries like America, Australia and by now also Western Europe have the highest percentage of fat girls in the world. Thai girls don't get fat—in Thailand it's easy to find a thin girlfriend and also the skin that western women are extremely jealous of. In the final chapter you'll find bar girls and hookers. You'll love this one. *I want to take you outside. How much do you want? That's too much.* If you make a Thai girl angry, and that doesn't happen much at all, she will forgive you anything, even having banged her best friend.

## 21

A large crane with a set of jaws has arrived in the capital.

## 22

I want to post on Facebook about being longlisted, but I don't want to post it myself because it'll look like I'm boasting. So you'll have to.

You read Alice her story, then.

And link to the story. The one with the picture of me, not the other one. But you'll need to say something about it, because it's the same photo they used in the Sunday piece, and people will be scrolling down and just think it's that story again and not read it.

What do you want me to say?

I'm in a hurry. I haven't got much time. Where's your laptop? Just say I'm so proud of my incredible and beautiful and perfect wife for being longlisted for the book awards. Here's a little baby, one, two, three . . . make sure you tag me in it. Then all my friends will see it, right?

Wait, what am I saying?

So proud of Catherine Chidgey for being longlisted for the book awards, announced today. What a talented wife. Something like that.

It doesn't sound like me.

Here's a little baby, one, two, three . . .

Do you just want to do it?

Okay. You read the story. So proud of Catherine Chidgey for being on the longlist for the book awards, announced today. All right?

Whatever you like.

Wait, that sounds like I was longlisted but didn't win.

You should say the New *Zealand* book awards, so my one thousand-plus overseas photography friends know what I'm talking about.

Very proud that Catherine Chidgey is on today's longlist for the NZ book awards—such a talented wife. Does that sound like you?

## 23

Shhh. Shhhhhh. Are your teeth hurting? Are you getting a new tooth? Shh, shh, shhhhhh. Do you want some Bonjela? Some banana? Shhhhhh. I don't know what you want. There's nothing to give you. What do you *want*? *What do you want?*

## 24

People who say methinks
Velvet upholstery
People who shop at K-Mart while I am shopping at K-Mart
Actors over-acting when they're eating
Gwyneth Paltrow
Students who can email to ask for extra help but can't email to say thank you
Newsprint
Dishwashers that don't dry plastic
Crooked postage stamps
Rhyming poems about Anzac Day and or dead grandparents
The breakfast-bar stools not pushed back into the breakfast bar
People who say peeps instead of people
People who say ta muchly
People who take pictures of their food
The sound of my own voice
The cold

## 25

Hairdressers who ask if I use conditioner
Newsreaders who chat with other newsreaders instead of just reading the news

Public spitters
My knees
Other people's children
Exclamation marks
Vacuum cleaner salesmen who say they will shampoo your entire living area for free so you make a time but when they arrive and have demonstrated how soiled your carpet is and how much filth that is probably mostly from your own disgusting body they can suck up on their white demo cloth they only do the bit of carpet by the back door.

### 26

Sub-editors who change what you said so it's not what you said, but everyone who reads it believes it's what you said.

### 27

Do you think I'm a negative and or an intolerant person?
You're not intolerant . . .
Right.
Perhaps you sometimes see the world through negative-tinted glasses.
Through black-tinted glasses.
No, through negative-tinted glasses.
Is negative a colour? Be concrete.
I feel sick.

### 28

Missing: ~~agonising truth~~

### 29

Six hundred attempts by the CIA to assassinate him, including a missile loaded with LSD.
Is that true?

Because they got desperate. Because they tried so many times.

What was the LSD bomb meant to do?

I don't know. I just read that. There were some bizarre plans hatched.

Like what?

I don't know. I'd have to read up on them.

How do you know that the LSD missile is true?

It's so stupid it has to be true. Just google CIA assassination attempts Fidel Castro.

Okay, so far I've got lacing a radio studio with LSD to cause him disorientation during a broadcast and damage his public image. It's a little bit different from an LSD missile.

Well I don't know. I read that the other day. I don't know where.

There were also—supposedly—poisoned cigars, exploding cigars, an infected scuba-diving suit, thallium salts to destroy his beard, a hypodermic syringe loaded with something lethal inside a ballpoint pen, and a booby-trapped conch shell placed on the bottom of the sea. The LSD plot was actually just bombarding the studio with an *aerosol* spray containing a substance *similar* to LSD. And when he started saying strange things on air, the Cubans would think he'd lost his mind, and stop trusting him.

That's not what I read, but okay.

## 30

One day everything will disappear.

Everything did disappear. It's a mystery. It's horrible. The library book you had sitting on your desk for three months—Getting Things Done—that's been returned, has it?

No. I don't know where it is. Oh, I just moved it.

You have a Post-It note on the front telling yourself off for not returning it.

I could at least put it in the car. All I need to do is take it back to Ōtara Library, for God's sake. I'm such a bad person.

I've got about forty dollars in fines. I haven't read it.

You could have bought the book.

I know.

Not mentioning names, but what do you do when you don't believe that it's a student's actual voice, but you can't find any proof? Because this is clearly not her voice.

Clearly not her voice. I don't know—what do you do? Every now and then it feels odd. She's just shoving a synonym in here and there to beat it.

Mm. A word's not quite right now and then.

Little shit. I can't find anything.

Feck. I'm not finding anything either, and I so wanted to. This website says ask the student to come to a private meeting, then say I was really impressed by your recent paper, it was an excellent piece of work, let's discuss it some more.

And then what?

And then what. Did you know there's a site called plagiarismtoday.com? Daily tips on how to get away with it.

Really?

No.

I wonder if I ever plagiarised. Did I?

You can't remember?

No.

It was different then, though. The internet didn't exist.

You had to look through books.

You had to go to the library, and look through books.

I don't remember . . . it doesn't mean I didn't, but I don't remember. I do remember not writing an essay, though, and at the end of the year the lecturer ringing me up and saying um, so your second essay for blah de blah . . . ummm . . . did you get a B+ for that? And I went yeah. And he went oh, okay then.

So he was having a panic because he couldn't find it.

Yeah. And he just gave me the same as I'd got for the other essay. And I knew very well that I didn't do it.

And you weren't going to fess up. Neither of you was fessing up to your crimes.

So I passed a paper that I didn't actually do the work for.

You're living a lie, Tusiata.

And another evil thing I did was I sent in an essay—you can record this—

I *am* recording this. Am I? I am.

—I sent in an essay on romantic poetry and prose three months late. I pretended I was in Samoa—I hadn't been to lectures forever. I put it in an envelope that I happened to have from the year before, when I was living in Samoa and had sent a letter home to my mother from just about the same date, and I smudged the year. I gave it to my friend, and told her to take it to the lecturer and say Tusiata had to go to Samoa, and she sent this and it got lost in the mail. I rumpled it up a bit. Made it look like it had gone on a journey around the world.

That's quite a lot of effort to go to.

I know.

And they bought it?

Mmhmm.

I was such a goody two-shoes at university. I remember regularly writing a note on my essays saying I realise the word count for this piece was three thousand words; I apologise that I have exceeded this by one thousand words, but I hope you will find that my work warrants it.

Awwww . . . cute.

Such a priss.

I took a year off between my second and third year and went to Samoa, but I spent that whole year nightclubbing and sleeping around, so I found it quite hard to concentrate when I got back. Because I kept nightclubbing and sleeping around.

It's all material.

I wish I knew a bit more about romantic poetry and prose now, though.

Have you said anything on Facebook yet about your dad?

No. I just can't.

You feel the pressure these days—if something happens, you have to mention it.

I haven't gone on Facebook at all. I think because I haven't been able to say anything about Dad, I don't want to say anything about anything. One of my young cousins put something on Facebook straight away and tagged me in it, so everyone knew.

That's the thing—you're forced to participate in events you don't want to participate in.

I didn't want it out in the world that way. Is this hidden fiction?

Is this what fiction?

What's this supposed to be?

I thought you said is this hidden fiction.

Sidden fiction.

*What* fiction?

Sudden. Sudd-en.

Sudden! God, sorry.

My terrible Kiwi accent.

Sidden fuction.

Sidden fuction.


I realised we never did our peer observation.

We did observe each other a lot. Under stress. Meaningful looks across a crowded room.

I don't know if that counts.

It's probably more meaningful than peer observation.

I'm glad that died a death. We never had to personalise and internalise a culture of continuous improvement in learning and teaching practice. We never had to use our scaffolded qualitative tool. What shall we talk about? Eavesdropping?

I've always been what my mother called an earwig. When I

was a kid, I was always listening in on adult conversations. And she could tell.

Were you an only child?

No, I'm the oldest of three. I remember hiding round corners and listening. Trying to piece together stories, and knowing—all the time knowing—that you didn't have the full picture. Not just because you might have missed something audibly, but because you couldn't see the looks on people's faces.

Did you ever overhear anything scandalous?

Only that Santa wasn't real.

Oh no . . . you overheard that?

Well I knew it already—but it confirmed it. I can remember thinking right, I'm never going to let on that I heard, because then he won't come. It was a New Year's Eve party, and we were at our family friends' place, and all the kids had been put down to sleep on mattresses in the lounge and all the adults were partying—well, the men were partying out in the garage and the women were inside having cups of tea. And I heard my mother say I'm pretty sure Sue knows he's not real, but she's not saying anything. And next morning I got up and I said is Santa real? I just couldn't stop myself.

Did your dad's watch turn up?

No. I think it slipped down the bed.

At his house? Or at hospital?

At his house. It sounds as if my stepbrother had a cursory look, but I want him to have a proper look.

Was it meant for you? Did your dad want you to have it?

I just took it off his arm. He was so skinny—it was right up here, at his elbow.

The ending is not the real ending. Let us keep our pain in perspective, please.

# [ DECEMBER ]

## 1

Oh my God. I was sitting there for over half an hour and nothing was happening. I imagine it's like giving birth. Do you push when you feel it starting to come, or do you hold off?

Don't strain.

I was straining. And that puts a load on the heart, doesn't it? Isn't that why Elvis died? But I don't eat deep-fried peanut-butter sandwiches.

You're probably not snorting cocaine, either.

My knees feel weak. Did you hear me jogging?

Jogging?

I was doing a lot of jogging. To try to move things along. At this stage I am considering a crochet hook. I am considering a melon-baller.

Be aware, slow down here. Too fast down this hill can kill. I want you to believe you're healing while you're listening to the word. Can everybody say amen? It makes me so happy when people can take the meat of the word, and you don't have to give 'em dessert. Amen? But we also need to be taught how to behave. No passing on painted median. No passing on painted median. No passing on painted median. Surely the only figure on the world stage who believes he was once abducted by aliens; they smiled and they laughed and they said you not make big evolution. You eat your brothers—animals, yes?—in restaurants. You understand which I mean. But there's no time.

## 2

We're all meant to be flipping our classrooms. Do you understand that? The flipped classroom?

No.

Have you heard of it?

Yes, but I don't know what it means.

Neither do I.

What does it mean?

Um . . . we're not meant to be standing up the front and lecturing . . .

Are we meant to be lying under the table?

We're meant to be fellow learners on the knowledge journey. No, I don't know—I made that up. We're meant to be getting the students to think about the concepts we'll be discussing before class, so that they come—

Fucking good luck with that.

—so that they come prepared to . . . enter the knowledge journey with us their fellow learners? We're kind of already doing that. Look at this reading and be prepared to discuss it on Thursday. But they never do.

No.

I've pocketed the $1.30 in change, finally, from Eleanor Catton's old desk.

You're a lot more honest than me, because I have eaten Eleanor Catton's tuna, and I'm now eyeing up her pictures.

Are they hers?

I presume so.

Why would she leave them here?

I don't know.

That one's signed. It's a numbered print.

We could sell these.

We could. We could hawk them on Trade Me. Why are they all here, though? It doesn't look like they were ever hanging on the walls.

No.

Hmm.

Hmmmm.

That's not Eleanor Catton's yoga mat, is it?

That's my yoga mat.

I'm not interested, then.

Anyway, I've put back on the eight kilos I lost on my grief diet.

The grief diet never worked for me.

Extreme emotions make me not eat. It's that low-lying disquiet—which is what I feel most of the time—that makes me eat. You know what, I snapped yesterday and I hit Tama. I can't even explain how awful he's being. I just fucking lost it. I grabbed him, shook him, and slapped him on the arm—it didn't hurt him—and then I started screaming at him. And I didn't feel sorry. I didn't. I was angry until half past one in the afternoon, and then I felt guilty. And then I forgot that I'd done it, and a few days later it came back to me, and it was all . . . um . . . it was all . . .

Hazy?

Hazy. And I couldn't remember if it was real or not.

What was he doing yesterday?

Screaming at me, being really rude. We were running late, again—and then just before we left the house I went to give him some Floradix, which he's supposed to be taking every morning, and he ran away from me. And I just lost it. I grabbed him and shook him. I started screaming at him. But at the same time, in the middle of my rage, I noticed how it made him stop what he was doing, and pull his head in. And I started screaming is this what it takes? *Is this what I have to do?* He won't respond to anything. I don't know what the fuck is going on; it's beyond me. I was talking to a friend of mine yesterday afternoon, on the way to pick him up—I was dreading picking him up—and she was saying look, you need to take the emotion out of it. Don't go and see a counsellor and tell them all your problems. For one thing, I couldn't tell them what I've done.

Couldn't you?

No! I would have CYFS on my doorstep.

There's no counsellor–patient confidentiality?

Not if you've hit your child. I would literally have CYFS on my doorstep.

Don't go down that route. You did that once before, eh?

Yeah. And I hadn't done anything. When he was seven months old I rang Parentline and I said I *felt* like doing something. And I had the crisis team on my doorstep the same day.

Jesus.

A team of people. And then I had CYFS following me around for three months.

Because you'd said I feel like I might hit him.

I feel like it, yeah. I didn't say I was going to; I said I feel like it. I knew I wasn't going to. I'm at the end. I don't know what else to do. I'm completely at the end of myself. He's like a fourteen-year-old—he's acting like a really bad teenager. Telling me to get fucked. You wouldn't know that from seeing him, because he's not like that with anyone else. He just unleashes this horror on me.

I remember you telling me about that feeling of wanting to hit him when he was a baby.

Or to throw him. I wanted to throw him against the wall. That's what I wanted to do.

And that energy coursing through your arms, and you can't do anything with it. I've felt that. I've felt that too.

Usually when I get to that point I will send him out of the

room, or I'll leave the room myself. But yesterday I just snapped. I don't have any give. So he went to school crying. He wouldn't eat breakfast. He got out of the car and I thought great, what a stereotype. No breakfast, tears running down his face, and I've just given him a hiding. He's really fitting into Ōtara .

PS I met a man at the reading in Tauranga last night who was in the British Army and guarded Rudolf Hess in Spandau Prison. I had my photo taken with him and was going to put it on Facebook, but Alan says that will make me look like a Nazi. What do you think?

3

I made the devil with my eggs: yellow eyes and white horns.

4

It's looking a bit shantytown next door, isn't it. The way they've shoved that salvaged ranchslider on the garage.

They've put framing up around it . . .

They haven't put framing up around it. They've stuck bits of four-by-two on either side to fill the gap, because it didn't fit. That's not framing.

No one seems to be sleeping in there, though.

There are beds. And an awful lot of extended family coming and going. And a power cord running from the house to the garage, through the horrible ranchslider.

You've got to focus on the up side. They're not likely to have a big dog running around. They're nice, civil people. They don't play loud music and have raucous parties. It could be worse, if we had someone with a gang affiliation and it was a shitbox from hell. At the moment it's just a shitbox.

With a power cord running from the house through the jerry-built garage door.

When I was growing up and we lived on Centre Hill, the

government funding came along and every house got a new corrugated iron coal shed. It wasn't connected to the power, but Dad was keeping foster lambs in ours, and he had a heat lamp for them, so he ran an extension cord out of the garage around the corner and into the coal shed. It went over the top of the door, and it chafed where it met the frame and the edge of the iron, and when I walked past I felt waves coming up my arm. I realised it was electrical current—the whole shed was electrified. The whole skin of the building. I could feel rings of waves going up my arm and spreading out. I told Mum, and she said John, John, you've electrified the coal shed, and he said oh, godverdomme.

You could have had roast lamb.

Everything was fine inside, it was just when you touched the exterior. Like I did.

We're going to see baby Tilly, aren't we, Alice?

Illy, Illy!

Your cousin or half-sister or whatever we're going to call her.

Cousin is probably the most acceptable term as they grow up and have to explain who they are. It's not making a dirty secret out of it.

You have a little sleep before we get there, okay?

That guy looked off his tree. He was covered in sweat. It might have been heat exposure.

Would you have stopped and picked him up if we had room? With Alice in the car?

I don't pick up hitchhikers any more.

You have a little sleep in the back seat. Night night. She's looking at me in the mirror: I don't understand.

Did you hear the cuckoo clock when we were there?

No.

Like the one she gave Alice. Is it fixable, our one? The cuckoo was coming out and not going back in.

I'll have to have a serious go at it.

Tilly's really changed. I look at her and I see Beryl—the face shape, the eyes, the build.

She's a lovely little baby. It's less weird now. Initially I felt guilt at not being a dad to her . . .

When I was going to read her that book about the pig, and I said oh, I'll have to read it upside down, Mummy will have to read it upside down, was Alice standing there too? Or did I say Mummy to Tilly?

I think you said *I'll* have to read it upside down.

No, I said *Mummy* will have to read it upside down. I know I said that. I'm just not sure if Alice was there. If she wasn't, it's kind of weird. Calling myself Tilly's mummy. My husband impregnated you, but I think of your daughter as mine because I am barren.

It's a confusing situation.

It's awkward. I mean I feel fine. When we made the decision it felt right, and it still feels right. If I dwell on it, now and then it makes me a bit sad that Donna has a child who's biologically yours . . . and I have one too, of course, but Alice isn't biologically mine.

You can only ever live with that. You can't get round it.

Though Donna called me her donor mum today. She was saying that some people assume that Tilly isn't hers—that she was a donor embryo from us. But she tells them oh no, they're my sperm donor mum and dad. That was nice. Did Tilly vom on my trousers when I was holding her?

No, I don't think so. It was just dribble.

I'll put them out to be washed.

Of course you will.

It is weird, though, that we get the baby who looks like Leila and Donna gets the baby who looks like you and Beryl.

If we had an Alice who was like Tilly—biologically mine, *and* a dead ringer for me and Mum—it would feel disproportionate.

Whereas the way things are now—it's fairer. When I see how much Tilly looks like me, I get a slightly off-kilter feeling—which doesn't compare to you not having a biological child, but it makes it fairer. You look at a lot of families with two siblings—one will take after the mother and one will take after the father, and they can look quite different. That's not uncommon; it's a fifty–fifty chance. You usually take after one parent, not both.

I think I'm a mixture of Mum and Dad.

Really? I don't see your mum in you.

I do. Younger photos of her.

Maybe. Maybe something around the eyes.

I feel like less of a failure as a mother, in terms of Alice's rather utilitarian bedroom, now that I know Donna has an interior design qualification. What are we going to get Tilly for Christmas?

I don't know. A book?

I think we should suggest a price limit of twenty dollars. Otherwise it could get awkward. Donna gets something really expensive for Alice, and we get Tilly a two-dollar-shop figurine.

You assume the scenario is us as the pauper cousins.

I was embarrassed about those roses. We shouldn't have given them to her—they were dead. That's the Huntly fruit and veg mart for you.

All those businesses will die when Huntly's cut off from the state highway—it's a kindness, really.

Put them out of their misery.

Yeah.

One-dollar bus fares, plus one-dollar booking fee. Where do you get to go for one dollar?

To hell and back. Those buses have toilets in them. A bus isn't a very big place, and someone inevitably has a bit of the dysentery.

Maybe they go to Huntly.

They pay *you* a dollar.

And waive the booking fee. Oh my God, I'm glad we didn't build in Huntly. We did look at some sections.

No, you did. I refused to go. I was never going to let us live in Huntly. Sometimes you don't have to see the bottom of the cliff to know what it's like to jump off the top. We just get the eternal damnation of Hamilton.

The grey death, as Sargeson said. But we're not really in Hamilton, we're in Ngāruawāhia, which is more like . . .

The poor man's grey death.


Are you running out of time?

There are some things I still want to include. I'll have to try to weave those in naturally.

I wouldn't be surprised if I woke up on the 31st of January with a slap in the face and a script shoved under my nose. A few last bullet points.

31st of December?

Did I say January? I meant December.


It's weird that the illusionist just disappeared, isn't it.

The illusionist?

Andre Vegas, Illusionist. The house on the corner. He just vanished.

The way he mowed his lawns, it was like he was never there anyway.


## 5

Why does one glass of wine make me try to kiss cowboys?


## 6

Just lie down and lift your feet. He reminds me of our drunk neighbour where I grew up—you know that ranting drunk man who's never been pulled up on anything? Like the truth, for example.

He's not your neighbour any more?

He's dead.

Oh. Of cirrhosis?

Of cirrhosis, funnily enough. He'd just go to the pub and sit there and rant and drink and rant: it's not that I don't like black people, it's just there's too many of them. He'd formed a clique of people with exactly the same opinion.

Like Facebook.

Except you're drinking heaps. And on Facebook, what you say is permanent, whereas at the pub you can say anything and it's gone. This area here is tight. All this is tight, and I think that's causing a lot of the tension. The good thing about where I grew up is that they hated the village next door more than they hated anyone else on the planet. It gave them something to focus on.

Where was it?

Kingussie, which is a wee town in the middle of nowhere. There's a TV series called Monarch of the Glen—that was filmed in and around my village. It's pretty white. About thirteen hundred years of inbreeding; your mother and your sister can often be the same person. There was one gay guy in the village, and he was known as John the Poof. Are you going to see John the Poof? Yeah, I'm off to see John the Poof. And we had this guy called Trevor in our year, and he would have been one-eighteenth Indian—a lot of Scots were posted to India in the army—and he was known as Trevor the Nigger.

Oh my God.

That's just how they referred to him—we've got Trevor the Plumber, and we've got Trevor the Nigger. I think I'll get you lying face down again.

And did Trevor the Nigger know that he was called Trevor the Nigger?

Yes. In the same way you know you're called Trevor the Plumber if you're Trevor the Plumber.

And John the Poof knew that he was John the Poof?

Yes. He was English, but he wasn't called John the English Person, he was called John the Poof. He regularly got dressed up in a wedding dress and sang Happy Birthday to big hairy Scotsmen. My parents ran a pub, and if it was someone's birthday he quite liked sauntering up to them like Marilyn Monroe and sitting on their lap in a wedding dress and singing Happy Birthday. I think that was his way of getting back.

I wonder what it's like now.

Worse, I should think. The bloody Polish. No—who do we hate at the minute? Romanians, I think. The Polish have all gone back to Poland. I'm pretty sure it's Romanians. Or Croatians. The problem with Polish and Croatians is they're white; it's quite hard to point them out. Decent racism's a bit difficult when you're not a hundred percent sure—and within one generation they sound like you anyway. It's not very fair.

No no no. Don't do it. It will be taken out of context. You will look like a Nazi.

## 7

What was in the parcel?

Landscapes, wildlife, mountains, natural wonders, people. When we moved off the farm, he threw out my childhood. All the boxes. All the reels. It didn't cost very much—twenty-eight dollars including postage. I can't remember any one particular image, but I remember I used to stare into them and think they were real. As a kid I never understood how it worked: two images that are the same but from slightly different viewpoints. Your own little secret world; no one else can see it. You hold it up to your eyes and light floods in and funnels through a dark space, and your eyes are covered, and you're immersed. I thought it was magical. I was looking back into time—that's how I feel about it now. I'm hoping one day I'll see some that remind me of my own. I'll see some that I remember. And I'll collect those, and I'll keep them.

8

Have you heard of it? I'll just refresh my memory . . . Twin Strangers. This Irish woman found her doppelgänger. Look at those two.

Wow. *Wow*.

So you post photos of yourself . . .

Please tell me you haven't.

I have.

Unbelievable.

You select your face shape and nose shape and eyebrows and everything . . . like an Identikit picture of yourself. You have to know your own face. Round? Or long? I don't know. I would say long. Probably. Do you think?

Oval? I wouldn't say round or square. Not really heart-shaped, are you. I would say oval rather than long.

And eyebrows—soft-angled, or rounded? And nose—Roman?

These are questions you don't sit around thinking about.

Vanity comes into it too. This woman's posted a photo of herself, looking mid fifties and grey, and one of Audrey Hepburn in her twenties. What's she hoping to achieve? If I was being honest, I'd probably say I have thin lips, but I'd prefer to say Cupid's bow or pointy natural. You set the lower and upper age limits, and ethnicity, and they give you your matches. Then you can put them into My Twins or My Strangers, and it discards the strangers. Most of the ones in My Twins aren't much like me . . . I mean there's a German baby. There's a *guy*.

So you can go with either gender?

I don't think so. He must have entered his gender wrong.

That would be pretty cool, though. To find not just your twin but your equivalent as a man.

Hmm . . . I can't change my gender. I thought I could. I'd have to rejoin as a man.

We should set up that site.

But some of them . . . look. There's something about her face. I can see a similarity there.

No, I don't think we're close.

And then I get a bit worried. Do I actually want to make contact with a double who doesn't know how to orientate a photo properly? She's upside down in all of them. I get very judgemental. It feels like internet dating: I see the picture and I think yes, she's extremely attractive, she might be my double. And then I click on her, and she's got a poorly executed tattoo . . .

Or she's chugging a Woodstock, with a bulldog in the background.

There was a potential match who had Perfect tattooed on one tit and Disaster on the other. I thought: no. No. That date is not going to happen.

Mm. What if you found your perfect twin and she turned out to be a trailer-trash hooker from Nowheresville, Kentucky, who dropped out of primary school?

That's the risk.

There could be a trash Cath out there.

There could.

God, people have a lot of photos of themselves, don't they. I can see something in her, but she's not your twin.

And her, I thought . . . she looks like a younger me.

Yeah . . .

Not that one.

No, not the eyes.

I'm a bit obsessed with looking to see if I have any new matches. Daily. It's the ultimate selfie-generation activity, isn't it.

When I lived in Auckland I used to get people telling me all the time oh, I did your aerobics class the other day. That was a great aerobics class. Ah, no, because I don't teach aerobics. People swore there was someone at the university gym who looked just like me. Even though I was at my unfit, overweight best in those days.

I can't imagine you overweight.

Bizarrely enough, before I had children I was much chunkier. Then they sucked every last cell of energy out of me, and I've never been the same since.

But you never found out who it was?

I never found out who it was.

I don't know. What is the motivation to find a double? You assume there would be an immediate bond, but of course there wouldn't be.

I think it would be quite eerie. It seems disturbing that the universe has only so many templates. That it's been forced to recycle you.

Anyway, so far no match.

If you found her, she could do all your publicity for you. You know how they have a stand-in for the king, so the king doesn't get shot.

So I wouldn't get bad reviews? Only the double would get the shitty reviews?

You could dress her up in art deco jewellery and send her out into the fray. Trash Cath wouldn't care about bad reviews. She'd just stick her middle finger up and say ah fuck 'em. That one—you can see something in her face.

Yes, I can see something there. It is weird, when you look at someone and you think yeah, the shape of the eyes . . . Not that one. And not that one. And definitely not that one. You should join. Go on. It would probably match us to each other.

Enough students mistake us for each other. I think sometimes people just see red hair and that's the only significant detail they store: red-headed lecturer.

What happens if I lower the age limit? Because clearly I look

412

much younger than my actual age. So we'll go down to thirty-three and see what happens . . . nothing. What if I change my ethnicity? Shall we try to find Asian Cath? Or Black Cath? Wait . . . why is it still only seven hundred and forty-seven matches? Maybe only white people do this.

Right, what do you want to say?

I don't know.

Well, how shall we open? Dear all . . .

Ah . . .

Something like Dear all, It's that time of year again . . .

I hope everything has gone well.

I hope everything has gone well for you in 2016. Then what?

I don't know.

Well, what's happened this year? What are the highlights?

Ah . . .

You moved to your new room. Shall we say that?

Yes.

I have moved to a new room . . . as my old one had become very noisy? Something like that?

And I'm very happy.

And I'm much happier, and sleeping much better. What about the view? Does it have a nicer view? I can look out at the trees . . . though the old one had a tree too, didn't it. It's north-facing? It has a lovely view of the gardens? It has a lovely view of the gardens. What else?

I don't know. I can't think.

Helen and co coming for Christmas?

They're all coming, are they? For some reason I thought it was just Helen and one of the boys.

No, that was the plan initially, months ago, but now they're all coming. They'll all be here for Christmas Day.

Oh, I didn't realise they're here for Christmas itself. That'll be lovely.

So we'll say I'm really looking forward to Christmas this year . . . which we'll spend at Catherine's place with Helen, Fred and the boys . . . who are all coming out to New Zealand. What else?

Something about Alice. Getting to know her.

I've had a lovely year getting to know my granddaughter Alice, Catherine and Alan's little girl . . . who is now eighteen months. Do you want to say about going to swimming with her?

Yes.

What do you want to say?

You just say it. I don't go into the pool.

I go to swimming lessons with her on Saturdays—I watch from the sideline while Alan goes into the pool with her. And we should say something about my book coming out—it's been a big year for Cath, blah blah—and something about the Mayalls. I'll ask Helen for a couple of lines and paste them in. And I'll put some photos in too. How do you want to sign off?

I don't know. Merry Christmas?

Wishing you a merry Christmas . . . and a happy 2017?

Yes. That's it. That's what I meant.

## 9

I've almost missed it. I should have been here earlier. Story of my life.

I love that periwinkle blue.

It's like the Wedgwood china Mum used to have. And that violet colour above the hills reminds me of the first evening we walked down to the beach at Ōpoutere, and we came through the forest—a pine forest, wasn't it?

Mm. And we went out over the dunes to the sea. I have a picture of the sky. I remember it was so startling when you came out from the darkness and the closeness of the trees, and then all of a sudden you were on the path through the dunes, and the sky was so huge and the beach was so huge and that violet sky so startling.

That trick was put to use at the Met, in the Egyptian galleries. On purpose you go through all these confined and crowded rooms, and there are massive bits of stone and you're right up close with them, and then you come through two doors and you're in this open space—the Temple of Dendur, which was a dam project in the 1960s. The whole thing was taken block by block to the Met in New York.

To make way for a dam?

Because it was going to go under water. It's in this huge hall, and it's the only thing there, and you go from being crammed into little rooms that you're shuffling round like you're a rodent in a maze—

Or like you're in a tomb.

And you come out into this huge space, and it's awe and it's spectacle. In New York, space is so expensive. It's the ultimate statement of extravagance, that most of the space is empty, and then there's this temple with a moat around it.

So did America get it because they had the funds to pay for it to be transported?

I guess. The Met is all about cultural imperialism. They go and take art and cultural artefacts from different countries around the world; they take it out of its context and its culture and they put it in a glass cabinet in New York. It does nothing for the culture it came from. It does nothing for them. They never get to see it, unless they're the wealthy ones who travel, and then they get to see a bit of their cultural history appropriated and claimed by an imperial power. I was very unpopular in New York with that idea, especially working at the Met. They said no, it's important to see the world's art in one place. Well, it's important for the people in New York. It's not important for the people in Greece or Indonesia or Egypt.

Mm. That bird felt very close.

It was on the roof.

I could hear its wings. Anyway, I don't think it was a trick, the forest opening out onto the beach at Ōpoutere. Unless God thought ooh, this would be quite dramatic.

Ah, but the Babel fish, you see, that's a dead giveaway. It proves you exist, therefore you don't, QED.

Are you quoting Hitchhiker's Guide to the Galaxy again?

Yes.

You can stop now. How can you remember all that, but you can't recall me saying Alan, you have a haircut in the morning? Alan, don't forget the endodontist?

Because you didn't say it in my formative years.

Hm.

He's put a mailbox up on the gate over there.

What were they doing today, with the big roller?

Compacting the road.

The whole house was shaking. The wine glasses in the cupboard were ringing—chiming against each other. You could feel it in your bones all afternoon, and it was too hot to have the windows closed. I don't like it. I don't want new neighbours.

That star jasmine is taking off.

I love that rose. Do you think you could tidy it up before the Mayalls come?

Yeah. I could get a ladder out, and trim some off the top.

You might have to.

It's because I took long branches and made arches, and it's formed a higher fence. Which has blocked out their window.

Yes, that's good. I don't like people. Can you take the Christmas letters tomorrow and get Mum to sign them? She just needs to put Pat at the bottom, forty times. She'll probably want to put Aunty Pat on some of them.

She'll want to write something on each one. A little note. Now, what have I done this year?

I'll go through the list and I'll tell her how many times to write Aunty Pat.

It won't matter. She'll still want to add a note. Now, who's this one to? I'm not signing anything till I've read it.

Ah, fridge.

And then she'll start to write a little note on each one. She does that every year.

Do you want me to give you the list of who they're going to?

No. I'll just say Catherine gave me these for you to sign so we can mail them out to everyone. I'll play dumb. There's nothing I can do—haven't got the list.

I can easily give you the list.

This is what I'm saying—I don't want the list.

I think it might be easier if you have it.

I know how to deal with your mum. She's always going on about how you organise me—I can just say I'm doing the boss's orders.

Mm. I'll count how many to write Aunty Pat on. That's all we need to do. The rest can be Pat, and then four or whatever saying Aunty Pat.

All right.

It's getting cold. I need to go inside now and not think about my life.

## 10

First of all, let me congratulate you for taking the initiative and requesting your complimentary Reading. I'm shocked at your timing, Catherine! Because I feel your life is at a turning point. I know you've felt it and yet it's most likely hard to understand or put into words. I get it because I know the feeling . . .

People like you contact me daily. And I'm here for you. I bet you've basically been swimming upstream against the currents which govern your physical life here on earth. This brief Reading shows the essence of who YOU are and a snapshot of the life YOU should be enjoying right now. That is to say, if you were aligned with the potential shown by your birth chart . . .

Of course, somewhere along the line, you may (by no fault of your own) have strayed from a life enriched by deep, meaningful relationships and a fulfilling career. The period that is fast approaching will allow you to begin living the life you were meant to live, since birth. The tools that will be at your disposal will show you how to navigate this time properly . . . I will divulge all in a minute. This period of great opportunity is about to begin, Catherine. Before that negative voice in your head, which wants you to keep 'living small', has a chance to speak up—complete your request on the next page to begin the process.

Your time is NOW, Catherine!

Catherine, it was exciting when our paths first crossed and you shared the greatest wish you had in your heart. Your timing could not have been more perfect. Catherine, you may be feeling this Transit Period right now! However, there's no guarantee that this window of opportunity will stay open forever, Catherine.

You made an excellent decision asking me for help, and at the right time it seems, too. You are extremely sensitive and insightful. Rather than becoming hurt or resentful because of your unusual sensitivity, you must learn to use this gift. I will divulge all in a minute, but I must tell you that it is a very special occurrence to realize one may be on the cusp of an extraordinary period of change. These revelations may be a bit on the optimistic side.

Your brief yet lovely Mini-Reading will paint a clear picture of how your life 'SHOULD' appear by this time in your journey. I must tell you though, there could be some not so good news in your future . . . I will explain that to you shortly as well.

Catherine, it's possible there has been some 'fog' pursuing you practically since childhood, and that you've had one problem after another. You know what I'm talking about—the anxiety and suffering you may have had to put up with, as well as your present problems too. (I'll explain in more detail shortly.) The opportunities are too good for us to let them go by without lifting a finger. And you have the great privilege today of being at the forefront of those who are going to benefit from this new harvest. With my help.

You have a right to 'happiness'. And you should know that there are no unlucky stars. (I'll explain in more detail shortly.)

It's too bad you didn't request a Reading sooner, Catherine. You could be living with all the fortunate events that have passed you by. But I'm here to tell you Catherine, that it isn't too late! You see, the TRANSIT PERIOD THAT IS FAST APPROACHING puts your life on 'steroids'.

Remember Susan Boyle? She was briefly deprived of oxygen at birth. She was bullied in school. When her mother passed, neighbors said that she stayed in the house, not answering the phone for 3 to 4 days. But then, Catherine, things changed for her. She received 'INTERNATIONAL STARDOM', having the top-selling debut album for a female artist of all time.

Catherine . . . the decision is yours! (I'll explain in more detail shortly.) Now is your time, Catherine! But you MUST act fast, Catherine. Please don't 'mull it over' and put it off, like so many opportunities in the past you have regretted.

It's important for you to know that to help you it is not absolutely necessary for us to meet personally. I will offer this Reading at a MUCH REDUCED cost from what I ask from my in-person clients because I know how much you have to gain . . . but only if you DO NOT SHARE this discounted arrangement with anyone else.

**TIME IS OF THE ESSENCE, Catherine.**

Believe me, it's absolutely essential for you to know what important events will happen for you in the coming months, and I'll be happy to tell you about them. (I will divulge all in a minute.) (If you take a false step, there is no turning back.)

What you discover in this detailed Reading has nothing

in common with anything you may have been told up to now about you and your future. You will receive a document that is more complete and more detailed than anything any other spiritual advisor may have done for you before. All I can say is that even though you may have unsolved personal 'problems' right at this moment, your immediate future holds several favorable opportunities.

I will help you overcome any feelings of 'solitude'.

BUT THAT'S NOT ALL, Catherine . . .

You know you'll never get another chance to discover so many amazing things about yourself and about your destiny. Transit Periods are not to be taken for granted, Catherine. You have to admit that IT WOULD BE A GREAT PITY NOT TO TAKE ADVANTAGE OF ALL THE POSSIBILITIES THAT AWAIT YOU, simply because you didn't act in time. Do it right away. There's no reason to wait another day.

You'll congratulate yourself for putting your trust in me.

**YOUR HAPPINESS, AND THE HAPPINESS OF ALL THOSE YOU LOVE, IS NOW IN YOUR HANDS.**

In all sincerity I remain,

Your devoted friend,

(I'll explain more in a bit.)

## 11

Which way is the Indian garden? That's my favourite—the carpet of flowers. We'll go there first.

Do we have to speak Indian?

No, Mum.

This is a camellia hedge. This is what I want. It's so sheltered in here.

Yes, this is a camellia hedge, but we don't have this much space. And we don't have gardeners. Little men to keep it clipped.

But the foliage. I like the foliage.

Oh . . . a wedding. Shall we go to a different one? Because

they're kind of hogging it. Let's hope they're not going to follow us from garden to garden. Shall we go to the Italian one? Through here, bubba. This way.

What can you see, darling? Yes, pretty flowers. Pretty. Don't pick.

Do you remember coming here with Helen's boys?

Oh yes. Often. We always had a walk around and then a cup of coffee.

Was it here that one of the boys fell into the water? Into the fountain?

Yes. Charlie, I think it was. Fred was saying to him don't go so close, and he fell in.

What are you doing, Alice? No. Stand up.

She's all right. We don't want a tantrum.

Shall I lie down beside her?

She's just relaxing.

Face down on the path.

They've put wires at the top of the stairway. They never used to have wires there. They must have had an OSH incident.

Somebody stupid did something.

Are you all right with the steps, Mum?

Yes. I'll just go slowly. I've never felt this old before. It's come on very quickly.

We should have brought some sunscreen for bubba.

We'll stay out of the sun.

Where's her hat?

I don't know. Probably in the car. We can't go back.

One of Helen's boys used to be frightened of those lions. I can't remember. Not always—when he was quite little. I think it might have been Charlie.

I think it was here that he fell into the water.

Yes, I think it was.

Aren't those pink flowers lovely?

What are they?

I don't know. I can't remember.

Sit down, bub. Make room for Nana. Oh, is that a dead leaf? Thank you. This does remind me of gardens I visited in the South of France and in Italy.

Oh yes.

Do you remember that garden we went to when you came over to see me—

Ohhh, yes.

—and it was owned by an English woman—

Yes.

It had been in her family—

Yes. Yes.

—for years and years. This reminds me of it.

Well yes. It is a bit. I had never thought about that, but yes. It was this type of garden, wasn't it.

Mm. The potted—

Yes.

—citrus trees, and the gravel walkways, and the little—

Yes.

—low, clipped hedges.

Yes. I can remember the little hedges. They weren't very high, were they. You took me to some lovely places over there. I'll always remember them.

Mm.

A couple of months ago I got out my travel diary and I read it. Ooh, you've got a banana! She eats well, doesn't she. That's good. You give her sensible things.

I do wonder what Italian people think when they come to visit the Italian garden. Or what Indian people think when they visit the Indian garden.

I took a daguerreotype of that fountain and a European person saw it on Facebook and he asked where in Europe it was.

Oh dear. What did he say when you said Hamilton?

I don't think he replied.

Oh! Oh, I thought she was getting into the water.

It's just an illusion. There's a pathway.

Yes.

A PowerPoint? Where?

A pathway.

There's a photo of you on that path—it looks like you're pushing Oscar and Samuel into the water.

Was it them? I thought it was Charlie. Mum said it was Charlie.

I think it was Oscar and Samuel. One of them, at least.

Who fell in?

Alan's nephew. Or nephews.

I thought Charlie fell in. But I might be wrong.

Did you used to go to the Christchurch gardens when you were little?

No. Because we lived out on the farm, and Dad milked twice a day, you see. By the time we got into town, we'd have to head home again. I didn't go out much as a child.

What about when you were older, though?

Oh, Les and I went a lot. Oh yes.

And what were they like then?

Oh, beautiful. They were the best gardens in New Zealand for years. But I don't know anything about them now. People used to come for miles, and there were always things in the paper about them. They were really lovely. Christchurch is good for gardens. The weather suits them. We went there on the Sunday after we got engaged and I was walking around with my hand . . . with my hand . . .

Flashing your ring around?

Yes! Les and I often went there. Well, we were saving to build a house, and instead of going somewhere and spending a lot of money, we would save it and go to the gardens. I must ring Joan before Christmas. I always give her a ring before Christmas and Easter and that sort of thing. And I try to do it early, because she'll ring me, and I know she doesn't have the money for toll calls.

Shall we go for a wander round the paths? I'll keep Booboo with me, all right, Alice?

I told the nurse this morning that something's happened to me. I feel like seventy instead of sixty—and she said you're bloody eighty-five. The nurses don't normally speak like that. She gives me lots of cheek and we have some good jokes. I'm very happy there.

Bee.

Beads. Yes, they're Mummy's beads.

Bee.

Beads.

I love those black beads of yours.

Bee.

Beads.

Where'd you get them? Overseas?

Sort of. EBay.

Are they old?

Bee. Bee.

They're 1920s.

I thought they looked old.

Bee. Bee!

Yes, they're beads, aren't they. Glass beads.

They're Nana's beads—I mean Mummy's beads. Has Nana got beads on? Yes. Nana's got pearls on. But they're only little. Little ones in comparison to Mummy's.

Come see the river.

Let's have a look at the water, bubba.

This is the most beautiful view up here.

It is lovely. You don't often get this close to the river in Hamilton. You can forget it's there.

That's right. Even if you're driving you don't see the river much.

Because it's cut so deep. It's not like rivers you see down in the South Island when you're going over a bridge—the river is the same level as the land.

What's that little bird up there?

Where?

There. It's not a sparrow.

Yes, a little sparrow.

No, I said it's not a sparrow—it's got a red face.

It's not a sparrow?

No. Alan, what's that little bird up there?

I don't know. It's not really a sparrow.

No, it's not a sparrow.

Might be a finch.

Looks like a sparrow to me.

Keep an eye on her. I don't want her tumbling down those steps.

She's okay running round. Let her have a run. The sky won't fall.

She's going to go down the steps. See? See? She would have bowled straight down if I hadn't been there.

If you say so. Are you all right getting down the steps, Mum?

No, I'm not. It's funny—I've never felt like this before. Your mother's got old and silly. I'm all right holding your hand.

You could jump in the pram. I could push you.

That's a good idea . . . but I think my legs might hang down. Ooh, look at the rhubarb.

We had a huge rhubarb patch at Frederick Street, didn't we.

Yes. I used to cook it quite a lot.

You used to stew it.

Yes. And sometimes make . . . that pie, with . . . you know . . . the crumbs over the top.

Crumble. Rhubarb crumble.

Yes! Rhubarb crumble, that's it. Les loved it. That's probably why I made it so often.

And those are marigolds in the centre, are they?

Yes.

Did we used to have those growing in the bed by the carport—

Yes.

—at Frederick Street?

Yes. They weren't quite as big as that. They were the same thing, but they didn't grow as fat.

There you are! Where did you and Daddy get to?

I found her hat, but she threw it in the water. I'm worried about her getting sunburnt.

She's all right. No, let her push the pram. You've got to let her try these things.

Can you speak Italian, Booboo?

Shall we put Booboo in the pram? You can push him, darling. Are you all right to keep walking a bit more, Mum?

Oh yes. Yes, I'm fine. As long as we go slowly. She's running away. The speed of it!

Who is that child?

You'd think the mother would do something.

She just needs a sleep.

You can't reason with her. You can't correct her behaviour at this stage.

Cuddling them doesn't make any difference.

Did you see the girl taking a selfie against the ivy, pulling her off-the-shoulder top even further off the shoulder?

A *lot* further off.

Come on, bub. Let's have some afternoon tea. You've still got those corn chips, haven't you, Alan.

I don't think she likes them.

Do I have to buy anything for Christmas, or have you organised it?

It's all organised. Here's Booboo. Oh, poor Booboo. You've got to hold him. Don't throw him. No. No. Don't throw

Booboo. I'd love to go back to Italy.

Oh, yes. I loved Italy.

We tried to see the Shroud of Turin, didn't we, but only saw the reliquary that holds it. Venice was my favourite, I think.

I loved that holiday with you. Places I'd never have been to otherwise. I loved all the holidays I had with Les, too, but we'd never done anything like that. Gone overseas.

Why do you keep pointing under there? Do you want your jacket? Are you a bit cold? No?

She's looking at something.

Water? Do you want some water?

Do you want your nappy changed?

We don't know what you want, bubba.

I don't think she does either.

You're just tired, are you? Pass me the bag, I'll see if there's anything in there that she wants.

There's a teething ring in the front pocket.

Is there something in here, bubba? No. You don't want that either. There's nothing else.

What time does Helen get in?

Some time in the afternoon. They've hired a people-mover so they'll pick you up and then all come out to our place for fish and chips.

And how long are they staying?

Only eleven days. They don't get a big holiday over Christmas.

That's long enough to have someone staying in your house. I'm not being awful.

They're not staying with us.

Oh, aren't they?

Where would we put five extra people, Mum?

I've never thought about it before. Where are they staying?

With the Dumbles.

That's right. I did know that.

Do you remember going to see the glassblowers in Venice?

Oh, yes! That was one of my favourite things. I underlined it in my diary. And it was good with you, because you can speak the language.

Well, I don't speak Italian . . .

No, but you were able to manage it. Excepting when I got eight cakes. I wanted four. There was a shop and we got buns for lunch—not a buttered bun, a sweet bun. Do you remember that?

No.

I can always remember, because I said four, and she put six in. I said no, four. So she put another two in, and was going to put in another two. I said no, that's fine. We went and fed the ducks with them. That was a lovely trip. It was my first venture on my own after Les had died—I always remember that. I was thinking the other day—I can't remember when Les lived with us.

He did. He did live with us.

I thought he did. But some people I think mourn forever, and you can't do that.

It has been twenty-one years.

Yes. Lena always used to go on about John, and quite frankly I think she was just showing off, because they fought half the time.

Didn't she visit his grave every Sunday?

Yes.

I remember buying some Venetian glass beads, after we'd seen the glassblowers. And you bought that P initial—P for Pat. That little glass pendant.

I don't know where it is.

I haven't seen you wear it for a while.

No.

You used to wear it a lot, didn't you.

I did. I wonder if it's been lost somewhere, because I've hunted high and low for it.

It's very little.

Yes, it was little. And I liked it. I haven't had it for quite a while. And I can't remember whether I wore it out one day, and I probably don't remember the day I lost it.

## 12

Here's what happens to a tree to be killed in different situations:

If a tree is a seedling, it is deleted from memory no matter why it died.

If a tree is a sapling or adult killed in a harvest, and the run is 'stump aware', the tree is converted to a stump.

Saplings killed for any other reason, or by harvest in a run that is not 'stump aware', are deleted from memory.

If the tree is an adult killed by harvest and the run is not 'stump aware', it is deleted from memory.

If the tree is an adult killed for any reason other than harvest, and the run is 'snag aware', the tree is converted to a snag.

If the tree is an adult killed for any reason other than harvest, and the run is NOT 'snag aware', the tree is removed from memory.

If the tree is already a snag, it is removed from memory.

Stumps exist only for the timestep in which they were created, and then disappear.

## 13

We forgot to read the little number 12 book on the advent calendar yesterday. Shall we look at number 12 *and* number 13?

It's hard enough to get through one.

Wait, no, bubba has to find it. We have to look for the numbers. It's an educational opportunity rather than fun.

Dada. Dada.

I'm not sure we looked at number 11, either. Now I'm reading out of order. The owl on top of the clock has come to life and it's no longer an owl. It's Herr Drosselmeyer, flapping his long black cloak like a bat.

I am the god of hellfire.

## 14

I don't know what to do next; I'll never have a story that good again.

## 15

Story about guard at lock-up storage facility. Lets himself into the containers and goes through the stuff stored there. Falls in love with someone who rents one of them, tracks her down.

Story about person obsessed with murder case, later meets accused who was found not guilty. He lets slip something that proves to her he is guilty, but she is in relationship with him by then.

Story about man who has same name as serial killer. All his life has been no one important, but now people look at him sideways. Women pay attention as never before. Starts to like it.

Story told from pov of a baby before birth. (Already done.)

Story about someone who overhears a story, records it—but isn't a story, is someone's real life.

Story about playing saints. (Not sure what I meant.)

Story about nightmare date—diarrhoea in hotel toilet.

Story about my Meridian Energy phone call—person scrawls ARSEHOLE CUNT across final bill. Then has to present final bill in court case.

Story about pupils who murder teacher. She seemed to fall as slowly as chalk dust, settling white on the wooden floor . . .

## 16

According to the book, many children by this stage can combine two words to form a meaningful phrase. Has she done that yet? Alice? Alice? Have you combined two words to form a meaningful phrase? We should be sitting on a blanket and asking her to bring us a flower, a leaf or a stick. We should be feeding her pieces of Emmental shaped like fish, and teddy croquettes, and merry meatball ponies. We should be arranging crunchily coated chicken pieces with green beans and sautéed potatoes to make this amusing caterpillar. We should be using fancy biscuit-cutters to shape peeled and cored fresh apple rings into clouds of steam.

## 17

Hello! It's so nice to see you all!

Shall I take my shoes off?

That'd be good. Hello Charlie! I mean Harry. You're Charlie. Eddie! You're unrecognisable. No little boys any more, Helen.

I know—they're enormous.

And Eddie's voice . . .

It's called growing up.

It shouldn't be allowed. That's Aunty Helen, bubba. You've seen her on Skype.

She's got to warm up.

Did you self-medicate on the plane?

I thought that would make it worse. Alice, we've got something special for you. Look at this. Are you ready?

She's not sure.

It's a singing Christmas penguin. I thought she'd be scared of it. You push here, darling. It can go for hours.

Oh. Lovely.

She got another present today and tore into it and the paper came apart. She was all upset and was trying to piece it back together.

I'll put this here, Mum, but keep an eye on bub. Hot hot hot. So you're thinking an early fish-and-chip dinner, before you all conk out?

We've already conked out.

How long was your flight?

Twenty-seven hours.

How many movies is that?

About ten. The great thing is you can speed through them.

Catherine does that. She records stuff on TV, then watches it double time if it's not very good.

Well, I feel I've committed to it by recording it in the first place . . . but also, life's too short. Charlie, you're looking so like Helen these days.

Who's that on the card?

Illy.

Tilly. That's Tilly.

Alice is very keen on Tilly.

Tilly's a big favourite. She looks exactly like Beryl.

Who's Tilly?

Tilly is . . .

Alice's half-sister, strictly speaking.

Biologically speaking.

Alan's sperm, and someone else's egg.

We've yet to come up with a term.

We were sperm donor to a friend of ours in Auckland, remember, Mum?

Oh, now I know who you mean. I didn't catch on. Let me see the card, Helen?

As they grow up we have to work out some all-encompassing term that doesn't have to be explained.

Cousins?

We thought cousins. We've been calling Poppy and Freya cousins. I suggested sperm sister today . . .

No.

No.

No.

What did you say you suggested?

Never mind, Mum.

What's happened to Baby Jesus? Where's the bubba?

Merry Christmas from Donna, Harry and Matilda. Oh, another Harry. That's lovely, isn't it. Can I read inside? Who's the little baby?

Tilly. We were sperm donor to Donna.

Oh yes. Yes, I know.

Christmas Penguin has replaced Baby Jesus in the nativity set. He's terrifyingly huge.

What does Baby Jesus do, though? He just lies there. He doesn't sing.

The penguin would be quite hard to crucify, with his stubby little wings.

Who's that on the card?

Illy.

Tilly, isn't it. That's baby Tilly, Mum.

Yes but I don't know who baby Tilly is.

She is Alice's half-sister. We were sperm donor to . . .

Oh yes, I know now. I see. She's lovely, isn't she. It's nice that you're going to keep in touch.

Shall we put Baby Jesus back in the crib?

Baby.

Baby. Baby. Here's the baby.

Baby.

Yes, here's the baby. Put him back in the crib? Don't eat him. Put his blanket on. Nice and cosy, with his mummy and daddy.

*

433

I don't like where this is going.

Oh God, neither do I. Why is it always the dog? Every fridging time. Whenever there's a dog in a movie, you just know.

Don't look. Don't look.

What's happening?

He's going to the door. He's looking around outside. There's nothing . . . oh, there's a bag on the ground. Don't look. Don't look. Don't look.

Poor Mads Mikkelsen. What are the subtitles saying?

That he's going to kill them. Okay, they're not showing it. But they still might, so don't look. Oh, that's awful. Christ. Don't look. Don't look don't look don't look don't look don't look. Don't. He's asking him to leave.

Who is it?

The godfather. Of the son. Don't look. It's an extended scene. He's digging a hole. Jesus Christ, just get it over and done with.

We could watch it on double speed.

Why do you *do* that?

### 18

Where was the wedding? Have you got some photos? She looked gorgeous on Facebook.

Down Old Taitap Road . . . do you remember . . . ? No, you were way too young.

That's a lovely one of the two of you.

That's Christopher's wedding suit.

Look, bubba. Grandad Brian in a suit.

I find it hard. You wait till this thing here gets to bloody twenty-eight—the same age as Erin is now—and you've got to get her married off. Your daughter. I never thought my daughter would get married off. When your son gets married—of course you haven't been through this—when your son gets married he's still your son. But when your daughter gets married you feel like you're losing somebody. And I'm not good at that. I didn't quite break down, but it was bloody close. She's my best mate, she really is. Always has been. And he's not a bad guy either. He's got these plugs in his ears, and tattoos, and the biggest beard you ever saw—but my God, he scrubbed up good.

I never understood that fashion—the things in the ears. They keep putting bigger and bigger ones in.

That started in the States . . . shit, it would have to be ten years ago. I thought those guys were dumbarses when I saw them over there.

They're called ear tunnels. One of my students told me.

Are they. So what. Stupid things.

I see Erin's got a horseshoe. We've got that photo of you giving Mum a horseshoe at her wedding.

We were talking about that. I had to make sure she had a horseshoe, because I said Aunty Pat had one.

That's cousin Erin, bubba. I don't know if you've met cousin Erin. And did you have to make a speech?

No, Lin did. I can't talk. No, Lin done very well. So Helen's here now?

They arrived yesterday.

According to Pat they've been here a week.

No.

And they're staying with you.

No, they're staying with their friends who have much more room.

I'll come and get you. I'll come and get you. I'll come and get you! Stay at my house?

That would be good, wouldn't it, Alice. We like that idea.

I know I don't see her very often—man, she changes every time I come here.

And how's Claire doing?

I'm not allowed to tell you something.

Is she pregnant?

I'm not allowed to tell you.

Okay, you didn't tell us.

God Christ, don't ever bloody mention it.

How far along is she not pregnant?

I don't know. I'm not telling you nothing. You don't know nothing.

We don't know anything at all.

She'd go off her bloody trolley.

Mintiemoo, were you looking for your water bowl and it wasn't there because someone keeps picking it up and turning it upside down? Come on Moo, I'll give you some water.

You're a beautiful pussycat, aren't you. Is this the deaf one?

That's Jiffy. This is Mintie. She's in possession of all her faculties. What are you doing on Christmas Day?

Probably nothing. I might be having brunch at Christopher's. That's about all. No one's coming up this year, because of the wedding.

Do you want to come here for midday dinner?

No no no no, I won't, no. I always get depressed on Christmas. I hate it.

Come round here.

No no no, I won't go anywhere. The year Lin left—I never really got over it.

We'd love to have you.

Yeah I know, thank you, yeah, no no—I'll go and say gidday to Christopher at some stage and call it quits.

Well you know where we are if you change your mind. We've got Rikk and Leila coming—you know, our surrogate— and their two girls, Poppy and Freya, and her parents are over from England. And Mum and the five Mayalls and us. So we'll have fifteen.

Just do a bloody barbecue out on the deck.

We don't have a barbecue.

Oh my God. Yeah, because you're veggie. Can I have a

cuddle of your penguin?

Show Grandad Brian your penguin. Show Grandad Brian. Show him. Take Nennee.

How does the penguin sing? You show Grandad Brian how you make it sing.

Push the button. Push the button. Don't go all shy. You push the button. You can push it. Show Grandad Brian the penguin.

She's saying some words, isn't she?

Yes, quite a few. It's just a matter of figuring out what they are.

Give Grandad Brian a block. I try to stack them up, but I can never get to the top before she smashes it all down.

What are you saying?

I'm not sure.

When I was down for the wedding I stopped outside Mum's house—the one that Les drew up, the one in Ledleys Road. It got quite badly damaged in the earthquake, and now it's totally altered. Remember it had a kink in it, and a little bit of a deck facing the road? That's all built in. And the car shed isn't under the house now—they've put it out to one side, and put a big deck there.

Did you ever know the farmhouse where Mum and Lena and Alice grew up?

Yeah, I stopped there too. It's a bloody disgrace now. Because Wally Williams—isn't Henry McGough your grandad? Same as me?

Yes. Mum's dad.

Well he sold it to Wally Williams. He was a little short fellow who spoke at about two hundred mile an hour—he was an auctioneer for National Mortgage for a thousand years, and mustered at Molesworth—he used to have the place looking like a million dollars. Every fence post was white all year round, there was never a blade of grass more than that long, the hedge was always perfect, the yard as you drove in was perfect . . . Now you can hardly see the house, and you can't even see the roadside fence—it's covered with grass and weeds and crap. There's about twenty acres there. That Wally Williams guy, he died about five years ago, but I think he used to have it as an overnight stop when the guys bought stock out of Addington Sale. They'd take them there and then shift them on the following day.

I'd love to see inside. It looks like a lovely old house. Or was.

Yeah. And Dad was born round the back.

Your dad?

Yeah. You go past Wally Williams's house, onto Taitap Road, and the next farm on your right backed onto that place. Down a long long drive. The house is still there. And that's where Dad was bloody born.

So your mum and dad grew up next door to each other?

Yeah. And you know where the Catholic church is in Halswell? Their classroom is behind there. It's still there.

Come and say hi to Grandad Brian.

I might come and get you! So have you made a million dollars out of this book so far? Cheques rolling in?

Not yet.

Soon though, eh.

He's going to get you!

I'll get you!

Run run run! Run run run!

I've got a shed full of shit right now. I went to mow the bloody lawns yesterday. I won't have told you this story—I bought the Corvette, I think I told you that, didn't I?

Yes, but you were having some problems.

It's like your Volkswagen.

You mean it's in bits?

Nice lady I bought it from in the States. Just like you and I. Her and her hubby had it for years and he died and she doesn't want to drive it around, a big goofy thing like that—it was really his cup of tea. She said there's nothing wrong with it, and she gave me all the paperwork, everything from bloody new, and I bring it out here and oh my godfather, I can't believe it. I can't get it VINned and I'm just having an absolute major with it. The VTNZ are just screwing me. But never mind, I don't want to go down that road. I'm sick of even thinking about it.

I was looking forward to having a ride in that.

I'm looking forward to having a ride in the VW. In twenty years or so.

I got a lot of the stuff done on the Corvette. It had to have all the rear suspension off. It's got sway bars up front—it's a racing car, really—and bushes and rubber things. Had to get them all replaced. Had to take it in and get the front and back realigned. Then I had to drive the thing home, and the bloody radiator blew up, and all the water poured inside the car. Into the passenger seat. You just wouldn't bloody believe it.

It's not like you to buy a lemon, Brian.

So I go to pull the radiator out, and mate, I might as well just burn the car down—it was so difficult. And then I couldn't get it back in again. Then I seen a tractor for sale down in Invercargill, so I thought I'll buy this bloody tractor, it's cheap. And I reckon I can get it home pretty right. It's four thousand to cart a tractor from Invercargill to the Waikato, but I knew a guy down there, because I've driven for him, and I knew he had his truck down there and nothing to bring home. So he said yeah, I'll bring it home for you, so I run him down $500 in cash and a box of beers. I thought that'll shut him up. And then that night the prick rang me up and said oh, would I do him a favour? And of course I couldn't say no, could I. He said would you come and pick up my truck and go down to Ōtorohanga and take a tractor to Cambridge for me. That was half a day's work and I had to do it for free. Another two hundred bucks. Anyway, prior to buying the tractor I asked the guy selling it four or five questions—are the hydraulics good, battery good, power steering and brakes and PDO . . . yeah yeah, this tractor's like a million dollars. So I buy this bloody thing, and I get it home, and you would never bloody believe it. For a start it had no power-steering fluid in it. It had no oil in the gearbox, therefore the hydraulics couldn't work—even if they did work they couldn't work, because they had no oil in them. So I go to pull the hydraulic lever up . . . oh, that's not sitting right. It is *broken off.* So I thought I'll just see if the power take-off goes . . . oh, there's no lever there. I get down off the tractor, walk round the back and have a look—the shaft goes into the back and it's broken off flush at the wall. So to cut a long story short it's about a thousand bucks just to get this one little shaft—a thousand bucks worth of parts. I rang the guy up and I said look I'm not going to put anything bad on Trade Me about you—I just can't be bothered—and he said if you don't do that, he said I'll find you some parts. Which he duly did. But I had to take this tractor to a million pieces, and I got it all back together again, and before I bolted it all up I even started it to make sure the power take-off went round, which it did. I bolted it back together again, put the oil in it, and now it won't go into gear. God only knows why. So I started pulling it to bits again yesterday.

You're not having a good run, are you.

When I got sick of the tractor yesterday I thought God, the bloody lawn's nice and dry, I can go and mow my lawn. I've got it down about that high, looking really good. I get the bloody lawnmower out, and I'm roaring round, flat out, and about halfway through it's just not looking like it should. So I drive it up on a bit of a bank so I can get underneath it, and turn the blade . . . yeah, the blade's going round. I start it up and carry on a bit more . . . no, I'm sure there's something wrong here. So I go back on this little mound and get underneath and have another look at the blade, and I turn it round, and I notice the bloody pulley up the top's not going round.

So the blade's not doing anything?

It was just turning with the wind. The bloody shaft that comes through spins the blade down here, but the pulley up here sits on this spline, and the bloody spline and the pulley are worn out. It's only about two years old and the spline's gone. Bloody disappointing.

That's disaster number three, so there won't be anything else.

No. Unless the car blows up. I'll come and get you. I'll come and get you! Anyway, I better get going. The day's wiggling away.

You spend all your time taking everything apart.

## 19

They clamped my hand in front of me and I had to lie face down on the bed and it started making alarm noises. You wear headphones and you're given a panic button and then it starts whirring away—it sounds like a very loud car engine. I thought they'd just stick my hand in.

You were right inside the machine?

I could feel the waves passing through me and then I was getting disorientated and thinking the bed was gliding forward and I had to bring my head up to see that I wasn't actually moving at all, I was just imagining that I was moving. I did try to talk myself down: they probably put fifty people a day through this machine and people do it all the time and it's fine. But even though I'm trying to be rational and think rationally, an involuntary response takes over and your mind starts to race and I felt nauseous and then the arrhythmia started up and I could feel myself going into a panic attack. And they were playing commercial radio at a very low level—

That would be enough to send you over the edge.

You couldn't quite hear it right. Just voices murmuring in the background: oh my God, he's going to explode. I said I didn't feel well. It had only been a couple of minutes but the whole thing takes quarter of an hour, sitting inside this whirring drum with these waves passing in and out of you.

You can feel the waves?

On my hand. Flowing back and forth. It was throbbing.

Like when the coal shed was electrified?

Yes. And I just couldn't do it. I can't do this. It was getting steadily worse. And then the walls of the drum felt very immediate and close and I was having a panic attack. I wasn't expecting that at all—it never occurred to me. And now my heart is sore.

Did you hit the panic button?

Yeah.

And they stopped it?

Yeah. They were like, what? And I said get me *out*. And so they retracted me from the vice and they talked to me for a bit and said do you want some sedatives? I said I'm not taking drugs. I don't do very well on drugs. Any sort of drug in my system, I'll have a bad trip.

It might have been the way to go. It's only Valium.

I just wanted out of there.

But they didn't get enough images . . . ?

No.

Don't do that. I don't like that. We don't throw things, Alice. Can you reschedule and be sedated and—

There's no fridging way I'm going back in there. I'm not ever going to have one ever again in my life.

I know it must—

No, I don't want to talk about it. It's back to the panic attacks when I lived in New York. I can't describe it. I'm not doing it. I'd rather die.

What about your wrist, though?

It's fridging sore.

No hitting. Do not hit Daddy. No. We don't hit people.

It's her dinner time. I'm ignoring you, aren't I. You're right in front of me and I'm ignoring you.

## 20

Santa's not here and there's no fucking sign saying when he will be. The throne's empty. I'll have to go to the fucking info place at the other end of the fucking mall and find out what his hours are. Hold fire on leaving the house.

I didn't realise there was going to be a queue. I thought if we got here right on ten, we'd be fine. They don't even have a sign saying what Santa's hours are. Well, they do, but it's round by the other entrance.

If you want to take the pram I can arrange the car seat so it's easier to get back in. I think you'll be hard-pressed to control her without the pram.

I don't know how to dismantle it. I'm useless. I'm a useless mother.

There's just two things to do.

It's all getting a bit hectic. I've got to buy something for Poppy and Freya—Leila said clothes, but the shop's way over there. I was going to try to do that now, but I've got no time.

You could. I can stand in line. What's the time?

You're going to need to get going to your appointment. It's five to ten. Unless I run. But then you'll get to the head of the queue and I'll miss seeing her with Santa.

They'll take a while. We'll be here a while.

But your appointment's at ten thirty . . . I'll run.

. . . No, it's not going to be enough time.

It's not going to work.

Her nappy bag's in the car if she needs a change. But unless I go and fold the seat down, it'll be hard for you to change her in the car.

She's lost a shoe.

You'll need the pram. I'll show you. See on this side? See how this button moves like that? You've got to hold that in, and on the other side, while you're holding it, you push that one in, and that lifts that up.

So I push that that way, like that, and hold the back thing in—

No no. No. Just push that and hold that there—it's got to be across—and then you push that in at the same time—see how it's got a spring in it—and then once that's off all you've got to do is hold that button in and flick both of those levers up, and then it will all collapse, and you put it in the car. Although at the moment it won't go in the back because of how I've got the car seat arranged. I better go down and make room.

So the first thing I do is push that forward and hold that in at the same time, then lift that off, then I push that button and flick these two levers up.

This thing here moves. And this moves. But they won't move until you push that button. And then the arm comes down.

Oh my God.

I better go. Don't forget to ask Santa for the Lotto win.

Have you got my keys? Ooh, here comes Santa, Alice. Look! Can you see Santa? There's Santa! Do you want to wave? Let's get your socks looking nice. There he is. There's Father Christmas. You can have a photo with him. He's saying hello to all the children. He's going to do a high five.

Up.

You want to come up?

Up.

All right . . . oh, our turn now.

No no no no no.

Darling? Do you want to say hi to Santa, and tell him what you want for Christmas?

No no no no!

No?

No no no! No no no no no!

Shall we get your penguin out of my bag? Who's this? Who's this? It's Nennee! Nennee the Christmas penguin! No?

No? Okay, I think we might have to call it a day. We'll have to give it a skip. Sorry, Santa.

That's all right. Do you want to give me a high five?

What about a high five, Alice? No?

You may notice the not-quite-dismantled pram in the front passenger seat. I don't want to talk about it.

## 21

I rang Mum. She's feeling much better now, and looking forward to Christmas Eve mass tomorrow.

My clock says 1:02. What time is it really?

Who knows. We're running on bubba time.

It's later than we think. I suspect interfering little fingers.

I'm sick of telling her not to put the baby in the rubbish.

Baby Jesus doesn't go in the rubbish, does He.

I think we should stitch Him into His bed.

No, because on Christmas morning Baby Jesus goes to lie in Mary's arms. That's why she's sitting there with her arms open for twenty-four days—she's waiting to hold the baby.

I really don't see it.

I'll show you. Give me the baby. See, Mary's hands go like that, and Baby Jesus goes there . . . but now we've done it before Christmas Eve. It's unlucky.

## 22

This is essentially your window of opportunity, Catherine. I can only show you the door. At this point I always get a little anxious. I have set up a special page where you will find an offer that is greatly reduced for you. I cannot keep this offer open forever. Soon this opportunity will be gone. I will watch my inbox. It is you that must walk through the door. You must hurry, Catherine. Or will you give in to your fears and doubts once again? Have you ever felt empty inside, Catherine? The window of time is closing, Catherine.

Let's take down the dead flowers. They're looking a bit sad.
No.
Throw the dead flowers away?
Okay.

## 23

I'm so glad you're not my mother ringing to cry down the phone at me.
I could if you like. I could do some weeping.
I'm at the end of my rope. Every phone call ends in tears. Anyway . . . I am recording.
I still don't know if I want you to use it.
There won't be any names.
People will know.
How will they know?
They'll just know. I can't believe you're making me do this.
You don't have an audience. Well, just my iPhone. Which is recording.
God. All right. You and I were in an asylum. And we knew it was an asylum, but no one else appeared to know. And we were us—we were writers—but we were also children. The place looked like a grand hotel—this huge banquet room at a grand hotel, and all the elite and well-to-do were gathered at high-tea tables, and we were racing around trying to escape because we knew it was an asylum even though no one else did. And it turned into a maze of running through weird spaces and corridors, and at one stage we were out, struggling through bush, but then we were back inside again. Somehow we got split up, and I found myself alone in somebody's hotel room, and I started testing windows and struggling, trying to get out, and then I turned around and I saw a handbag on the floor. I opened it up, and as

soon as I opened it I knew whose it was—your reviewer's. And so I squatted over it and pissed in it for you.

## 24

The stockings were hung by the heat pump with care . . .

I think if we sit as near to the front as possible.

I'd like to sit at the side, in case we have to get out in a hurry.

Yes, at the side, but near the front, so bubba can see what's going on. Because if she can't see anything but the backs of people, she won't last.

Those sorts of seats are always long gone by the time we ever get there.

But we're early this year, because we're organised.

Are we?

Yes. One year we got there at five thirty and we were basically first in the church, and last year we got there at quarter to and it was already full. Or did we get there at five thirty last year and it was already full? I can't remember.

Shall we take bets on whether Mum is waiting out the front for us?

She won't be there.

On the phone, when I said can you come out the front, she said you mean right out to the gate? Shall I come out to the road? Maybe some other passing family will pick her up instead. I wonder if we'll sing the carol about the ignorant brown people.

What's that one?

Te Harinui. The Māori people heard the great and glorious word.

Oh dear.

It's half an hour after her bedtime.

She did pretty well—she just hit the wall at the end there.

I thought she was amazing.

She was trying to get out into the aisle when all the people were going by. I think she was kicking a few communicants.

She was.

I decided to go up for a blessing. I can't remember the last time I had communion—I mean, I'm a coeliac atheist—but I thought a blessing couldn't hurt. I was trying to remember what you do. I think the priest who normally takes that mass used to say if you just want a blessing, put your hand on your heart . . . or something. The bishop didn't say anything this year, though, so I went up and put my hand on my heart and said just a blessing please, and the woman giving out the communion didn't seem to know what I was talking about. She had the host ready and she went to sort of grab my hand . . . it was awkward and weird.

You'll take your gluten Jesus and you'll like it.

How do we get out of here, Pat? I'm not sure.

I'm not sure either.

I think you go that way.

No, you go right.

Pretty sure I go down the back here.

Well that car's going right. I don't know.

Is there anyone behind me?

You're fine. Oh, you can go out that side street, can't you.

I think Baby Jesus was Filipino. And Mary was twice the height of Joseph.

Did you see the angels? Those little blond girls ripping their wings off and whacking each other with their ballet slippers.

I was wondering how their mother felt.

We were first down the aisle after the bishop. No mucking around.

I was ready to get out.

Don't kick me. I don't like being kicked.

Okay.

Not on a snowy night, by star or candlelight . . .

Thank you for taking me. I would get lost going home; I wouldn't remember where to go.

Google presents [light holiday music] [chuckles] [music continues] [eerie whirring] [brakes screech]

I had to give her five dollars for the collection plate. And then she forgot that she had it and when people started rustling around for their money and the basket was coming I said where's your handbag. She said I don't know. I said I gave you five dollars just before. Oh, oh did you? No recollection.

I wasn't sure if you were upset because your mother was clutching at you, or if you were upset in general.

I always feel emotional at Christmas Eve mass. It's partly the focus on The Mother and The Newborn and Birth, and I remember that awful Christmas Eve when we'd had the positive-but-not-really-positive pregnancy test and I was waiting to lose the embryos, and we sang When a Child is Born: it's all a dream and illusion now. And it reminds me of Dad, and I remember his voice, and I can hear him singing next to me. And it's also that I don't believe any more. It's that loss too.

In some ways it seems simpler to believe. But once you unknow . . .

It's so attractive, though. It's so attractive to believe that one day we'll be reunited with everyone we've ever lost.

We don't know. There are unanswered questions.

No. As a rational person, I can't believe that.

There is no evidence that there is, and there is no evidence that there is not.

There is evidence: when you die, you're dead.

I think you can still have faith without having a religion. I think I do.

You believe in God?

No, not that sort of faith—faith that things will be all right.

If in the moment it works, if it keeps you calm . . .

I don't believe in self-delusion.

You can have faith in the good side of humanity. That's not unscientific.

No, but . . . people are shits.

[music ends]

## 25

What do you call a man with a paper bag on his head?
What do you call a man with a spade on his head?
What kind of cough medicine does Dracula take?
Why did the golfer wear two pairs of trousers?
Why did the mechanic sleep under the car?
What does an angry kangaroo do?
What lies in a pram and wobbles?
What animals need oiling?
What do ghosts eat?

I came to offer assistance, but I know there's nothing more annoying than somebody in your kitchen putting things in the wrong place and getting in the way. I could stand here and make unhelpful comments . . . ? Though when you're holding a knife like that, Catherine, I agree with whatever it is you're saying.

At kindy, I can take Gingernut home. Maddisynne's having Gingernut now.

Who's Gingernut?

Someone from kindy.

Is it an animal? You don't need to go through there with your chocolate, Freya, thank you. And don't touch the curtains either.

We thought you'd be back in England by now.

You're not alone—we thought they would be as well. We believed them when they told us.

We believed us when we told you too. It wasn't what we intended.

Things don't always work out.

Blame Nigel Farage.

That's an excuse.

No it's not.

I think it is.

It's not, actually. That was what swung it.

Well, it sounds like—

Wonder Woman didn't used to wear trousers, did she?

Leggings.

She used to have a little skirt. In the seventies I think she had a flirty little skirt.

A very small skirt. But this is high-school Wonder Woman.

Yes, she did used to wear a skirt.

It was a very short skirt, wasn't it.

Yes. Yes.

And she used to have a bra thing rather than those shoulder decorations.

I think she did, yes.

I'm trying to remember the name of the actress.

Lynda Something.

Lynda Carter. We wanted to be her.

She had hotpants.

Oh, hotpants. So basically this outfit but without the spencer underneath. And without the gold thing here. And a strapless bra top. And without the tights. She wore a lot less in the seventies.

This is the new one.

It's quite Xena Warrior Princess, isn't it.

That is a little bit analytical. I have watched Xena Warrior Princess on television many times, but never in English. What is it all about?

The leather bikini, I think.

451

I've seen it in Turkish and German and Arabic . . . I can ask for two beers please in any language in the world, but I've no idea what's going on on the television in all these hotels. It's always Xena Warrior Princess.

Whose is she?

Poppy's.

Mine. She should be wearing short shorts.

I think this is her winter outfit.

This is her feminist outfit.

Can you shut the door, Poppy, please?


You show two cards, and then conceal one. The spectator can never guess which card remains. Secretly turn the card behind your back over and expose the opposite side and say 'No, you are wrong, that is the card I have in my hand.' Whichever card they name, you show they are wrong.


You two must be exhausted—have a rest. Now, are we seeing Helen again, or has she gone?

We're going out to Brian's tomorrow to see them there.

Brian Coakley's? How did that all get organised?

I said to Brian shall we come and visit you on Boxing Day and he said yes.

He hasn't rung me for Christmas. I can't believe it.

He called you the other day.

How do you know?

Because he said so.

Oh. I don't remember talking to him. But I forgot, obviously. I think I've just asked you, but are we seeing Helen again? Or has she gone?

Yes, we're going to Brian's tomorrow.

Oh, Helen's going to be there too. I get it now. What time are we going?

Just after lunch, so we'll pick you up about one.

Has Brian been away?

Ah . . . not recently.

It's just I haven't heard from him for Christmas, and I've rung him twice and never got a reply, and it's most unlike Brian to not ring me for Christmas.

Well he's been down in Christchurch, with Erin getting married.

Erin getting married?

Yeah.

Oh. When did she get married?

Last weekend, I think.

I wonder who she married.

Her fiancé.

I suppose so. I didn't even know she was engaged.

Oh dear. Oh dear oh dear oh dear.

The pav's catching up with you, is it?

What?

I had a bit of dairy today.

He shouldn't really have dairy.

It plays havoc with my digestive system.

Oh. It's not often that people eject Mary . . . ah . . .

Eject Mary?

Ah . . .

No room at the inn?

Yes.

It's reasonably common.

I never heard that before. I never realised it would upset people. You should go to bed.

There's another round of dishes to do yet.

They'll still be there in the morning, Alan.

Alice really enjoyed today. She loves Poppy—she's been carrying round a photo of her and saying Poppy Poppy Poppy.

Oh, there's the Queen.

What's she going on about?

Not all of us can do great things, but we can do small things with great love.

Did you hear him? Over dinner? He said he has a number of little plastic rulers from inside crackers, and he keeps them at work because they're perfect for measuring people's tumours.

Yes. Over Christmas dinner.

I wanted to get some stain remover on the tablecloths. Are you ready for me to take you home?

I was just going to say—when can someone take me home? Yes, I'm quite ready to go home, thank you. It's been a lovely evening.

It's been a lovely evening all day.

I think your door is open.

I should know this car by now, shouldn't I. Where's Helen?

At the Dumbles'.

That's good for you.

They've been staying there the whole time.

Yes I know—but I thought they might have been coming here for Christmas.

They were here. We've had Christmas.

Yes, we had it earlier, didn't we.

The same time as everyone else.

What's today?

Christmas Day.

Oh, I thought it was Christmas Eve.

No, we went to mass last night.

Yes. I was just trying to work that out myself. But I couldn't. When's Brian coming?

We're going to see him tomorrow, after lunch.

So you'll just pick me up in the afternoon. Where did you say Brian was having Christmas Day?

With Christopher, in Cambridge.

Where?

In Cambridge, with Christopher.

I thought he might have been going to one of the family's. Was somebody coming to his place?

No, he was going to Christopher's, because he's just been down in Christchurch for Erin's wedding.

You said that this afternoon, but I didn't know she was getting married. I wonder who she married.

A guy she's been going out with for a while.

Did you know she was engaged?

Yes—so did you.

Pardon?

So did you. We all did.

I must have forgotten. Look at the corn. Every year they grow corn there. Your . . . ah . . . surrogate mother. What's her name? I can't remember.

Leila.

Leila. That's right. She seemed to be taller today. I suppose I've only seen her a couple of times. It's nice that Alice knows her. Are you going to have a bit of a rest? You look tired. Now, what's Helen doing? I'm very confused about Helen.

They're meeting us tomorrow at Brian's, and then they're off first thing on the twenty-eighth.

Where's she staying?

At the Dumbles'.

I haven't heard from Brian for about three weeks, which is quite a long time for Brian. I guess he's been busy, getting near Christmas.

Mm.

And when did you say Erin's wedding was?

About a week ago.

Oh. Brian hadn't told me that.

Mm.

I didn't even know she was engaged. He must be getting forgetful.

Mm.

I wonder how old she is now.

Twenty-eight.

I thought she would be getting near thirty. Nearer thirty than twenty. Look at all the roses. Twice of recent times somebody told me that a man came to see me and I wasn't there. And I'm wondering if it was Brian.

Kill me. Kill me. Kill me kill me kill me. What have I missed?

He's in New York City. He was scared by a lady full of pigeons.

A lady full of pigeons?

Mm. And now they're sitting in the high attic of the Metropolitan Opera.

Why is he racing against the clock?

To get to the toy store. Because the two idiots are going to rob it. I just wanted to have something familiar in the background.

Where is his family?

Florida.

I'm going to reach out to you this one last time, Catherine. This incredible period of change is going to **come your way** *whether you are prepared or not*. Catherine, I cannot help you achieve your goals if you're unwilling to let me in. Hurry.

Ghoulash.

Mice, because they squeak.

A jelly-baby.

Get hopping mad.

He wanted to get up oily in the morning.

In case he got a hole in one.

Coffin medicine.

Doug.

Russell.

Motherfridger. We forgot to put Baby Jesus in Mary's arms yesterday. She appears to be nursing a lamb. That can't be good.

And now George Michael is dead. And Mintie just threw up some grass.

She's coming out my bathroom window. She's been using my toothbrush to freshen up.

We're still good mates—I invited them to the wedding. We went to the Halswell, Springston, Lincoln and Taitap pubs and showed them where Dad and his mates used to drink.

The dads always drunk at one pub and the sons always drunk at the other. And the daughters sat in the car and Dad snuck them out a sarsparilla. Les's uncle had a pub in Christchurch, and when it was six o'clock he used to open the front door and everyone would come out. And they'd walk round the block and come in the back door. Alice, come and see me. Come and see Nana.

I think she wants to go outside with Charlie and Mia. Go play with your cousins.

Are they cousins?

Distant cousins. Because you and I are first cousins, so Christopher and I are . . .

First cousins once removed.

Is that right, Mum?

You're cousins if your mothers or fathers are first brothers and sisters, and if one of them's the second brother or sister they're . . . ah . . . cousins once removed.

No, you've lost me.

So what are these guys to me? Are they my second cousins?

Helen's your first cousin.

Yes. They're your first cousin once removed.

So what would a second cousin be? Is it the same generation?

Would a second cousin be like one of Dad's brothers?

Yes.

Oh.

I'm not sure . . .

That's right. Or if you get married, your wife.

Hmm. Okay.

Well they stopped first cousin once removed and all that years ago. You might find it on the computer still . . . but when I was young, if I went in for something and I had to sign who I was a cousin of, I would have to put that Lena would be my first cousin once removed.

Except she was your sister.

Yes. No. I forgot Lena was my sister. But you know what I mean.

Is it lunchtime or is it dinnertime?

Afternoon tea. She had her veges and hummus earlier.

Alice has had a wholesome lunch like I have.

Beer?

Half a box of chocolates.

Why did you eat half a box of chocolates?

Because there's no room for the other half. Don't worry about it, Fred, if it gets on the roof—I've got a ladder. It would be good if Aunty Alice and Uncle Tom'd had some kids.

I don't think that would have been quite possible. He was sixty-four when they got married and she was forty-two or something.

He was twenty-six years older, wasn't he?

Yes. Yes.

And he was a friend of your father's—is that right? Mum?

Yes.

Yes. And I don't know how the hell Les Chidgey met him, but he used to go up there shooting deer, and it's one of the places where this earthquake has done a lot of damage. Have you boys followed the earthquakes in Kaikōura over in England?

We hear about them, but we don't know much.

Because you were born here, weren't you?

Yes, all three of them were born here.

We hear about stuff when there's a big earthquake, but we don't look too far into it.

Well Kaikōura was very badly damaged in the earthquake, and this guy Tom Rainey, who married Aunty Pat's elder sister—

Alice. That's where the name comes from.

—they lived up in this valley. You'd only get up there on a fine day—you had to drive on the riverbed. When the weather was right and the rain had stopped you'd make a new track along the stones.

When Alice and Tom went up there to live it was the back of beyond.

It still is, I can tell you. Have you been up there? If you ever go for a drive to the South Island with Alan and Alice you want to take your little four-wheel-drive with you, not your car. And when you get to the Hāpuku River you turn right and you'll go up to where Alice lived.

Did they build the house there?

No, they lived in a woolshed.

A converted woolshed?

It was the woolshed, but it had a little bit for sleeping in.

I don't remember that.

They had a townhouse. They lived in Kaikōura.

Right. So what was this other place?

That's where the farm was. Up the valley.

And he lived there, long before he met Alice. And Les Chidgey—your dad—somehow got to know him. I don't know when that started, but there were deer up there. And he went up with a mate one day—they went on motorbikes—and old Tom says you can walk over my farm and find a deer and I'll come and pick you up down the riverbed tonight. So bloody Les Chidgey, he walks all bloody day trying to shoot a deer,

459

and not a damn thing. Ten o'clock at night this bloody old Buick car comes wiggling up the track and by this stage your old man and his mate are absolutely stuffed, and old Tom says you sit on the headlights there, boys, and just down the track you'll be able to drop one. Well he turned round the old '28 Buick—it would have had lights like a torch—and poof! They got a deer each.

We've probably got photos of that in an album.

Bound to.

I don't like looking at them. Goose Bay, where the Chidgeys used to go camping every year—that was damaged in the Kaikōura quake too. They were cut off.

There was a house, way up on top of the hill. And a woman lived there, and she was a musician, and she used to start at twelve o'clock every night, and play her piano and sing. You could hear it in the distance.

## 27

There are times in the liturgical year when the laity assist in specific acts of blessing, such as the blessing of throats or the distribution of ashes. These are clearly indicated in the Book of Blessings. The practice of giving blessings in lieu of Communion was popularised by the priest who started Life Teen. This was then exported all over the US and overseas and has infected many Catholic Churches. It should be not only discouraged, but discontinued. I myself am rather queasy about touching people on the head while simultaneously administrating the sacred host on the tongue of the next person in line.

## 28

Increasingly it's about preservation, not pillage and plunder. Now they don't open the tombs. They don't excavate. They just drill tiny holes, have a look inside with a camera and record what's there, then seal it back up. Even Carter said that their very breath was destroying the artefacts.

Well, the actor playing Carter said that.

Live coverage: Star Wars actress Carrie Fisher dies 2 minutes ago.

Catherine, I want you to imagine life without fear.

### 29

Where are Helen and Fred? Why haven't they come to say goodbye?

I want to switch off my memories, so I don't keep seeing them.

I don't think you can opt out of memories.

There's no setting?

Not that I've seen. There might be. I'm not the all-seeing eye.

Notifications?

On This Day. I think that might be it.

On This Day. I can select Highlights, All Memories, or None. None. Because some pop up that I don't want to see again. I don't want to see Daisy. Or dead people. I had a People You May Know suggestion the other day, and it was a dead person. It was prompting me to add her as a friend.

Dead people don't post on Facebook.

Some of them do. If you were dead and posting on Facebook, it would be did I turn the oven off?

Did I lock the front door?

If I choose All Memories, do I then see every post I've ever made, regurgitated every day? How does that work?

It's for the truly self-obsessed.

You'd have no time to do anything other than look back at your own past.

You wouldn't see anything from anyone else. You'd be so inundated with all your past days.

I know I just rang you a few minutes ago about Helen and Fred not coming to say goodbye, but I *know* they haven't been, because I left the door open and the door is still open.

## 30

Where has the time gone? As if it's waiting somewhere, as if it's dropped behind the couch like coins. There aren't enough days left for all the things I meant to tell you: that I'm related (sort of, by marriage) to W.B. Yeats. That the cuckoo still won't go back in the clock. That pickled quail eggs, for instance, are increasing in popularity. That I wonder how they decide which three-letter words to skip on car number plates; that I saw a FEK once, but I assume there are no FUKs. That I looked online for reviews of the Vengaboys' Hamilton gig, but it's as if it never happened. That I wish I saw my dad in airports the way you see yours. That I'll have to settle for Peru if I want to see pyramids, because of the terrorists. That I'm looking for my doppelgänger and German Cath is sixty if she's a day; that she's had a budget glamour-shoot and is wearing not very much lace. That we need to agree on the colour of the middle traffic light; that I and the rest of the civilised world say orange. That I have picked the eyes out of the year. That Your Body Will Send 7 Signals That Dementia Is Coming. That #5 will shock you. That the Virgin Mary says coconut yoghurt is not good for me, but that she's a bitch. That he gave me his business card and told me his wife had died, which was why her name was crossed out in biro. That whatever you do in bed, Sealy supports it. That we may be accidentally eating an ingredient blamed for fifty thousand heart attacks a year. That we need to imagine our imaginary carpet shampooer sucking all the imaginary dirt out of our imaginary carpets. That I can still feel the glass under my skin. That I'm sorry. That Alice has to learn to wait; that we are making a rod for our own backs. That white spotting can be present on a cat that is also a dominant white, and that of course white spotting on white is invisible. That if you close your eyes it sounds like JonBenét's mother says what did you do? That The Thoughts With Which a Christian Child Should Be Taught to Look on the Works of God, framed, sold for £370,000. That Ernest Hemingway requires no introduction. That a small German town was unknowingly built inside a meteorite crater; that the buildings are made up of tiny diamonds. That we never did find our wedding certificate, did we; that it can't be *lost* lost; that it still has the rain-spatter on it. That it's true we might have crashed that day; we might have swerved across the centre line—but we didn't, we didn't.

## 31

Catherine, I'm concerned . . . I want you to know that you are not alone, but time is running out.

There's not a breath of wind. The trees are hardly moving. Christmas has been and gone.

Never again.

You've got a very intelligent little girl there. She'll be ready for school at four.

Some days it seems like she'll invade Poland at four.

She's a smart little tot. Aren't you? You know too much for a little girl. No, that's your foot. Her hair's going darker.

Alice's?

Yes.

It's going lighter.

I could see the two colours and I thought it must be darker. I can't remember what it was before.

It was dark brown when she was born.

I'd forgotten that. Yes, it was quite a dark brown, wasn't it. She's growing up so quickly.

Cat.

What are you going to do for New Year?

Nothing. Try to stay awake till twelve, then watch the neighbours' fireworks from the deck. We're having the other neighbours over this afternoon. Every year we mean to get together for pre-Christmas drinks, but we always run out of time.

I think it's good to keep friendly with your neighbours, instead of fighting with them. Are you going to stay up till midnight?

We'll see if we can stay awake. After Alice has gone to bed we usually just collapse.

She's so lovely, but she doesn't just sit and play. I think she's going to be fairly brainy. Do you?

Don't know.

Oh, I'm sure. She's very observant. It amazes me.

Mm.

Cat.

I hope he doesn't drop her.

Look at the bromeliads. Why don't our bromeliads look like that? Alan?

Gardeners.

What are they called?

Bromeliads.

Excuse me—hay fever.

One for a wish, Cath.

That would have been a cute photo. There are other people in it now.

Look at those little orange lilies. Beautiful. I love through here—it's sort of natural, not like a garden. You hold Nana's hand. See the wee blue flowers? I'm here, darling.

Shall we sit down somewhere and give her a bit of lunch?

Where do you want to go?

Alice, look—here's Alice in Wonderland. Lift her up. Oh. She's picking Alice's nose. Now she's picking the Mad Hatter's nose.

We haven't been here before, have we?

Yes we have, but not for a long time.

I've been here once with one of your friends. I can't think who it was.

It must have been Helen.

No, no it wasn't. Somebody who's a writer too, I think. I can see her face, and I just can't put a name to it.

Kate Camp?

Pardon?

Kate Camp?

I think it might have been.

I don't know.

She doesn't cry very much, does she.

At certain times of the day . . .

Oh yes, well they all do, but some children weep and cry.

Shall I post that? Of her picking Alice in Wonderland's nose? What's the caption?

Something about the rabbit hole?

Something about that's not the way to the rabbit hole, or . . . that's not the rabbit hole, darling? Will people get that?

No. Alice is curiouser and curiouser?

Hmm. No. Shall I say at least it's not her own nose? Shall I say that? At least it's not her own nose?

I don't know. I don't know. Could you get her water out? Do you want a drink of water? Of course you don't, that's why we got it out specially.

Bad behaviour at the tea party? Bad behaviour at the tea party will do. Or something about manners.

Nana!

Yes, Nana's coming. Nana's here.

Shall I just say how meta? Alice picking Alice's nose.

I don't know. Whatever. It doesn't really matter.

It doesn't really meta.

Mm.

It doesn't really *meta*.

What a lovely looking meal. Rice, vegetables—this looks so nice, Nana wants to eat it. When I see what some people feed their children . . .

Tayto.

Do you want the potato? Nana will give it to you. Here you are. Potato. Potato. Nana used to get a shilling when she picked up a row of little potatoes. We had sixty acres, and before there were machines the men went round and picked up the big potatoes and left the little ones. And I used to go round and pick up the little ones and I got a shilling when I'd done I forget how many rows of potatoes.

What happened to the little ones?

They used to go to Nazareth House and . . . I can't remember the other places, but they were places where children were. You know. What do you call them, the children in those places . . .

Orphans?

Orphans. Thank you. They weren't really orphans—the mothers were unmarried, but people used to say they were orphans. My father donated them. They were always funny shapes. Have some more?

In your mouth, bub.

Nana didn't put it in the right place, did she. Silly Nana.

It's nice here. No one else around—just the way I like it.

Sounds like a recipe for mass murder.

Get rid of Nana? I think I might go.

Who would feed the baby?

I'd take her with me.

It all becomes a bit of a game, doesn't it, Alice. This is getting way too messy.

No!

No no no. I'm going to get through this. You can't always have what you want, you know. You don't get to call the shots all the time. Eat that. I'm not going to start being a slave to her. She gets her way most of the time as it is.

Not with me she doesn't. Mummy's a bitch.

She wears me down. Pumpkin. Put it in your mouth.

Nana doesn't want to see your food when you're eating it. No. She's just a normal little child—like you probably were.

You can hold it yourself, bubba.

Good girl.

All finished.

No! No!

Is there more?

Yes, but—

Why can't she have it?

Because she—I don't want to repeat myself. Finished. Finished.

What nice sensible food. These tins of stuff they buy must be revolting.

They're handy to have on hand, but . . .

We've never really used that.

It came in when you girls were little and I generally had one tin for an emergency, but I never used it. Our neighbour had a child the same age, and she fed it all tinned food. And then she had terrible trouble when—I can't even remember his name now—got a bit older and was sitting at the table—he wouldn't eat anything because it wasn't tinned. *Terrible* trouble. I felt like saying to her ages before, for goodness' sake give him some proper things.

All finished. That sun's so bright—I wish I'd remembered to bring her hat.

Just put the pram hood up.

Hat too. Hat too.

Daddy left it at home. Never mind.

Aunty Carol sent her a Buzzy Bee hat for Christmas and she loves it.

Did Aunty Carol make the Bruce Springsteen cake?

No, Helen made that.

What was it?

My Bruce Springsteen birthday cake.

Oh. For whose birthday?

My birthday. My fifteenth.

Did I go to that?

Yes.

I can't remember it.

Well it was in 1985.

I thought you meant this birthday—you know, now.

No, my fifteenth. I didn't have a Bruce Springsteen cake for my forty-sixth.

Okay. Righto.

Shall we go to the Tudor garden?

Oh, thank you, darling. Lovely. A nice little leaf. How long do I have to keep this for?

You can probably let it go now.

I've been to a fair few gardens in New Zealand and I reckon these are the nicest ones. I used to think Christchurch was, but these are better than Christchurch. Don't keep going forward, Alan, will you.

I'm surprised they're allowed to have that drop.

It's an odd thing. They've put the wires across in the Italian garden. In a workplace you wouldn't be allowed to have that.

What?

I surprised they don't have to have a rail, Mum.

This is new. This didn't used to be here.

Look how weathered it is—it's been here for ages. Is that honeysuckle? No. I don't know what it is.

A plant.

They must have to work hard to keep that view of the river.

It'd be nice if you could go up in the little tower.

It's probably ornamental.

No, you used to be able to go up there. I'm sure you've been up there, haven't you Catherine?

No, I've never been up there.

Maybe I was here on a trip—I remember being up in the tower. It was a long time ago.

Look at the brickwork on that side—see how some bricks are in and some bricks are out?

Is that because it's meant to look old? They don't look like they've even got mortar. Maybe it's just a veneer.

A façade. A skin on the outside of another structure.

Up the stairs, bub. In your sedan chair.

Can I hold your arm, Cath? In five days I've got ten years older.

You always say that.

Well, it's true. I seem to get older in lumps, not gradually.

Hello.

Hello, sweetheart.

Hello.

Hello.

Hello.

Hello.

Hello.

Hello.

Hello.

Hello.

Hello.

Hello.

Hello.

Hello.

Hello.

Hello.

Hello.

Hello.

Hello.

Hello.

Hello.

Hello.

How long's this going to go on?

Hi.

Hi.

Hi.

Hi.

Hi.

Hi.

Hi.

Hi.

Hi.

Hi.

Hi.

Hi.

Hi.

Hi.

Hi.

Hi

Hi. Mummy. Mummy. Mummy. Mummy. Mummy. Hi.

Hello, darling. She picked me some daisies yesterday, didn't you. Or was it the day before?

She put them in the tray of her trike and said Mummy, Mummy.

How are you doing, Mum?

I'm all right . . . I'm just so upset.

Why's that?

Because they didn't come.

They didn't what?

They didn't come when they said they would. I stayed up till half past eleven.

No, they came to say goodbye the day before they left.

Bye.

They did, Mum. I've got photos on here. Look.

Bye. Bye.

They were coming in the evening for coffee.

No, they came in the late afternoon, and we sat in the big communal lounge.

Bye bye.

Yes, I know. But they said they were coming back after they'd been to the Dumbles'. I know you don't believe me, but it's the truth. Do you believe me?

Ah, well . . .

No. You don't. I am *not* confused. I've got a note the nurse wrote down, and it says they were coming. And *she* wasn't confused. I know you don't believe me.

I think you've probably got the wrong end of the stick, Mum. Helen wouldn't do that. And they—

Well just forget it.

—they were getting up at five in the morning.

I know that. Just forget it!

And I was there when we said our goodbyes.

Okay okay. I've probably got it wrong. Forget it!

Cat.

Back to the car, bubba? We need to put Teddy in the car.

Where's Teddy?

Where's Ted-Ted? Here he is.

Nana will carry Teddy.

Oh look, we could have had a golf cart.

You wouldn't want to be run over by that, would you.

A slow death—two miles an hour.

It would be slow. It might just break my legs. Nana's

471

coming, darling.

We're nearly there.

But this is the secret that I want you to know, Catherine—this reality is actually not reality at all! It only exists because we believe it to be true!

You might as well flay yourself as hard as you can before the finish line.

It's a no-win situation—it looked like I was dumping her on their doorstep and hotfooting it out of there. And the truth is I do want to get the hell away. She just makes shit up. But what do we do?

If we play along with it, we make it worse, and she gets upset. So we contradict her, and she says you don't believe me, and she gets upset. We're boxed into a corner.

Every time I see that, I think it's a dead animal.

There's a few of those around here. Sandbags, from construction. I wonder if we'll find out today whether Margherita and John are advancing on their property development.

I think we should ask.

I know it's a fantasy, but I'm very interested in the back half of their farm. There's a building platform on top of the hill, and there are only so many hills where you can do that. I went up there on a sunny day and took a panorama. You're elevated, and you've got the whole of the Hakarimata Ranges, and you can't be built out. It feels regal. Like a citadel. But we still don't know where we want to be, and every place has its hook and its barb. I'd like to go back to Dunedin, but you don't want to because of exes . . .

And the cold.

We both want to go back to Wellington, but for me there's always that feeling of being hemmed in by the mountains. God forbid Auckland.

And that's where I have a job.

I don't know what the answer is. The default is we stay in the holding pattern till we've run out of fuel and have to emergency land.

Or we make this our home. We make it what we want it to be.

She's gone to sleep.

Sometimes I think we should have bought David and Peta's property. We could have built up trees around it . . . faced the house to the sun. I do second-guess that now and then.

So do I.

Not that he would have sold to us—he's such a belligerent guy.

He called you a queer cunt.

Anyway, in the end the road will go through and you'd be right next to it. But on John and Margherita's you'd always have that moat—the creek, and the distance from other people.

That's what we want.

The issues are access. At the end of the paper road there's another paper road that goes up the hill. There's a whole lot of strings attached to that. And then Alice would still be going to the local school in Ngā. Which may not be so bad.

Or going to the local Catholic school and pretending she's a Catholic.


So this is it, dear one. You will be able to perform **shockingly accurate** predictions about the future, and gain clarity from the past. Catherine, you will understand a good portion of what I take into account when conducting your Reading, which I feel will bring a deeper meaning to it all.


Cute dress.

This was from her surro. Her surrogate . . . ah . . . parent. My favourite one went in the wash, because she—

We won't talk about that, dear. John and Margherita don't want to know about that.

You smell good now. You didn't smell very good before, did you.

Yes, all right.

We had to head to the shower. I had to hose her down. New prisoner in D Block.

Lean on the wall and stay still.

Put your hands on the hand marks—

I'm going to try to make it to midnight. I used to be a night owl, but since she's been on the scene I've been conking out at nine thirty. It was a Chidgey tradition to see the sun rise—Dad always used to see the sun rise on New Year's morning, but that's not going to happen.

I've only ever seen it once, and that was 2000.

That was very disappointing. I was in Auckland and we went to the Domain to watch the fireworks and it was raining, so we were huddled under a tarpaulin looking at these tiny little orange smudges that may or may not have been fireworks. And then it was overcast in the morning, and we went down to the waterfront to see the waka come in at sunrise, and we were like is that it? I'm not sure, and it's starting to rain, and has the sun risen? I can't tell. I didn't see it rise, but it must have.

We stayed up to see if the world came to an end. Nothing happened.

That's right—Y2K. Your mum still has that magnet on her fridge, doesn't she, Alan. Have you got your bottled water and your tinned food and your batteries?

Every computer was going to grind to a halt and that was going to be the end of it.

And nothing.

Remember all those plane executives were made to be in the air at midnight? To keep confidence up.

I was in New Orleans, staying at a bed and breakfast, and

they said don't worry, it's got an iron roof. Because at midnight on New Year's Eve, everyone goes out and shoots their guns, and the year previous two tourists had been killed by falling bullets.

Falling bullets! Ha ha!

Makes Ngāruawāhia seem more attractive, doesn't it.

Are you going to stay awake?

No. We'll probably go to bed at eleven. We normally give up.

Could be the last one, with Trump as president. The world might end this year.

Next year.

Don't say that.

I still can't believe it's actually happened.

It's a cosmic joke. They're pulling our leg. There's something going on here—a very late April Fool's joke.

Someone's going to point out the camera any minute now.

I read an article the other day that blames the downfall of western civilisation on the TV series Friends. It said that the anti-intellectualism exhibited in it—like Ross the scientist always being laughed at—was the start of it. And then reality TV became so popular, and everything started going downhill. Fake news. Trump. Trump is not a great evil man, but he's the product—the end result. He was always going to be. We were always going to get to this stage. It's a degeneration.

No feet on the table, please.

The status quo continues; it just gets a little bit worse.

We took Mum to the gardens this morning. She gets these ideas every few months and the latest one is that my sister didn't come and say goodbye to her before she left. I've got photos of it; I've got a video of it. But that doesn't make any difference. She says no, no, they were going to come round that evening—but they weren't, because they had to leave at five the next morning; that's why we did it in the afternoon. She said no, they were coming round for coffee in the evening, and I sat up till eleven thirty and they never arrived and they never rang, and I left my door open and I *know* they haven't been because the door's still open. This is days later.

Ha ha! Days! Ha!

She didn't leave her door open and it never happened.

No, it never happened. But the thing is, the more you say to her no, that's not right, Mum, you're a little bit confused—you don't believe me, do you! And then she gets more upset, and quite aggressive. So the options are we disagree with her and she gets upset and angry with us because we don't believe her, or we just let it go and say oh well she must have forgotten and so then Mum thinks that her other daughter didn't care enough to say goodbye.

John was going to ring his mum about a gift he hadn't given. I said just tell her that you did. And he said no, I can't lie to my mum. And I said well she's starting to lose it, you're going to have to learn how to lie to her.

No no—not a whole one. Number one choking hazard for children.

I'll get a knife. So did you lie to your mother?

Yes.

Some days she's got no memory of anything, next day she'll be fine.

Very repetitive. Very repetitive.

The repetitiveness is exhausting.

It is.

It is. Having the same conversation over and over. I've been having the same conversation with Mum for about eight years now. What's Margherita cutting up? Say thank you.

She's too busy. Exit stage right.

You didn't need those fingers, did you?

It's like feeding a horse.

Stage right!

You get so many warnings.

She's fine. Don't give it any attention and it'll go away.

John's mum used to give Hannah cards that played Happy Birthday, and you knew they had a life, and Hannah would be in bed and we'd be opening and closing the thing, opening and closing it, trying to run it out. I remember one time we wedged open the card and cut the back of it. They do like repetition. Which I can understand is learning, but . . .

We don't need to learn it too.

Gentle. Gentle.

We've been reading your book. How did you work it all out, Catherine? I haven't read that far.

I had to keep a timeline of what happens when, and align that with what was happening historically to make sure I wasn't making any gaffes. It's weird to be at the very start again. I have lots of ideas, but they're all historical. Can't I just write something set now? In Ngāruawāhia?

You wouldn't get into fantasy? Like Lord of the Rings?

Ah. No.

Well there's nothing on TV. We don't watch the news. We record programmes, and fast-forward through them.

I do that too.

She'll get bored with a series but she has to get to the end, so she'll watch all the episodes sped up. I can't bear it.

If you fast-forward on Sky you miss the talking. It's silent. We just tape everything.

Record, Margherita—*record*. You're showing your age.

I bought one of those things that you can plug into your computer and play your video cassettes, and then record it onto TV. You can't download it—you have to play the video in real time. You're supposed to have updates, but none of them work. It's just getting used to everything all over again. But once you get used to it, eventually you can't remember how it was and why you found it so hard to change over.

477

I need to do that with some old old things that I want to keep. There's a videotape of my debutante ball, which has the tiniest snippet of Dad—the only video we have of him, and the only recording of his voice. This is 1988. It's very much on my mind that it's rapidly deteriorating.

Have you got any resolutions?

I can't keep up with the years, let alone the resolutions.

At the gym I go to, the personal drainer—no, the personal trainer—fasts every Monday. He just has water. But I thought: that doesn't suit my body style. Sorry, I missed that.

I had to go for an MRI on this hand and I was rushed and I was trying to get work done, and I went off to the appointment and I had all these things in my mind. And I got there and I had to lie still, and I could feel the magnetic waves going back and forth, and I started thinking well I have low-level mercury exposure from making daguerreotypes: what if the mercury in my brain is wobbling around, and my head's going to explode?

That's likely.

Do you have to wear a mask?

I have a fume hood, just in case. But I've been doing it for seventeen years, and mercury is cumulative—so any small exposure is a risk. And the fumes are odourless, colourless and absorbed through the skin. People say oh, as I kid I used to pour it into my hand.

I remember doing that. I remember Mr Ash in fifth-form science passing round a petri dish of mercury, and we were all touching it.

That's fine, because that's probably the only time in your life you'll handle mercury.

Well Mr Ash is dead now, so how do you explain that?

So have you thought any more about Council's plan to build a teeming metropolis across the road?

All that's effectively happened is they've rezoned the front of our place to residential. But the back is still zoned rural.

And a developer would only be interested in the front.

The guy down there said it was going to be forty thousand to put the power on to his place. We'd be close to double that. If what he told me is right, they've got solar power and a generator.

Ready for the end of the world. Do you know him very well, John?

No, I only talked to the father. I haven't met the son. And according to the father that concrete shed is just to store his toys.

But it's *massive*! Such a high roof. It's a bunker.

He's got an army tank and jeeps—that's my recollection of what he said.

Tanks aren't that high, are they?

Unless you have an anti-aircraft missile.

Is he planning to take Huntly or something?

He can have Huntly.

When they first put the doors on Catherine said why have they painted that over? I said it's because you're just not seeing the black space any more.

Mm. I couldn't see it.

So would you keep the whole back block as one, or would you subdivide it?

My understanding is we can only keep it as one. The plan for the long term is that it would be residential as well, but you're talking at least ten years, maybe fifty years.

And we can't find any pieces of land that we like. Whereas up there we've got rolling hills, we've got no neighbours, we can build in the middle and be away from everything, it lies perfect for the sun—it's ideal. Why would you give up that? We've been told by one of the real estate agents that the moment it's been rezoned we could have a developer come within the hour, and within a couple of hours they'd have a cheque to us.

The paper road is gone. Stopped. Dissolved. The paper road that goes along our trees is no longer there. It wasn't a good spot to put a road.

We could show you concept plans from the engineer—he's got the driveway here and the house here, going out over the gully. There's no land. The house is above a big hole.

There's nothing there.

Catherine would like to build again.

I'd like to upgrade from this place. With a special room for Jiffy, so we can't hear him at night.

Lead-lined.

Underneath the ground.

I'll just finish this. Can't you get a thing that you put on their collar and it takes their voice away? I don't mean cruelly. I don't mean that.

Like shock therapy?

I think it's pretend. It's a little box, and you put it on there, and it nullifies their voice. I think it's a fantasy. What did you say?

She kept pointing me in other directions. She gets lonely, and she's looking for me. She'll walk howling round the house, trying to find me, and I'll call out to her.

You look into her eyes and you know she's truthful.

We've got another ten years of this.

I know. She's looking frailer and frailer, but it's not like they die early, is it.

I missed the important part—whether you were talking about the cats or my mother. I thought I could wing it.

You were blank. I was talking about your mother; thinking about what's in store for us. I know everyone's different.

Christmas was when she lost the plot, but before that, for a good six months, she kept saying that her hip was aching, and she was going to the doctor's and he wasn't doing anything, and she just seemed to get weaker. I went to the doctor's with her. He did nothing. Discounted everything. She had somebody come in and assess her. They say can you shower yourself? And she goes yes, it takes me two hours because I can't lift my hands and I can't do this and I can't do that—and they go yes, she can shower herself. Let's move on to the next question. I said to Mum you are going to have to be quiet and let me say things that are going to upset you because I'm going to make you sound very fragile and dependent. So when they turned up and went through the questionnaire again, and Mum said yes I can shower myself, I said Mum, you need to say what you mean by that. It went from a tick for everything to a cross for everything. Within hours she got help. And she was complaining of a pulse in her stomach, and feeling sick, so he finally organised an X-ray and a scan. We knocked on the door, the door was open—and nothing. Nothing. So we went in, and we were calling out—nothing. I think she'd started to give up. I can't remember the exactness of it. He pulled me aside and he said this is what your leg should look like, even in an elderly person, and this is what your Mum's got. She had no bone left, from about mid thigh. Just nothing left. The doctor all the way through had kept saying well what can you expect for your age? Disgusting. She had a massive aneurysm just below somewhere which meant that they couldn't do much. The end result was—let me have that and I'll cut it for you. Say please. Please can I have another grape. She was there while we were talking about the X-ray, and she was there while we were talking about the aneurysm, and looking back now, I would have pretended. I would have talked to the doctor and said pump her full of as much pain relief as you can and don't say a word. Not even tell her about the aneurysm. Because Mum basically gave up the ghost. Within minutes she gave up.

And her hands stopped working. And she lay miserable in bed.

She woke up one day and she was crying. She woke up one day and said I think I'm dying. We got the ambulance and the ambulance took her into hospital and she became the Queen of Sheba. She started telling the nurses that they were working for her. That she was paying their wages. But she wanted to die. She spent her whole time saying I want to die. It got to March for her birthday and we had the party but she stayed in her room.

Everything was wrong. She lasted till winter.

John's mother is very repetitive, and it's getting worse. And his brother's wife's mother had Alzheimer's and she constantly wanted to go home. This is a visit: I want to go home now.

And she already was at home?

She was in the home. But that was all she talked about for three or four years: I want to go home now.

It's all deteriorating right at the end.

And after they're gone, what you'll miss or what you'll want back is what you didn't have for so many years anyway. I would have loved it if Mum was nice up until the end, but it didn't happen. All I can do is go back to a year before she died and remember those times. Like Christmas lilies—that's Mum. So I have Christmas lilies, and every night the perfume's stronger. But I'm not missing Mum as such—I'm missing a memory.

All you have to do is take the first step, Catherine . . . and then watch as a new and exciting journey unfolds before you!

Out of the gate and off for a walk went Hairy Maclary from Donaldson's Dairy. That's his favourite post, isn't it.

That's where all the other dogs have urinated.

Cat. Cat. Cat too.

No, that's a mailbox.

It sounds like they want no one around them.

But I think they know we're interested, if they could divide it in two. After we get back from holiday, not to give you too much time to think about it, I'd like to take a half-plate daguerreotype portrait of you.

Of me?

Yeah.

Hm.

I'm thinking, either shoot at the far end for morning sun, or when there's afternoon sun shoot under the eaves and get reflected light. Control the light.

Oops. We skipped some.

. . . straight back home to bed. What a good idea. The end. Finished. Okay bubba—bedtime.

No, two! No, two!

We'll have one more book. That's Not My Lamb. Okay?

Where's the mouse?

Good! Where's the bee?

Bzzzzzzz.

Where's the little bee? You found it!

Where's the flower?

Very good.

Good girl.

Four flowers. One, two, three, four.

Four.

Four flowers.

Daddy.

Did you find the mouse?

Where's the mouse?

Where's the mouse? Yes, there's the mouse. That's not my lamb . . . Butterfly. That's a butterfly.

Its ears are so soft.

Its ears are so soft. Where's the bee? Where's the bee? There's the bee. Where's the little mouse?

He's saying bye bye.

Here's the mouse.

Bye bye.

Good night.

Bye bye.

Good night, Alice.

Bye bye.

That's what the mouse is saying. Bye bye.

Nighnighs.

See you next year.

No. Two.

No, bedtime now.

No!

Bedtime now.

Definitely bedtime now.

No!

We could have one more. Shall we have Tickle My Ears, translated by Mummy? This is Little Rabbit. Tap him on the shoulder. Will he turn around? Tap him on the shoulder. Alice. Alice. Tap him on the shoulder. It's late. Little Rabbit must go bed. He's brushed his teeth. His pyjamas are ready. Clap your hands—he'll put them on. Clap your hands. Pakipaki. Good girl. Daddy clapped his hands too. A little bit late, but never mind. We're almost there. At last Little Rabbit can go to bed. He's very tired—look, he's yawning.

Say hippity hoppity.

Or hoppity hop, as Mummy translated it.

Where are his ears? Tickle tickle tickle.

. . . The end.

No!

Yes. No more putting it off. The time has come.

I said her surrogate parent today.

I know.

I was lost for words. I couldn't think—her surrogate what?

Just our surrogate. Full stop.

Her surrogate. Because I'd already said her surrogate . . . and then paused.

It does sound weird to people outside. It sounds quite clinical. We say surro, but other people don't understand what that means. Wind up the music box.

*

Will you take that step, Catherine? Will you claim the destiny that has actually been yours all along?!

In a fitting end to 2016, the poo was on me. I'd been wandering round her room, smelling poo, but it was on my shirt.

You were holding her. And then you passed her to me. And so I now will have trace faecal matter on me also.

Not on purpose. I know you think I do these things on purpose.

Do you want to come out on the deck and watch the last sunset?

I've got to make a curry.

I don't think you have time to make a curry before the sun sets.

I need to pee, though.

Quick.

Can I pee before the sun sets?

I don't know. How much beer have you had? Quick. *Quick.*

I am so proud that you have made it this far. I want you to be one of these people, Catherine. It is your time, your destiny, and your moment to seize. I am waiting for you . . .

Oh my God, you were taking your time.

Is it the apocalypse?

Yes. It's the end of my novel. Quick quick. Quick quick quick. No, that's my chair. Did you know we get an extra second today? There's a leap second. It's because standard time lags behind atomic clocks, so they have to add a leap second every so often.

What's standard? Atomic clocks are better than the sun going round the earth?

If they didn't do it, eventually clocks would be showing

midday before sunrise.

I think that's Fleetwood Mac.

Yeah, it is. It's not from that house there—it's further away than that. Or is it that house?

I think it's that house. It's bouncing off the trees and coming back.

They were playing Come On Eileen before. Could be a long New Year's Eve.

The burning ball of fire is disappearing into deep space.

Are you quoting Hitchhiker's Guide to the Galaxy again?

No.

You could see the sun before it went behind the clouds, but that's when you were having a pee, so you missed seeing the sun disappear.

It's probably still there.

How do we know?

Because I can see you. It's light.

It's still light after the sun goes down. For a little while.

But it's the sun reflecting up off the clouds which is the real sunset. That's when you get all the good colours.

Has the sun set yet, or not? It's hard to tell. See, just between those pine trees, you can see a little glowing speck.

You can too.

Is that it?

That's it.

Just about to go down behind the hills. Do you really think standing up will make it last longer?

Maybe I could be like Lippity Rabbit, and jump a bit and see if I can reach the stars.

Have another Coruba and Coke and maybe you will. Oh, Coruba and cola. It's not even proper Coke. Here it goes. Hold my hand. Be romantic. Say something romantic.

Ah . . . I love you.

I love you too.

2017 will be an exciting year, with my book coming out overseas.

I worry about what's going to happen in 2017.

Why?

International geopolitics.

Right. I thought we were talking about me.

Not everything in the universe revolves around Catherine Chidgey.

Does this? Oh look, it does. For the tape, as they say on CSI, I'm moving my middle finger around my head.

Mintiemoo's here for the end of the world.

Then she will be Queen! Won't you, Moo. And Jiffy will be your court jester. There's an echo.

The echo has substantially increased since that concrete storage shed was built.

His bunker?

Mm.

For his *tank*.

Better not piss that neighbour off. Better have him over for drinks.

I think the sun's gone down. There's a greenish tinge just above those glowing clouds.

The sun has disappeared below the horizon, but it's still not yet dark.

Are we going to sit out here till it's dark? Because I'm hungry.

I want to see the light show. There's a certain span of time where the colour shifts quite quickly.

That thing at the gardens today, set into the concrete with all the rings around it—is that a sundial? A sundial of human involvement. I wrote a short story called that once. You stand in the middle.

I think it is, but I don't know about human involvement. Why, because it's life size? And you stand there?

You cast the shadow.

You're the obelisk.

Is that what it's called? Obelisk?

No. No.

Needle.

Arm?

The pointy thing in the centre.

I'm out of alcohol. My can's empty.

You can't go now. You'll miss the colours.

There's a little bit of green there too, behind that band of white.

Why is a rooster crowing at eight thirty-eight in the evening?

It's the end of the world.

It's been taking lessons from Jiffy.

Probably got into its owner's stash of P.

It hasn't been keeping up with the leap seconds.

It's doing it now so it can sleep in tomorrow morning. Oh, nice blues. You know, I didn't make a single daguerreotype in 2016.

Didn't you?

2017 though. Damn different story.

That's tomorrow.

I'm going to make stereo daguerreotypes. That's my New Year's resolution.

I do like that photo Helen took of me.

It looks like an author photo.

It does. And you can see a bit of my tits.

Possibly. I'd have to have my glasses on.

Thank you very much.

To see your *phone*. I think I need a new prescription.

So you can see my tits?

Is that the sun coming back up over the horizon over there?

I was just thinking—there's that same little spot of light between the trees.

Time is now going backwards. You're going to have to unwrite the novel.

Oh God.

You'll have to do it every day for a year.

Oh my God.

You'll have to untype letters.

No. I think it was just behind the cloud before.

Or, time is hurtling backwards.

Or that.

You have to keep an open mind about these things.

Mmhmm.

You lose the perspective of distance in the clouds, because the light is highlighting different areas. It doesn't look like a standard—what do you call it? Regression to depth?

I know what you mean.

It was a term in art history, I remember that. The Coruba is muddling my mind. *Recession* to depth, I think.

We'll google it when we go inside.

Can you see a big feather, with one dark half and one light half?

Where?

That big band across there, where it's darker on the top and light on the underside.

Oh yes.

And the embers burning down there at the sunset.

We should have bought David and Peta's section. Built a house on it, put tenants in there, and subdivided later.

Mm. We should have done that. But those macrocarpas cast an enormous shadow.

We still should have.

Yeah.

Did you say you closed bubba's window?

I did. And turned the fan off. She's not going to overheat.

*Now* the sun's gone down.

We'll be forty-seven this year.

Next year. Forty-seven next year.

Okay, but in the next six months, we'll both be forty-seven.

You will be in the next six weeks. I am clinging to forty-six for a bit longer than that.

Soon we'll be fifty.

Oh my God.

Half a century old.

Not for a few years.

I want to have—

Soon enough.

—two more books written by the time I'm fifty. Not counting this one.

I want you to fulfil your dreams and everything, but also I don't want you to miss out on bubba.

I know.

We're the inverse of a stereotypical husband and wife. You're the workaholic, and . . .

I'm not a workaholic, I just do what I have to do.

But think of Mad Men—Don Draper coming home from the office carrying his briefcase and his hat and whatnot, saying I'm not a workaholic, I just do what I have to do.

I would love to be writing full-time, and spending more time with bubba, but . . . we would have no income.

I know . . . I don't know.

I think that's it for the sunset.

The clouds that were white have now gone dark.

The best bit is over.

It's turning to ashes.

Let's go inside. My feet are cold. We'll come back out for midnight.


The names and images of our astrologers have been changed to prevent instances of stalking or harassment. Obviously, we cannot guarantee the accuracy of astrological information, and we are not responsible for how you interpret or apply it.

Smells like gunpowder. Oh, now it's Kenny Rogers. They'll be going all night. Know when to walk away . . .

Are you going to see in the New Year on your phone? Just you and your Facebook addiction?

No, I'm trying to find the clock for the countdown. Is there a digital one? I can see the teeny little hand on there, but not really.

I need my glasses. What does that say?

Wellington, today.

What does that say?

Waitangi, tomorrow, 45 minutes ahead.

Why is . . . ? No. Impossible.

That's what it says. I think it's . . . I don't know what it is. Never mind. We don't have time to worry about that now.

I have no idea. Waitangi's on the same time zone.

I think it's somewhere else. On an island or something.

An island.

Yes. We don't have time.

Hmm. I can't find the digital clock app on your phone.

What's the time?

Eleven forty-seven.

Let's just use my laptop.

Wait . . . got it to work. I don't know why it was doing that. Is it digital? Can you make it digital?

Yes.

Does it show the seconds?

Yes.

This does too.

Close that. We'll use this. It's too bright. Can you close it? Thank you.

Is it next year yet?

No. Still counting down. Eight minutes till the end of the novel. Till you stop recording me.

What about now?

Two two two.

What does that mean?

I'm counting off the last three numbers.

No, that's not helpful. What did you say my big finish should be? Something about a mask. The other day in the car—you were talking about what my big finish should be. I meet someone who's me.

I forget how I phrased it now. You meet someone with a mask, and you pull it away, and it's yourself. Looking back at you. It's been done before.

In what?

The Prisoner, for one.

I am not a number.

My life is my own.

Is it next year yet?

Three three six.

Not helpful. Just say not yet.

Almost.

How much longer?

Exactly . . . six minutes. There's Orion.

Is that the three stars in a row?

The pot.

I can see the three in a row. Where's the rest of the pot?

Okay, this way is the triangular bit.

That way, you mean?

Yes. So you follow the three down, and then there's two stars which are the other end of the boat.

The boat? What about the pot?

The three are one end of the boat—aft—and then forward is those two stars.

Is one slightly brighter than the other?

You really have trouble visualising things, don't you.

From the three, do I go left?

Yes. And then there's one bright star up in this corner. And then there's one below it. So that's the bottom of the boat. And then in between, but this way, there's a small line of stars, and then there's some more faint ones and it makes a sort of lid to the crock pot. A little triangle.

Is it a boat or a pot or a crock pot?

It's a New Zealand thing.

The crock pot.

Yes.

I've heard of the pot before, but I always thought it was a saucepan.

People say it down here, but in the northern hemisphere they say Orion's belt. They see it the other way round most of the time. I guess.

Do they?

I don't know. Yes. It does tend to rotate. Doesn't it? I don't know. Five five five.

Stop that. It doesn't make any sense. How much longer?

Four minutes.

Remember we get the extra second. The leap second.

I have to endure the novel for an extra second?

The great black night scooped out . . . How about now?

It won't get to six six six, will it, because that would be over a minute.

Just tell me how much longer.

That was something deflecting off the roof. We almost got hit by a sky rocket.

Did we? But we didn't. How much longer?

A minute and a half.

U2. Of course. I . . . want to be with Moo again . . . I . . . want to be with Moo aaaagain . . . Counting down. I can't see anything but smoke.

Thirty-three seconds. I hope that's not waking bubba up.
Now?
Ten seconds.
Five. Four. Three. Two. One. One.

## Acknowledgements

The book's title is a translated phrase from Proust's *In Search of Lost Time* (published in the French 1913–1927). The original French phrase is 'les battements de l'aiguille'.

Thank you as always to Victoria University Press: Fergus Barrowman, Ashleigh Young, Kirsten McDougall and Craig Gamble. Thank you also to my agent Caroline Dawnay and her assistant Sophie Scard, and to Fiona Pardington for permission to use as a cover image the glorious photograph of one of Nabokov's butterflies. I am very grateful to everyone who let me record (and shape) their words, particularly Donna Adams, John and Margherita Allan, Tusiata Avia, Brian Coakley, Helen Mayall and family, Oliver Russell, Tracey Slaughter, Leila Sparrow and family, and the members of my book group. Very special thanks to the three people on whom I imposed the most: Alan Bekhuis, Alice Chidgey and Pat Chidgey.